twenty thousand nurses
tell their story

A Report on Studies of Nursing Functions
Sponsored by the American Nurses' Association

WITH A FOREWORD BY
AGNES OHLSON
President, American Nurses' Association

twenty thousand
nurses
tell their story

EVERETT C. HUGHES

HELEN MacGILL HUGHES

IRWIN DEUTSCHER

J. B. LIPPINCOTT COMPANY
Philadelphia & Montreal

foreword

"Twenty Thousand Nurses Tell Their Story" reports those studies which resulted from the decision made by the House of Delegates of the American Nurses' Association in 1950. All of us who were present when the plan for a five-year program of research in nursing functions was presented, thoughtfully considered and approved, will remember the feeling almost of dedication with which we began the task. We had faith that nursing functions could be analyzed and delineated, and that better patient care would be the outcome of that study.

During the first two years, the project was financed by State Nurses' Associations. By the third year, the ANA Board of Directors decided to finance the program from the regular budget of the Association. Nurses invested, throughout the four years of the study, a total of $400,000 in support of twenty projects from seventeen states.

The wisdom of the decision in 1950 has been demonstrated. The preliminary report of the five-year program of studies of Nursing Functions, "Nurses Invest in Patient Care" by Dr. Clara Hardin, outlined graphically the scope of the study. The present volume gives us not only a synthesis of the findings but the implications for the nurse as a practitioner, her relationships to others in the work situation and the future of nursing.

As we look back on the years since 1950, we realize how much we have learned and how much there still is to learn. As we read this book and as we study the individual research projects themselves, let us be alert to the implications. Where can we improve nursing practice?

We have answers to many questions. There are many others which still need study. With the help of those who are more sophisticated in research techniques than we, and with the skills which we ourselves are acquiring we will find these answers.

The American Nurses' Association thanks everyone who contributed to the success of this program. We are proud to present "Twenty Thousand Nurses Tell Their Story."

AGNES OHLSON
President
American Nurses' Association

acknowledgments

The story of the evolution of the ANA program of Studies of Nursing Functions has been told elsewhere. In one sense it has no known beginning and no ending. Officially known as a five-year program of research and studies, it was the outgrowth of many exploratory conferences prior to the action taken by the ANA House of Delegates in 1950. No one could give adequate acknowledgment to all of those individuals who participated in the development of the idea, the creation of the administrative machinery and the implementation of the plan.

As one who was fortunate enough to participate in the beginning of the program and still is privileged to be a technical advisor to those administering nursing research, I must pay tribute to the entire membership of the American Nurses' Association and to the successive Boards who guided the program during the administrations of Dr. Elizabeth K. Porter and Miss Agnes Ohlson, and to the alert and understanding Executive Secretary, Miss Ella Best.

Two people stand out in my memory for their leadership in planning the program and interpreting it to the members of the State Nurses' Associations: Dr. Elizabeth L. Kemble of the University of North Carolina, who was the first Chairman of the Technical Committee appointed to guide the studies; and Miss Elizabeth S. LaPerle, who served as Associate Executive Secretary, ANA Research and Statistics Unit, through the first two years of the program. Dr. Kemble remained on the Technical Committee throughout the entire program as did Dr. Katherine J. Hoffman of the University of Washington, who succeeded Dr. Kemble as Chairman, and Mrs. Margaret Filson Sheehan, University of Chicago Clinics.

With me were non-nurse members of the Technical Committee: Dr. Victor Karabasz of the University of Miami, in Florida, who served for the "duration"; Dr. Launor Carter of Santa Monica, California, who helped launch the studies; and Dr. Daniel M. Wilner who served from 1954 through 1956 before moving to his present post at the Johns Hopkins School of Hygiene and Public Health.

The Technical Committee was assisted by the able leadership and guidance of Dr. Clara A. Hardin who succeeded Miss LaPerle in September 1952, and Mrs. Roberta Spohn, Assistant Executive Secretary, ANA Research and Statistics Unit (1952-1956).

The individuals named here are only a few of those who stand out in my memory of stimulating and productive meetings. Close by always were members of the staffs of the ANA Public Relations Unit and the nursing journals, eager to keep nurses and the public abreast of the new studies and the latest findings.

In the preparation of the present volume, I am particularly pleased to have had as collaborators my wife, Helen MacGill Hughes, and Irwin Deutscher. My co-authors and I are greatly indebted to Dr. Thomas S. McPartland of the Greater Kansas City Mental Health Foundation, for writing two chapters of the book, Chapter 3—"Student Nurses," and Chapter 11—"Careers;" and to Mrs. LaVerne Southard, Community Studies, Inc., of Kansas City, who typed our manuscripts and assisted in the proofreading.

Although some nurses kindly read the manuscript and made some technical suggestions, they in no sense took away from the freedom of the authors to write their own report. The document as here presented is therefore the authors' own and for this product we are content to be labelled "responsible."

My warm personal thanks go out to the American Nurses' Association and to my colleagues.

EVERETT C. HUGHES
Professor of Sociology, University of Chicago

note

The studies on which this book is based are listed beginning page 278. These works are keyed into the text by number, and are referred to from time to time by the appropriate number which appears in parentheses immediately following the text reference. Wherever practical, these have been added to facilitate consulting original sources.

Some of the original studies have been published, some not. A few that appeared in a limited mimeographed edition may be out of print as this volume is released. In almost all cases, these materials will be available, if not from the publishing institution, then on loan from certain libraries.

table of contents

introduction

by

EVERETT C. HUGHES

studying the nurse's work

Nothing North American is so much so as the North American nurse. Nursing is, of course, an activity as old as, if not older than human culture; it is one of the universals of human behavior. In that sense it is not especially American. Nor was that founding mother of the nursing profession, Florence Nightingale, with some of her formidable British traits, in any way American. But it is on this continent that the revolution which she started has continued with the greatest vigor. This is the part of the world where nurses themselves are discussing the nature of their work, and of other people's work as well. For most nursing takes place where there are several other kinds of people at work so that any change in the work of one must alter the work of others. *Twenty Thousand Nurses Tell Their Story,* puts the spotlight on that work.

Nurses initiated and between 1951 and 1957 some 175,000 of them paid voluntarily out of their own pockets for the research that this book reports. This is not an especially American way to pay for research; an aspiring profession usually turns to a foundation for the money with which to assess its progress or to state its case. Even the richest of the professions get research about themselves paid for out of other people's pockets. Seeking, receiving and using foundation or public money for research designed to improve the services of any profession essential to our welfare is not an unworthy task for a professional person. Certainly the major cost of nursing research in the future will have to be taken from fatter purses than those of nurses; but the reader should know what is here reported came straight from the slim purses of nurses. There never has been a whisper of suggestion that the aim of the research on nursing functions was self-interest or public relations; the talk has been of making nursing better, much better than it has ever been.

Nurses, at least those I have been seeing these past few years, are terrifically American in that they love to talk shop. This book is shop-talk of nurses about nurses and about the other people involved in their work. It is very American indeed for the people in an occupation to be vocal about their work; self-conscious about the direction, the degree and the desirability of change in it. Generally, such talk is done by people who want to improve the standing of their profession—thus their own standing; the quality of its services— thus their own competence; and its income—thus also their own. True, not all people in an occupation on the move will be equally concerned over these matters. But it is a very American thing for some group within the profession to initiate a movement, or several competing movements at once, to bring about discussion and changes within the whole profession and in the other people and institutions involved.

We might call the nursing profession a "more so" case; it is like many other occupations, only more so. That is what gives the study of nursing a wider interest. The things which are happening in it and to it are of the same order as those in many other occupations but are more strikingly visible. We who are students of society cannot produce whole human institutions or social movements in a laboratory, using some as controls and inducing change in others. Generally we have to make do with what society produces for us, keeping our eyes open for such "just like the others but more so" cases in which change is taking place more rapidly and more visibly than in others. In order to make the best use of such a case we construct models, taken partly from nature and partly from our imagination, with which to compare our special cases in which a lot is going on. For instance, we can think what things would be like in a profession that had everything and in which nothing appeared to be changing.

Now *profession* has become, in the English language, the word to designate an occupation of the highest possible prestige and status. So our model profession would have all the prestige an admiring society could heap upon it and well-developed prerogatives (status) to match. Since it had the most prestige, power and standing, it would not seek more of them but might resist sharing them with others.

Even more fundamental to our model is the name of the occupation. It would be an historic name, known to all within and without, to professional and layman alike. Custom and law would have made it clear exactly who was entitled to the name, and when it was to be used and by whom. When the name was mentioned, people—again lay and professional alike—would believe that they knew what work the people of that name do and would accept their right—their license—to do it and to be protected in the right to do it to the exclusion of others. The boundaries between their work and that of others would be clear. They would also recognize the right—the mandate—of the people who do the work to decide how it is to be done, whether it has been well done, and to tell the community at large how it ought to be done.

To be sure, the knowledge of the outsiders, the laymen, would not be the same as that of the insiders, the professionals whose esoteric knowledge the layman must take on trust. When the layman heard someone addressed by the historic name of the profession, or saw someone wearing its historic costume or badge, he would recognize in that person a proper bearer of the license and the mandate of the profession.

The young person, thinking over what his lifework might be, would hear early the name of this profession and would learn its value. There would be a clear course to run of hurdles, choices and accomplishments for entry to the profession. He (perhaps there would be no *she* in this case which has everything) would have an accurate idea of the length of the training and of the rewards at the end. Naturally, as a layman, and as a youngster, he would not know in advance all of the esoteric knowledge or be able to perform the skilled work. But he would meet a minimum of rude surprises in the course of his training and in pursuit of his profession. He would be sure as a human being can be that the knowledge and training he got would be good for as long as he should have strength and wit to practice. He would not fear that technologic or social change would pull his professional feet from under him in mid-career. One could predict what all people concerned would do, not only now, but for so long a time as any man might hope to have need of assurance and stability. To make prediction doubly sure, the whole system would be supported by a philosophy accepted as true by all concerned.

Now no such occupation exists; nor could it in our society. But one will come to your mind as being the nearest thing to it; it will be—medicine. Medicine, in our time, is devoted to improvement—hence, to change—of its underlying knowledge and its techniques. This is a drastic departure from our model; there are others. Still, the literature on professions in our time shows clearly that medicine is the prototype of professions in the minds both of physicians and of other people who seek the respected designation of profession for their own work.

Here we have a difficulty; for we have just admitted that medicine is the "most-so" profession, thus apparently going back on the proposition that nursing is a "more-so" case; but we do not mean that nursing comes closer to the model set up. Rather, we mean that nursing is an occupation in which changes are taking place in nearly all the features of the model. If it is the living reality, the processes, we are interested in, then nursing is indeed a high-lighted and challenging case to both practical and theoretical students of human work.

Social scientists themselves are a "more-so" case in their disposition to use more energy in deciding whether the living reality fits their words than in finding words which aptly and penetratingly illumine the reality. They have aided and abetted nurses and others in the fruitless argument whether or not nursing is a profession. Now if the word "profession" is to be used only for that occupation which, in any system such as the medical, occupies the pinnacle of prestige and power, there can be only one profession in it. So long as medicine occupies the pinnacle, nursing could not be a profession.

This absurd argument will, I trust, make us more content with our main business, that of analyzing various kinds of human work in the systems of interaction and institutions in which they are carried on. Nursing is certainly a "more-so" case in that it is so obviously carried on inside such complex organizations and in such lively interaction with other kinds of working people that no one can even flirt with the illusion that the relation of nurse and patient could be studied as if it occurred in a social vacuum. Nurses know they work and have their being in a complex social setting and frankly discuss their work in terms of it.

The respects in which nursing is undergoing change will be apparent to any reader of this book, although anyone in the medical world already knows. The name "nurse" itself is historic, as are the uniform and the badge. But almost at the moment when, through licensing laws, the name Registered Nurse came to have clear and commonly recognized meaning, changes in medical technology and the organization of hospitals led to a redistribution of the nurse's work such that it is no longer clear exactly who may be called Nurse. Laymen don't wait to read in the fine print on the badge whether it says R.N. or P.N. before addressing the "Nurse." Certainly the content and the boundaries of the work are far from clear and agreed upon; one can scarcely think of an occupation in which changes in both content and boundary of work are so great and so numerous.

Certainly also, the standing of the nurse is changing; not in some simple way that affects all nurses equally but in complicated ways which reflect the demand of the modern medical establishment for a great variety of functions and for corresponding variety of people to perform them. A nurse may be at the bedside in a small general hospital; she may be directing doctors around in a sterile operating room; she may be dean of a graduate school. She may administer, hire and fire, a staff of thousands of nurses. She may wear the insignia of a brigadier-general. As the standing of all nurses changes somewhat, and the standing of some changes a great deal, the relative standings of all other people who work in their vicinity change as well. The change of position of nurses of necessity affects the position of physicians.

In the medical system of things, the nurses are a little like a minority in society at large. Their very self-consciousness makes others self-conscious as well. But if they are like a minority in society at large, they are also like the higher noncommissioned officers in the army and like certain people of second rank in many organizations. The people in second rank are apt to know more about the whole organization and to be more immediately sensitive to its inner workings than those at the very top. Doctors "visit" the hospital and make rounds at stated times, while the nurse lives there on her wards. This is not completely true. Some physicians do all of their work in hospitals, but they tend to work in laboratories and operating rooms. And more and more nurses do work at some distance from the bedside. Yet the basic distinction holds; the physician, the company commander and the manager visit the organization; the nurse, the sergeant and the foreman are there with it all of the time. It may well be that, apart from the fact of the greater changes in nursing, her position is a better one from which to view the working organization of a hospital or other health agency. Hers is a position of great sensitivity, less insulated from the on-going life of the organization than the position of the physician.

Around the clock proximity to and sensitive contact with the on-going activities of the sickroom, the ward and the clinic put upon the nurse the burden of using more authority than is formally allotted her. The very absence of the physician during many hours of day and night constitutes a delegation of authority. It appears to be a law of organizations that the person at the top of the hierarchy of authority is invested with more power than he can ordinarily use, while the second in command must often exercise more than she (sic) is formally allowed. As the organization increases in complexity, perhaps the resulting internal changes more quickly and visibly affect the second position (that of the nurse) than the first (that of the physician). Hence, the nurse may be the person to watch if one is interested in medical organization.

Nurses also offer a highlighted case of the role of research itself. When, at least in our age, an occupation seeks to redefine its position in the world it usually engages in self-conscious study to determine the nature and the boundaries of its work. Research itself lends a certain glamor and prestige to an occupation; the research career adds another rung to the ladder of success; but those who lead the educational effort in a striving occupation will soon ask themselves what basic kinds of knowledge underlie the arts which they practice. Nursing is now in this phase. The several answers to this question and the history of such answers will form an important part of the history of nursing and, indeed, of medicine and of social science.

The ultimate course of such answers is still not clear. When the American Nurses' Association undertook to study the functions of the nurse, various kinds of projects were proposed. Each proposal rested on the assumption that knowledge of some particular kind is basic to nursing. Some studied the motions of the nurse and the time devoted to various activties. Others proposed to study organization in the large and in the small. Some studied social interaction. Some studied the social origins of nurses, their conceptions of nursing and their careers. Still others studied nursing as education of the patient. We will neither catalogue the projects nor the kinds of knowledge which they implicitly emphasize. Nor will we predict what the future emphases will be. The trends can be studied in the many research projects now going on in the country, for there is more research into nursing than ever before; but who will not follow with interest the natural history of the knowledge considered pertinent to the developing profession of nursing?

There are a few predictions which anyone may safely make about nursing here, and probably eventually all over the world. They are, in effect, predictions about the course of the treatment of illness and the maintenance of health. The medical standard of living of all people and all peoples will rise, in that better medical knowledge and techniques will be developed and in that people will demand distribution of the best to all.

The medical division of labor will continue to become greater, in that there will be more different kinds of things to be done and in that the health institutions will be more complicated and require more different kinds of people to operate them. In the course of this, physicians will learn more new techniques and will continue to reorganize their work by delegation to others, especially nurses, of many tasks and responsibilities. The preparation of operating rooms, the keeping of records and much scheduling, many actual procedures —once rare and now routine—have already been so passed on. The doctor will keep control over the economy of his time by continuing such delegation, although, naturally enough, he probably will continue to complain that the woman to whom he delegates work and responsibility is not always there when he wants her on a moment's notice.

The physician's work will become more and more difficult and demanding; he will ask for help and will get it—and probably have to pay for it in changes of behavior and position which he will not especially like.

There will be more work for nurses to do, and more and more kinds of nurses will be required to do it. Some difference of opinion about the solution of the many resulting problems will be chronic, but people will continue to work at them. Research will be part of the effort.

We who have written this book are sociologists: two of us actually planned and carried out projects which are here reported. We do not assume or believe that sociological studies of nursing should be cultivated more than any other kind. Since all human work brings people into relations with others and generally so within the framework of institutions, some study of work will be sociological. Nursing is highly social and most of it occurs in large and complex institutions; its social aspect will continue to receive attention. But so will the psychology of illness and health, and of the activities of the nurse herself; so will the physical, the biological, the economic and the other aspects of nursing.

We have not gone beyond our assignment, which was to report within the space of one book, the studies resulting from the original plan of the American Nurses' Association to study nursing functions. Unreported is the impressive amount of research which has been done and is being done under other auspices. One who wishes to master any aspect of nursing research will have to go to original reports, those which were the basis of this book and others as well.

We have written with a sociological pen; many of the studies could have been written in some other style. We hope that we have done our work in such a way as to be immediately useful and to encourage future study designed to improve the care of the sick and the maintenance of good health.

who were studied and how

Although the nurse and her work were the focus of all the American Nurses' Associations' research projects considered in this volume, of necessity many dealt with groups other than graduate nurses which are involved physically, psychologically, or socially in nursing. There being little or no tradition of research in professional nursing, there were in the beginning few nurses with the necessary qualifications, either by experience or training, to execute research projects on their own, but their number has been growing very rapidly. It is obvious that the nurse and her work cannot be studied in isolation from those with whom she must work, whether they be her patients, her colleagues, those whose orders she must carry out, or those who carry out her orders.

This chapter describes the kinds of people who conducted the research, the kinds of people they studied, the locale of the studies, and the methods used to uncover the findings which are the subject of this volume.

who did the research and whom they studied

It is sometimes difficult to ascertain exactly who has primary responsibility and most influences a given piece of work. However, to the best of our knowledge the major responsibility for the 34 documents—books, monographs and reports—to be discussed in this volume is as follows: 15 were conducted by sociologists, 6 by nurses (either individually or in committee), 4 by psychologists, 7 by interdisciplinary teams (all of which included a nurse and one of them included an M.D.), 1 by political scientists, 1 miscellaneous assortment. There is no study in which nurses did not participate in some research capacity. The grants with which these people conducted their research have been administered by state nurses' associations, universities, hospitals and nonprofit research corporations.

Whom did these people study? Perhaps more than any other group, institutional nurses were the objects of analysis, and among them the general duty nurse receives the most consideration. Others, however, were also placed under the research spotlight: supervisors and head nurses and those in such special fields as private duty, industry, education, psychiatric, obstetric and operating room nursing. At least two studies included every conceivable type of position in which a graduate nurse was found, whether institutional or not: these, also, are unique in their inclusion of nurses who were not employed at the time the studies were conducted. A wide range of auxiliary personnel was also examined. These included practical nurses, professional and practical student nurses, nurse aides, orderlies and nurse-technicians. Finally, some of these studies view other groups and some of the more important relationships that they have to the nurse: physicians, hospital administrators, patients, hospital housekeeping personnel, and a variety of technicians—medical, x-ray, dietary, and so on.

The program sponsoring the research began in 1951, and the first reports were completed in 1953. They have continued to appear since then, and the last were issued in 1957. Three studies, that of Theriault in New Hampshire (22), Wendell I. Smith who surveyed industrial nurses in Pennsylvania (31) and the Metropolitan State Hospital project in Massachusetts (24), appeared while this book was being written, and the writers regret that not until the last half of this compendium could they be given much consideration. Late-comers, of course, have a natural advantage in being able to draw on the earlier studies and in providing more recent facts.

Geographically, the projects encompass a wide area of the United States. In the northeastern region of the country New York is represented by results obtained from medical and surgical wards in 12 urban hospitals in both New York City and Rochester (1), in addition to another study conducted in the obstetric division of a large New York City hospital (20). A series of investigations concerned primarily with psychiatric nursing have taken place in the Boston Psychopathic Hospital (6), and another study was made at a mental hospital in Massachusetts (24). Registered nurses in Pennsylvania participated in a state-wide project (19), and those employed in industry in central Pennsylvania (31) and in the Ohio Valley region were studied (21). Observations took place in 11 hospitals of varying size and type of support in the state of New Hampshire (22), and the work of private duty nurses in the District of Columbia (30) was analyzed.

The West Coast is covered by an intensive study of 2 rural and 2 urban hospitals in Washington (2) and a survey of 40 hospitals scattered over the state of California (4). In the Midwest there have been 2 studies covering 91 hospitals in Minnesota (3, 8) and another which includes 23 hospitals in the state of Kansas (5). Two additional projects in Missouri were concerned with nurses in nonmetropolitan hospitals (9, 28), while a third series covered a metropolitan area which included segments of both Kansas and Missouri (11, 12, 25, 26, 27).

In the South, private duty nursing has been studied over the state of Georgia (7), while 3 hospitals were subjected to study in Alabama (10). The faculty of a nursing school in Nashville, Tenn., undertook a self-study (13), and the work of the psychiatric nurse was observed in 7 hospitals in North Carolina (29). A study of 10 Arkansas hospitals resulted in reports on the operating room nurse, the general duty nurse and auxiliary nursing personnel (14, 15, 16, 17). Finally, research in one of America's largest hospitals, located in New Orleans, has culminated in a significant volume describing both the work of the nurse in a great metropolitan general hospital and the special problems found in a premature-infant center (18).

These research projects, in covering a variety of states and regions in the United States, survey a wide range of nursing personnel, working under very different conditions. The hospitals in which the studies took place are both urban and rural, large and small, and differ in their sources of support and forms of control. The effects of the differences on the nurse and her work are discussed in Chapter 4, while nurses employed outside the hospital are the subject of Chapter 5.

how nurses were studied

Taking their cues from the ANA Master Plan for Studies of Nursing Functions[1] the research teams identified a wide range of problems for study and approached them by a variety of methods. The Master Plan itself contained a number of important assumptions which, in turn, were influential to a degree in the selection both of problems and of methods. One of the more important reasons behind the financial venture of the ANA into the research field doubtlessly is the crucial shortage of nursing personnel—a shortage for which no easy solution in the near future was in sight. The Master Plan, by focusing on the nurse's functions, recognizes that recruitment alone is not the answer. With the increasing popular use of health facilities, the growth of the population, and the expansion of hospital construction, even the most intensive recruitment could not be expected to keep up with the demand. There is currently a personnel shortage in many fields, but in nursing the problem is intensified by the need for 24-hour service. When a new school is built, it may be difficult to find a teaching staff; when a new hospital is built it is nearly impossible to locate *three* shifts of nurses.

It has become necessary, then, to seek an answer to this problem along avenues other than recruitment of new personnel, although recruitment certainly must continue at the maximum rate. First of all, the Master Plan was devised to guide research into the nurses' work. Once their work is understood, their services may be used more economically by the reallocation of functions. It is assumed that if there is a shortage of skilled professional nurses and if new recruits cannot be obtained and trained in sufficient quantities, then the work of the professional people should be modified so that they do not engage in time-consuming tasks which can be carried out by other occupational groups with a shorter period of training, who can be obtained with less difficulty. Before any such reallocation of duties and responsibilities can be carried out, one might like to know: How do professional nurses allocate their time under present conditions? How do auxiliary nursing personnel allocate their time under present conditions? How does the use of time vary in different parts of the country and in different kinds of hospitals? Are professional

---

[1] Cf. Nurses Invest in Patient Care, New York, American Nurses' Association. May, 1956, p. 61.

nurses expending large blocks of time on functions which conceivably could be carried out by others, for example, practical nurses or nurses' aides or even orderlies or by the dietary or housekeeping departments?

A number of research projects sought direct answers to these kinds of questions by modifying the methods developed in industrial time studies and applying them to the work of the nurse in an institutional setting. Indeed, the studies of timed functions are the core of the whole program of research into the nurses' work. Although the technique varies somewhat from study to study, its basic form involves observers who shadow nurses on the job, classifying their activities on a precoded checklist and noting the amount of time spent on each task. Later analysis reveals the proportions of time spent by various personnel on different activities.[2] Sometimes categories of activities are employed, such as "Professional Nursing," "Nonprofessional Nursing" and "Non-nursing" (1). The time study was the exclusive or primary method of a number of the inquiries (1-5, 8, 13-17). In other projects this method was used in part or to complement other research methods (6, 18, 22).

The authors of a series of time studies conducted in Arkansas (14-17), point out that this work differs considerably from the usual industrial time research in that they observed most of the nurses' activities as within a social context rather than as isolated. The time and the nursing activities are related to the work setting and variations in it. Variables considered include size and type of control of hospitals, rural or urban setting, service, shift, auxiliary personnel, patients, and the nurse as a person. We have attempted in Chapter 6 to present an overview of the results of these and all the other direct studies of nursing functions by drawing out the general propositions for which there is evidence, regardless of geographic area of the country or the type of service or institutional setting. In addition, we have pointed out the ways in which certain variables tend to qualify other kinds of propositions.

Aware of the fact that there are numerous institutional and social-psychological obstacles to any deliberate shifting of nurse functions from one category of personnel to another, several investigators have

---

[2] Standard techniques have been adapted especially to the study of nursing. Cf., How to Study Nursing Activities in a Patient Unit, Public Health Service Publication, No. 370, Washington, D. C., U.S. Department of Health, Education and Welfare, Public Health service, 1954

devoted their efforts to seeking knowledge about the informal workings of hospitals and the kinds of role relationships which exist among nurses and between nurses and other kinds of personnel. Objective measurements have not yet been developed which will enable the social scientist to understand such subtle phenomena as these. The tool kit for studying informal structures and role relationships consists largely of varying degrees of participant observation in conjunction with loosely structured face-to-face interviews. The work of Habenstein and Christ (9) and Ford and Stephenson (10) began with the exclusive use of such methods, but both studies follow up their initial findings with attempts to scale the attitudes of nurses toward the functions and the tasks recorded in the time studies (28). These analyses get at the discrepancies between who actually is responsible for certain tasks and who, nurses think, *ought* to be responsible for them. They also seek to understand which tasks are looked on as desirable and which undesirable and why. Informal observation techniques and interviewing are used to great advantage to supplement and help interpret other kinds of data in such studies as the Arkansas series mentioned above, the New Hampshire project (22) and the New Orleans project, a part of which focuses directly on the formal and the informal organization of the nurses' work (18).

Data derived almost exclusively from lengthy, loosely structured interviews (mostly electrically recorded) provide the keystone to the study of career lines and contingencies of Kansas City nurses (27) and the North Carolina analysis of psychiatric nursing (29). Three studies which leaned heavily on the interview technique incorporated experimental controls into their design. These include one aspect of the Boston Psychopathic Hospital research which involved an attempt to change attitudes of personnel and patients in order to reduce patients' fears (6), the study of nurse students undertaken in Kansas City in which both entering and graduating students were interviewed in order to determine shifts in conceptions of self and nursing which occur during the educational process (26), and the study of a New York maternity hospital in which the needs of women during the maternity cycle and the nurses' awareness of them were studied. This involved interviewing the same women early in the cycle and later reinterviewing them toward the end of puerperium. Incidentally, this study also illustrates the maximum use of participant observation; one of the investigators, expecting a child herself, participated along with her objects of study, in all of the voluntary educational programs at the hospital (20). A fourth study which attempted to incorporate experimental controls into its design was conducted among private duty nurses in Georgia. In this case the control was intended to measure the effectiveness of workshop sessions among private duty nurses who were seeking to solve certain problems in their field (23).

Two projects were attempts to obtain an over-all picture of what a nurse "complement" looks like. The complements include all graduate nurses in a given territory, whether or not institutionally employed: in one case the state of Pennsylvania (19), in the other the Kansas City Metropolitan Area which includes four counties in the states of Kansas and Missouri (25). It is a coincidence that both of these studies obtained questionnaires from nearly 2,500 graduate nurses. It is not a coincidence that both utilized the technique of mailed questionnaires to gather their data, for this is the only means by which so many nurses could be represented economically in a study. The rate of returns, estimated for both of these studies at 63 per cent, is unusually high, for market research analysts consider a return rate of 30 per cent as satisfactory; and, indeed, this was the approximate rate obtained in a mail survey of private duty nurses in Georgia (7) and another in the District of Columbia (30). The Kansas City and the Pennsylvania studies provide much of the available data on noninstitutional nurses, but there are others, such as the Georgia and the District of Columbia studies just cited, which focus specifically on certain fields of nursing. These provide comparative and contrasting data within nursing and permit some generalizations which include all nurses rather than only those employed by hospitals.

The Georgia study makes explicit the use of two techniques used widely throughout these research projects. One they call the "method of involvement," which means that as many nurses and other interested persons as possible are drawn into the conduct of the research. This is a common technique in the study of community relations and one which supposedly assures greater understanding and therefore greater co-operation by the respondents. In varying degrees it is utilized in all of the studies considered here. The other common technique made use of explicitly in the Georgia study is the "Critical

Incident Technique."[3] This is a method often utilized by sociologists in interviewing. It involves the location of points of stress and strain in a social organization through the revelation by respondents of incidents in their experience in it which appear to them to be unusual or critical in some sense. This method, although unnamed, was employed in all of the studies of informal organization and role relationships discussed above.

The Georgia studies were unusual in several respects. There is an attempt to explore the nature of interpersonal relations by means of sociograms—diagrammatic representations of who associates with whom. They also made an effort to move from survey to experimentation in a follow-up study (23). Problems isolated in the earlier research were introduced to experimental workshop groups which attempted to solve them through discussion. Their effort to maintain a control group so that comparisons could be made between it and the workshop groups has been mentioned already. The other study of private duty nurses, conducted in Washington, D. C. (30), is like the Georgia research in that it makes explicit its use of the critical incident technique. Although its conclusions are based in part on returns from a mailed questionnaire, interview materials with nurses and others, along with rating scales of tasks and job satisfaction, were also used.

Among the studies of special groups within nursing, the Vanderbilt time project dealing with nursing educators has been mentioned earlier (13). There remains two studies which are unique in dealing exclusively with the industrial nurse and her problems (21, 31). Based on mailed questionnaires, observations in industrial plants, and interviews with nurses, workers, employers and others, their conclusions concern the industrial nurse in central Pennsylvania and the Ohio Valley. The Ohio study also employs another method which has not yet been mentioned but is used in several of these research projects—the pencil and paper test. In the Boston studies (6) Army Alpha and Beta Intelligence Tests were administered to student nurses and the results related to their reasons for choosing nursing as a career. The Arkansas investigators administered the Strong Vocational Interest Test for Women to each nurse they interviewed (14-17). Projective tests such as the Sentence Completion Test and the Thematic Apper-

---

[3] Named and publicized by J. C. Flanagan, in "The Critical Incident Technique," *Psychological Bulletin,* 1954, 51, 327-58.

ception Test were used in the New Orleans, the Washington, D. C. and the Georgia studies (18, 30, 23). Another application of test materials is found in the Pennsylvania report where the investigators used the personality tests their respondents had taken when in nursing school and also made use of the scores they had achieved on their state board examinations (19).

There are two reports which deviate both in purpose and method from all of those mentioned to this point, being analogous to consumer research in seeking to discover the impressions the "public" has, not in this case of a product, but of a profession. The first deals with a special "public" which stands in a peculiarly significant work relationship with the nurse—the physician (11). It is a statistical analysis and interpretation of questionnaires mailed in by a representative sample of physicians in the Kansas City area. Although none of the other studies focuses specifically on this problem, several contain interview data which can be used to supplement the poll. The second study of public opinion, also in Kansas City, was conducted from house to house, using a sample census to ensure representativeness (12). It sought to discover something of the way people in all walks of life esteem nurses, recognizing that what other people think of nurses has an effect both on what nurses think of themselves and the relationships they are able to establish with others. This report provides the core of Chapter 8.

A considerable gamut of methods has been employed in the research projects whose findings are reported in the following chapters. Each has its strengths and its weaknesses; there are kinds of knowledge which each can and cannot contribute. As professional nurses become continually involved in the conduct of research they will find themselves confronted with various schools of research methodology and, although competence in research equips one to select whatever method is most appropriate to the problem under investigation, there are extremists who make the excellent advice given by Milton Greenblatt (6G) worth reproducing:

When she works with a group the nurse will find herself face to face with problems of interdisciplinary research—which are many. There is a great variation in research approaches to problems with polydiscipline meaning, and there is considerable bias among different specialists as to what constitutes the most fruitful and illuminating method of attack. Research patterns of investigation tend to vary all the way from tight experimental designs—such as characterize the school of experimental psychologists and physiologists, to the less-structured, impressionistic investigations—more characteristic of the *modus operandi* of anthropologists and psychiatrists. High objectivity is claimed by proponents of the first method and high subjectivity is admitted—and defended as a positive value in research concerned with human personality, by supporters of the second school.

Among the projects being considered here, the Reissman and Rohrer volume (18) contains data based on one of the widest ranges of method. Rohrer compares conclusions and data derived by various means and bearing on the same phenomenon and states that they "showed almost perfect agreement. In no case was there any significant deviation of the pattern of role behaviors described by the two collecting techniques." His conclusions echo our own assumption that good research will produce valid results, regardless of the specific techniques applied:

In comparing the high degree of agreement that was obtained by the structured interview schedule, the projective role cards, and the observational techniques, the conclusion was reached that all the techniques were satisfactorily valid and reliable for obtaining the kind of data needed for the study.

Although we have not attempted a critique of method in this chapter, it is certainly true that these studies vary not only in quality but in their general applicability and the reliability and the validity of their conclusions. This variation is recognized; necessary qualifications will be placed on conclusions as they are discussed in the following chapters. Our task in this volume is to collate, integrate, compare and contrast the results of these studies undertaken by different kinds of people all investigating aspects of nursing in different parts of the United States. Some of them corroborate others; there are instances of contradiction. But it must be remembered that each study is of a time and a place. And while many findings will not match others and will be true, perhaps, of only their limited sample, still they will not fail to shed their light on the whole picture.

this company called nurses

What kind of people are nurses? What are their social and geographic origins? What do we know of their age, sex and race? To what extent are they active in the social life of their communities? How do they spend their off-duty hours? From what kinds of families do they derive? How many are married? What kinds of families of their own do they have?

These, and such other personal characteristics as religion, national origin and income, are the questions addressed in this chapter. Although research has contributed much information in some of these areas, some, as we shall see, need further exploration. Perhaps the greatest gap lies in the almost complete lack of comparative data with other occupational groups which in certain respects are similar to nurses. If more were known about social workers, teachers and librarians, the significance of the data on nurses would be much greater. Nurses are people, but because they are involved in this profession, we might expect that they differ in many respects from other people. As will be seen in later chapters, nurses in some fields certainly differ sharply from their own colleagues in other fields.

social origins and social mobility

It is a part of the "American Creed" that all of us have the opportunity to move up in the world and make more of ourselves than our fathers did. But in order to move "up," one must first be "down." So the creed also implies the existence of different levels in our society. Few Americans would deny that in almost every community there is a "right" and a "wrong" side of the tracks, a "Four Hundred" or some other elite such as the "old families," and parts of town where people in general live in houses, engage in occupations, attend churches and schools and have incomes—all of which are different from those in other parts of town. These different levels have become known as socioeconomic strata and the people who occupy them, as social classes. The important thing about all this, from our point of view, is the freedom to be mobile, i.e., to move from one level to another—either "up" or "down"—and the fact that people do move. This movement we call *social mobility*.

One of the most reliable indicators of socioeconomic status is a person's occupation. In general, lawyers, physicians and business executives are of different social strata from store clerks, typists and technicians of one sort or another. All of these can be differentiated from those engaged in such occupations as maids, shoe-shiners or street-cleaning.[1]

From the Middle West, the East and the South comes evidence that nurses derive from middle-class backgrounds. The evidence is derived not only from widely separated geographic regions but from very different kinds of universes: a metropolitan area (25), a state (19) and a large urban hospital (18). Table 1 shows that the greatest proportion of nurses' fathers—whether in the Kansas City area, the State of Pennsylvania or in Charity Hospital in New Orleans—are or were engaged in middle-status occupations. In each of the three studies, this includes about half of the fathers, the remainder being divided nearly equally between upper- and lower-status occupations. Backing up the data are additional, although not comparable, facts from North Carolina (29) and New Hampshire (22). About 25 per cent of the psychiatric nurses in the North Carolina study had

---

[1] A great deal of knowledge of social stratification has been accumulated since about 1930. The pioneer works in this field include Lynd, Robert S. and Helen M.: Middletown, New York, Harcourt, 1929; and Warner, Lloyd and Lunt, Paul S.: The Social Life of a Modern Community, New Haven, Yale, 1941. For recent and current research in this area, the reader is referred to the Index to the American Sociological Review under the categories "Social Class" and "Social Stratification"; also, *The Am. J. Sociology*, **58**: 1953, and other issues.

Table 1. Occupational Status of Fathers

	Place		
	Kansas City	Pennsylvania	New Orleans
Occupational Status	%	%	%
Higher	22	27	26
Middle	53	51	44
Lower	25	22	30
Total	100	100	100
N	2056	2035	43

Source: (25, 19, 18). Data from these three studies are reclassified where possible in approximate comparable categories.

In general, "higher" status occupations include professional, managerial and executive positions. "Middle" status includes white-collar occupations, skilled labor and farmers. The "lower" group is composed mostly of unskilled labor and personal-service occupations.

Table 2. Occupational Status of Husbands

	Place	
	Kansas City	Pennsylvania
Occupational Status	%	%
Higher	47	43
Middle	26	36
Lower	27	21
Total	100	100
N	1692	317

Source: (25, 19). Naturally, these figures are for married nurses only. In addition, the Pennsylvania data include only those nurses who graduated in 1950.

fathers in lower-status occupations, while the remainder were in "middle and upper" and "farm" occupational categories. In New Hampshire, the most frequent fathers' occupations are skilled trades and employment in industry. Farmer appears third, with white-collar occupations ranking fourth. Professional and salaried executives appear in "a very small number of cases."

How do these occupational characteristics of nurses' fathers compare with those of men in the general population? An answer to this question was sought by Kephart and Bressler in Pennsylvania. Without very reliable data to go on, and clearly recognizing their limitations, they point out that nursing obtains an excessive proportion of the daughters of professional, managerial and skilled workers in Pennsylvania. It is of interest that in spite of the fact that the absolute numbers of daughters of professional men going into nursing are small, they are larger than what would be expected on the basis of the frequency of professionals in the general population. The authors conclude that the nursing profession is attracting more than its appropriate share of applicants from the upper end of the social class scale.

One way of determining the direction and the extent of social mobility among nurses is to compare the occupational status of their fathers with that of their husbands. Comparable data on husbands' status from the Kansas City and the Pennsylvania studies are shown in Table 2. By comparing Tables 1 and 2 we begin to understand the social mobility among graduate nurses: although more fathers were engaged in middle-status occupations, more husbands are found in higher-status occupations than in middle or lower. The process appears to be increasing steadily. When the data from the Pennsylvania study are divided into the three graduating classes of 1930, 1940 and 1950, the percentage of nurses that marry professionals rises steadily—from 24 to 28 to 36 per cent (each per cent is based on numbers well in excess of 500 nurses).

Upward mobility among nurses is further confirmed in Kansas City, where 55 per cent of the more than 2,000 nurses surveyed have either married men with higher occupational status than their fathers' or (if single) have achieved higher occupational status by becoming nurses. Twenty-one per cent of this group show no mobility, while 24 per cent have either married down or (if single) have lost status by entering nursing. A larger proportion of the single than of the married are mobile upward. The authors suggest that "the difference lies not so much in where they ended up as in where they came from," their point being that although nurses who do not marry appear to be more mobile, this may be because they had further to go. This observation is verified by the finding that the fathers of single nurses tend to be of lower status than those of married nurses (25).

The New Orleans study (18) introduces a very different kind of evidence to support the contention that nurses are ambitious to climb in the world, namely, that of the Thematic Apperception Test.[2]

---

[2] The Thematic Apperception Test is not unlike the "inkblot" tests. To discover an individual's attitudes, the examiner shows him a set of picture cards showing persons singly or together in various attitudes and situations and asks what he thinks is happening.

Among other things, two recurring themes were revealed. One is that "The daughter is attempting to raise her standard of living above those of her parents by getting an education." The predominant theme read into another was: "That is a woman or child going up the stairs to get someplace—a climb toward success or to achieve a goal." Rohrer, the analyst, explains that both of these themes are mobility-motivated and that the nursing profession is seen as a way of climbing up in the world. When these findings are combined with the data obtained on fathers' occupations, he concludes that the profession represents moving upward for most of the nurses studied. It is worth reminding the reader that these are statistical generalizations which may or may not apply to any individual nurse. There are certainly sizable minorities for whom they do not hold, for example, the nearly one quarter of the Kansas City nurses who were found to be mobile *downward*.

There are some disconcerting bits of knowledge which do not jibe as neatly as they might with the Kansas City, Pennsylvania and New Orleans findings. Although Theriault, in his New Hampshire study (22), also demonstrates a trend upward among nurses, he finds that this is not restricted solely to nurses. In comparing nurses' brothers with their fathers, he finds that the younger generation of men are somewhat upwardly mobile in the scale of occupations. Possibly, this suggests that there is a general trend toward intergenerational upward mobility, that is, for children to rise above their fathers. In part, it is to be explained by increasing mechanization and automation which relieves human beings of much of the work thought of as "dirty" or of low status.

The study of North Carolina psychiatric nurses provides a clear case of findings contradictory to most of those cited above (29). The authors do find a slight increase of husbands over fathers in what they call the "middle and upper" status occupations: 25 per cent of the fathers of their 103 psychiatric nurses fall in this category, in contrast with 33 per cent of the husbands. Although this indicates some upward mobility, the other end of the scale must also be examined. Both fathers and husbands are classified equally (25 per cent) in their "lower" group. However, for husbands, they introduce a new category—"One third held jobs which did not fit into the groups mentioned; most of them were themselves mental hospital attendants." The occupation of hospital attendant falls within the lower category as it has been thought of here, making, therefore, a total of 58 per cent of the husbands in the lower occupational category. This is a far larger proportion than can be found in any of the other studies and is obviously attributable to the large number of psychiatric nurses who are married to attendants.

The observation made of Arkansas general duty nurses (17), that over half of their husbands are in occupations which rate lower than nursing, is not particularly relevant to the problem in hand, insofar as the crucial question is whether or not the husbands have occupations which rank higher or lower than the fathers. Although many of the husbands may be engaged in occupations which rank lower than nursing, they may rank higher than the nurses' fathers. Nurses, by and large, have had more education than their parents, but this is too general a trend in America to be construed as a sign of rising socially (18, 22).

geographic origins and geographic mobility

In what size of community are nurses born? Are they likely to be farm girls or from big cities? Are there regional differences in their origins? Do they travel far to seek employment or do they tend to stay near home?

In six of the eight areas from which data are available, over 25 per cent of the nurses studied are of rural background. All six of these are in the South or the Middle West. Of the 107 general duty nurses in the Arkansas study (17), two thirds had "rural backgrounds." Fifty-five per cent of the North Carolina psychiatric nurses came "from rural areas or communities of under 2,000 population" (29). Among the New Orleans sample, 40 per cent were from "farm," "country" or "a village of less than 2,500 population" (18). In the Kansas City area, 37 per cent of the graduate nurses stated that they grew up on a farm, an additional 22 per cent came from places of less than 4,000 population (25), while of nonmetropolitan Missouri nurses, 31 per cent are reported as having "attended rural schools" (9). A study conducted by Robert P. Bullock in Ohio (33) describes 27 per cent of his sample as having grown up "in the country."

In contrast with the states in the South and the Middle West, in which over a quarter of the nurses appear to have rural derivations, data from two studies conducted in the Northeast indicate that only small proportions of nurses have such origins. The Pennsylvania survey found a mere nine per cent of its nurses identifying their father's occupation as "farmer" (19), while in New Hampshire, "rural farm origin" was specified by only 13 per cent (22). According to the United States Census, 36 per cent of the population was "rural" in 1950.[3] (The Bureau of the Census defines "urban" approximately as any incorporated place with a population of 2,500 or more.) Obviously, this array of figures from a variety of sources is only roughly comparable, but it does provide at least a crude picture of the degree of "rurality" of American nurses.

Table 3. Nurses Having Rural Origins[a]

Study Area	Per Cent of Nurses with Rural Origins	State	Per Cent of Population Rural
Arkansas	66[b]	Arkansas	67
North Carolina	55[c]	North Carolina	66
New Orleans	40[b]	Louisiana	45
K.C. Met. Area	37	Missouri & Kansas	39 & 48
Central Missouri	31[b]	Missouri	39
Ohio	27	Ohio	30
New Hampshire	13	New Hampshire	43
Pennsylvania	9	Pennsylvania	30

Source: (17, 29, 18, 25, 9, 33, 22, 19) and U.S. Census Bureau (see footnote 3).

a. The various definitions of the term "rural" used in these studies are described above in the text. Wherever possible, the present authors have regrouped data in order to obtain more nearly comparable definitions. This was not always possible, however; for example the 9 per cent of nurses with "rural" origins in the Pennsylvania study is clearly an underestimate resulting from the fact that this includes only those nurses who gave their father's occupation as farmer.

b. This study includes institutional nurses only.

c. This study includes psychiatric nurses only.

A state-by-state breakdown appears in Table 3, where it can be seen that in every case the proportion of population which is rural exceeds the proportion of nurses with rural backgrounds. Considering the limited comparability of the data, it is probably safe to say that in all of these states nursing has been obtaining its fair share of recruits from the rural population—with two exceptions: New Hamp-

---

[3] Summary, General Population Characteristics, 1950, Population Census Report P-B1, Reprint of Vol. 2, Part 1, Ch. B., U. S. Govt. Printing Office, 1952. Table 58. p. 105.

shire and Pennsylvania. In both of these states, the percentage of nurses with rural origins is far below the percentage of population which is rural. This may well be indicative of a regional variation in recruitment.

Table 3 compares graduate nurses of all ages with general state populations. In order to determine the extent to which recruitment of rural girls into nursing is successful at any given time, a different kind of comparison should be made—one for which no data are available. That would be a comparison between student nurses and the proportion of the female population which has rural origins within a specific age group—say 17 to 20 years. The state data in Table 3 include people of all ages and men as well as women. A closer approximation of this kind of information can be found in a study of over 200 student nurses in a variety of nursing schools in the Kansas City area (26). Thirty-five per cent of these students had rural origins, but the two states from which most of them are drawn are 39 and 48 per cent rural. The Kansas City survey of graduate nurses (25) observes that although nurses traditionally may have tended to come from rural areas, there is evidence of a trend toward more urban origins. An examination of the relationship between age and the size of the home town reveals that the percentage of nurses who come from farms decreases steadily from the older to younger age groups.

Table 4. Graduate Nurses Who Grew Up on Farms

Age	Number of Nurses In This Age Group*	Per Cent Who Grew Up on a Farm
20 – 29	696	30
30 – 39	715	34
40 – 49	474	44
50 – 59	256	45
60 and over	128	53
All Nurses	2269	37

Source: (25). Sample is from Kansas City area.

* Nurses for whom either age or place of origin or both is unknown, have been eliminated from this distribution.

Table 4 shows that of those who are now 60 years or older, over half grew up on the farm, in contrast with only 30 per cent of those under 30 years of age. Their data indicate that the same trend is visible among nurses who grew up in large cities (100,000 or over) with only 10 per cent of the 60-and-older group having originated in such cities, as contrasted with over twice that percentage in the younger group. Certainly, this is a reflection in part of a general decline in the rural population, but it may also indicate a growing appeal of nursing to the urban girl or a declining appeal to the rural girl.

The comparison between characteristics of nurses and the population characteristics of the state within which they are employed implies that nurses are natives of that state. To what extent is such an assumption justified? Sometimes it is said that nurses are a restless group, always on the go from one place to another. Let us examine what information exists on the extent of their geographic mobility.

Ninety per cent of the institutional nurses in New Hampshire were born and bred in New England, with half of them being natives of New Hampshire (22); 34 per cent of these nurses are actually working in their own home towns. A fifth of the central Missouri nurses are working and always have worked in their home towns, while a total of 55 per cent of them always have worked in the state (9). Fifty-six per cent of the Arkansas general duty nurses were born in Arkansas (17), and over two thirds of the psychiatric nurses studied in North Carolina were born in that state. Eighty-five per cent of this North Carolina sample were born in southern states (29); 72 per cent of those surveyed in New Orleans were natives of the south central region, a fifth of them having been born in the city itself, and half being natives of Louisiana (18).

Despite the fact that nurses are in a seller's market, and despite the favorable pay differentials in some other parts of the United States, about 60 per cent of Kansas City nurses never have worked outside the two states in which the metropolitan area lies (25). Almost half of them always have worked in that area and less than a fourth of them came from outside Kansas and Missouri. These Kansas City observations are further corroborated by the nurses' history of state registrations, which indicates that well over half of the working nurses in the Kansas City area have been registered in only one state. When we consider that the area itself includes parts of two states, this seems to indicate a remarkable degree of geographic stability.

Thus, by and large, nurses are a home-grown product. However, the statement needs to be qualified. When the Kansas City nurse is compared with the nonmetropolitan Missouri nurse (25, 9), the patterns of geographic mobility are found not to be the same: a much smaller proportion of the nonmetropolitan nurses are rooted to a single community—only 20 per cent as compared with 47 per cent. Of course, it is impossible for a small community to produce sufficient nurses to staff its local institutions, so that inevitably a higher proportion of its nurses must be imported from outside. The point is made in the Arkansas study (17) that the younger woman is not attracted to the small hospital in the small community. Unless it is her home town, she is otherwise not likely to come to it for employment. Four out of the five single nurses in small hospitals in the Arkansas sample were found to be working in their home town, while 18 out of the 20 married ones came from outside after marriage. The authors of the Arkansas report observe that by far the biggest part of the nursing staffs of the smaller hospitals is of nurses who married into the community and came there with their husbands, and that this is a source of supply which the administrators of the small hospital find is not adequate. On the other hand, a metropolitan area, because its demands are higher and its facilities better, produces large numbers of home-grown graduate nurses, many of whom stay at home to work after graduation. Theriault concludes in New Hampshire that, "These findings illustrate dramatically the highly important function of middle-sized and larger cities as sources of professional registered nurses for their hospitals" (22).

Although we have no data here about patterns of geographic mobility in other professions, it is probably safe to hazard the guess that nurses are as stable geographically as most other occupational groups, if not more so.

the nurse and her family

The Family of Origin. An individual typically has two families. The family of origin consists basically of a person's mother, father, brothers and sisters, although in some cases grandparents and even uncles and aunts may be included. The "family of orientation"—to use the anthropological phrase—is the one which an individual creates through marriage and consists basically of a spouse and children, although certain in-laws are occasionally incorporated into it. Each family imparts decisive personal characteristics, some of which have been discussed already. To consider others, data in three of the research projects bear on the nurse's position among her brothers and sisters—her sibling position. Psychoanalytically oriented observers sometimes attempt to explain supposed attributes of the nurse, such as her choice of occupation, as the consequence of her position within the family. On the one hand are those who state that nurses are youngest or only children who are drawn into their occupation by their need for an authoritative "father-figure," the physician, whom they can look up to and who assumes full responsibility in the work situation. Others claim that nurses are eldest children accustomed to giving orders and needing to dominate others, the patient providing the dependent whom they need. Finally, some claim that nurses are middle children, who find their occupation suitable because of the way it places them between the doctor and the patient. Although any one of these may be a reasonable hypothesis, not all of them can be correct.

First of all, which are nurses likely to be—older, middle or younger children? We find that 36 per cent of the 161 graduate nurses in the central Missouri sample are eldest children—"first-born" (9). A comparable category can be obtained from the Kansas City study by combining "only children" with "oldest children" (25). This results in approximately the same percentage as the central Missouri study— 31 per cent of the 2,194 nurses of whom sibling position was known. Sixteen per cent of 94 nurses in the New Hampshire sample were "only" children, as contrasted with eight per cent of the Kansas City group (22). The New Hampshire study goes on to point out that institutional nurses in that state appear to come from families in which girls outnumber boys at a rate of almost two to one. It is not possible to determine the proportion of middle or youngest children in either the central Missouri or the New Hampshire sample. The Kansas City analysis indicates that 44 per cent of those nurses have both older and younger brothers and sisters, while 25 per cent of them are youngest children. This may be a "high" percentage of middle children, but interpretations are limited by our lack of knowledge of sibling distributions in the general population or in other occupations. How can we describe something as peculiar to nurses or nursing when there is a dearth of evidence relating occupational choice and sibling position?

Wherever data are available, they lead to the conclusion that graduate nurses are primarily native Americans. Only two per cent of the group studied in New Orleans were foreign-born (18) as were five per cent of the New Hampshire sample (22). The last-named were all Canadians, and their presence is easily explained by the nearness of the Canadian border. In addition, in two of these hospitals there were Catholic sisters from Canadian orders. In both Kansas City (25) and central Missouri (9), about 85 per cent of the nurses sampled are found to have two native-born parents; the remainder are split about evenly between those with one native-born parent and those with none. Obviously, nursing does not have that peculiar appeal to ethnic and other minority groups which characterizes some occupations.[4]

Further support for this contention is found in Kansas City (25) where only eight per cent of the local nurses identify a member of their family as belonging to a minority, and not all of those identify themselves as belonging to one. Of those who so identify a member of their family, about one third are Negro; one third Catholic; and the remainder divided among other religions and nationalities. Of course, this is no indication of the actual proportion of Negroes or Catholics in the Kansas City sample; rather, it reflects only those members of such groups who think of them as minorities. It is probable that this includes most Negroes. However, whereas 552 nurses in the sample identified themselves as Catholics, only 58 said that a member of their family belonged to a minority which they identified as Catholic. Curiously, the reverse is true of the Jewish nurses. Only six identified themselves as Jewish, while over twice that number said that a member of their family belonged to a minority which they identified as Jewish. This provides a partial explanation for the small proportion of Jewish women found in nursing. Being Jewish apparently means different things to different people. To some it is a matter of religion, while to others it implies a cultural heritage or a nationality. It is certain that there are nurses of Jewish parentage in Kansas City who did not identify themselves as Jewish.

There are little or no data in these studies on the proportion of nurses who are Negroes. The Kansas City survey (25) found that about three per cent of the local graduate nurses identified themselves as Negroes; the city of Kansas City, Mo., which includes most of the

---

[4] See, for example, New Kong-ming, Peter: Social Processes in a Minority Profession: From Osteopathic Manipulation to Osteopathic Medicine, Kansas City, Community Studies, Inc., 1955. Mimeographed.

area's population, is about 10 per cent Negro. Only six per cent of the New Orleans sample of graduate nurses were Negroes (18), while one third of the population of the state is Negro. (This, with the data on national origins, leads us to believe that there is a reservoir in the minorities which is not being tapped by professional nursing. To what extent is the opportunity afforded by the presence of displaced persons and refugees not being taken advantage of by nurse recruiters? Are intelligent Negro girls, especially in the South, made aware of the fact that they are sorely needed in nursing?)

Family of Orientation. To what extent do nurses marry and have children of their own? This is an important question when we con-

Table 5. Nurses Reported as Never Having Been Married

Study Area	Per Cent Nurses Never Married
Pennsylvania	10[a]
New Orleans	20[b]
Kansas City	12[a]
North Carolina	24[c]
Central Missouri	25[b]
Arkansas	26[b]
Georgia	26[d]

Source: (19, 18, 25, 29, 9, 17, 7).
a. Includes nurses who are not working.
b. Institutional nurses only.
c. Psychiatric nurses only.
d. Private duty nurses only.

sider the degree of the nurse's professional involvement and her career line (Chaps. 10 and 11).

As can be seen in Table 5, from one fifth to one quarter of nurses never have been married—with one exception: the Pennsylvania state-wide survey reveals that only 10 per cent never have married. This deviation from the general pattern is difficult to explain. It is true that the Pennsylvania study includes nurses who are not working and, to the extent that marriage draws women out of the labor force, we would expect a sample containing nonworking nurses to show a higher proportion of married and a lower proportion of unmarried women. However, this is not sufficient explanation because the Kansas City study encompasses an even greater range of nonworking nurses than the Pennsylvania survey, and its percentage of unmarried nurses is similar to that found in most of the other studies. The prob-

Table 6. Current Marital Status of Working Nurses

Study Area[a]	Per Cent Single	Per Cent Married	Per Cent Other[b]	Total
Kansas City	31	56	13	100
Arkansas	26	58	17	100
Georgia	26	50	24	100
Central Missouri	25	64	11	100
New Orleans	20	60	9	89[d]
New Hampshire	[c]	48	[c]	100

Source: (25, 17, 7, 9, 18, 22).

a. Notes to table 5 describe peculiarities of these samples except for the Kansas City area, where only working nurses are included in this distribution.

b. Includes widowed, divorced and separated.

c. This study reports only that 48 per cent are married and 52 per cent are unmarried.

d. Marital status could not be determined for the remaining 11 per cent of this group. Percentages for the other studies exclude those for whom marital status was not known.

lem must remain unsolved for the time being. The current marital status of nurses as reported in six studies is shown in Table 6.

The Arkansas report (17) states that many of the unmarried nurses were less than 25 years old and, although only 22 per cent of the Kansas City nurses never had been married, nearly half of those under 25 years of age were unmarried. Another way of looking at it is that nurses under 25 years of age constitute only 11 per cent of the whole Kansas City sample, yet they are 21 per cent of the single nurses, nearly twice as many as would be expected in a random distribution (25).

Comparisons between it and Table 6 are revealing. There are only two categories of employed women which contain more single people than nurses: the professional and technical workers and the clerical and sales workers. On the other hand, service workers, operatives and the proprietor-manager group all have proportionally fewer single women employed than does nursing, as reported in the six studies for which data are available. The Kansas City report (25) compares its complement of nurses with other women in the metropolitan area on the basis of Census data. They find that 10 per cent of all women in Kansas City who are 20 years and older are single,[5] in contrast with 22 per cent of all graduate nurses in the same age group.

[5] Department of Commerce, Bureau of the Census: 1950 U.S. Census of Population, Missouri, Detailed Characteristics, Report P-C25, Reprint of Vol. 2, Part 25, Chapter C; Table 57, p. 173 and Table 70, p. 207, Washington, U.S. Government Printing Office, 1952.

Table 7. Marital Status of Employed U.S. Women

Occupational Category	Per Cent Single	Per Cent Married	Per Cent Other	Total
Professional, technical and kindred workers ..	42	43	15	100
Clerical, sales and kindred workers	38	46	16	100
Service workers	24	41	35	100
Operatives and kindred workers	19	59	22	100
Proprietors, managers and officials	14	61	25	100
All employed women ...	29	49	22	100

Source: Women's Bureau, U.S. Department of Labor: Women as Workers, Table 25, p. 67, Washington, U.S. Government Printing Office, 1950.

They also compare women in the Kansas City labor force who are 20 years or older with working nurses, 20 years or older, and find again an excessive proportion of single nurses—31 per cent, in contrast with only 23 per cent of other working women. However, when the "single" and "other" categories are combined, nurses and other working women are about equally unmarried. This is because there is over twice the percentage of widowed, separated and divorced among all the working women, as among the working nurses in Kansas City.

Of course, nurses vary among themselves in all these attributes. For example, we shall find interesting variations in different New Hampshire hospitals (22) and important differences between the fields

Table 8. Per Cent of Nurses (Ever Married) With Children

Study Area	Number of Nurses	Per Cent with Children
Georgia	315	47[a]
Central Missouri	113	67[b]
Arkansas	79	68[b]
Kansas City area	1827	75
Pennsylvania	738	88
All U.S. women (married)	—	79

Source: (7, 9, 17, 25, 19) and Demographic Yearbook, 1955: table 17, p. 582, New York Statistical Office of the United Nations, Department of Economic and Social Affairs, 1955.

a. The percentage for the Georgia private duty nurses appears to be based on all nurses in the sample rather than just those who have been married.

b. Institutional nurses only.

of nursing are described in Kansas City (25). Such variations are considered in more detail in Chapters 4 and 5.

The percentage of nurses having children is reported in five studies (Table 8). At first glance it would appear that there is wide variation, but there are fairly simple explanations. The Georgia private duty study (7) did not eliminate unmarried nurses in the computation, so it is quite natural that the percentage of nurses with children is smaller than in the other studies which report only the nurses who ever have been married. The high percentages observed in Pennsylvania and Kansas City (19, 25) result from the inclusion of nurses who are not working in hospitals, as well as those who are not working at all. Note that these two percentages approach the figure for all married United States women who also may or may not be working. This point can be clearly made by removing all but the institutional nurses from the Kansas City group and recalculating the percentage with children. When that is done the percentage drops from 75 to 67—practically identical with the other studies reporting on institutional nurses only (9, 17).

Not all children are dependents, and not all dependents need be children. The Georgia study reports that 62 per cent of its sample of private duty nurses have persons other than themselves dependent upon their incomes (7), while in Arkansas it was found to be true of 38 per cent of the general duty nurses (17). The Arkansas and Central Missouri studies (17, 9), both focusing on institutional nurses, report the average number of children for married nurses in their samples as 1.9 and 1.4 respectively. It will be seen in our discussion of career lines in Chapter 11 that the number of children a nurse has may be important in keeping her in or drawing her out of the labor force. This argument is most clearly presented and supported in the Pennsylvania study (19).

personal characteristics

We now have at least a rough picture of the graduate nurse as daughter, sister, wife and mother. The following section deals with some of her individual and personal characteristics.

Age. The age distributions of working nurses vary widely with the kind of work in which they are engaged. It can be seen in Table 9, for example, that the two groups of private duty nurses have considerably smaller proportions of people under 50 years of age than do most of the other samples reported. At the other extreme, practically all of the psychiatric nurses studied in North Carolina are under 50. An explanation for the relatively low percentage of younger institutional nurses found in the nonmetropolitan Missouri study can be inferred from a finding of the New Hampshire study: a consistent increase in the percentage of younger nurses as the size of the hospital increased; moreover, central Missouri's hospitals are all extremely small in comparison with those in which most of the nurses in other studies were employed. The Georgia research team compare their private duty nurses with those in a national study (34), and the results are parallel, although there appears to be a somewhat higher percentage of older nurses in private duty in the United States as a whole than in Georgia.

Table 9. Nurses Under 50 Years of Age

Study	Number	Per Cent Under 50
North Carolina (psychiatric)	106	94
Kansas City (general duty)	489	87
New Hampshire (institutional)	—	85*
New Orleans (Charity Hospital)	45	80
Central Missouri (institutional)	181	74
Georgia (private duty)	315	70*
Kansas City (private duty)	220	68

Source: (29, 25, 22, 18, 9, 7, 25).
* Includes those 50 years of age.

Except for the two private duty samples and the central Missouri group, the studies noted in Table 9 report nearly half their nurses as being under 30 years of age. The percentage over 60 years of age ranges between 3 and 6 per cent except for the private duty nurses. In Kansas City, 12 per cent of the private duty groups are over 60 years old (25). Although age variations in the different fields of nursing will be discussed further in Chapters 4 and 5, it is worth mentioning at this point that the Kansas City survey found 3 groups of nurses to be generally older than those in private duty: school nurses, administrators and nurses in public health. Only 27 per cent of the last were under 40, and 15 per cent of them were 60 or over. Using Census data, the Kansas City team answers the question, "How does the distribution of nurses compare with that of other working women?" The team finds no marked discrepancies between the two, although on the basis of minor differences they make the general observation that nurses tend to be slightly younger than other working women. In comparing their own metropolitan nurses with those in nonmetropolitan Missouri (9), they observe that the nonmetropolitan nurse appears to be slightly older than her metropolitan counterpart. The explanation offered by Theriault on the basis of his New Hampshire investigation seems to be sufficient to explain this difference (22).

Martin and Simpson express concern over their finding that little more than a quarter of the North Carolina psychiatric nurses are over 40 years of age (29). They pose the question this way: "Is this peculiar to psychiatric nursing or is there a general quick drop in the number of persons in active nursing after the age of 40, or do nurses beyond 40 like other types of nursing, or do mental hospitals as a matter of policy not employ nurses of that age?" Some of these questions are answered by other studies. First of all, the situation appears not to be peculiar to psychiatric nursing. Institutional nurses in New Hampshire and general duty nurses in Kansas City show the same pattern of youthfulness. The Kansas City survey also shows that office nurses, nursing educators and industrial nurses are relatively young. The Kansas City data indicate that not only is there indeed a general quick drop in the number of persons in active nursing after the age of 40 but also a similar drop after that age in all employed women, whether or not they are nurses.

There is certainly a relationship between age and career in nursing, and it will be discussed in some detail in Chapter 11. As an example, we need mention for the moment only the observation made in the study of operating room nurses in Arkansas (16): that the age range among the operating room nurses is from 22 to 45 years, with an average of 29. Floor nurses in the same institutions range from 22 to 59 years old, with an average of 34.

Religion. The historic and traditional connection between nursing care and religious ideals and organizations leads to the question: To what extent are nurses affiliated with religious denominations, and does any denomination supply nurses out of proportion to its numbers in the general population?

Since there are no reliable religious censuses which would enable a comparison between nurses and the general population, these questions can be answered only partially. Data from Kansas City (25), central Missouri (9), and Ohio (33) indicate that Catholic women are found in nursing in larger proportions than they are in the general population. The Catholic church in Kansas City estimates that the local Catholic population is about 12 per cent, while 23 per cent of the nurses in the sample were Catholics. The existence of church-supported hospitals staffed in part by nurses who are members of religious orders no doubt is partially responsible for this inflated proportion. However, there are other explanations. The fact that Catholic families tend to be larger would make it more difficult for those families to educate all of their daughters. Nursing, being a respected profession with a relatively short period of inexpensive training, offers a means of successfully launching daughters into a secure and worthwhile career. However, it is not universally true that Catholic women are overrepresented in nursing. The North Carolina study of psychiatric nurses found only three Catholics among the 103 nurses reporting religion. This would suggest that there are some parts of the country or some special fields in nursing in which there are disproportionately few Catholics.

Jewish women, in contrast with Catholic, appear to be grossly underrepresented in nursing. Less than one per cent of the nurses in Kansas City (25) and in nonmetropolitan Missouri (9) gave their religion as Jewish, and only four per cent of those in Ohio (33). It has been noted earlier that there were more nurses in the Kansas City area who identified their parents as Jewish than who identified themselves as Jewish. The fact that being Jewish may or may not be regarded as a matter of religion obscures the state of the case.

A final observation on religion is derived from the Kansas City survey of 2,441 nurses, of whom 86 per cent claimed some sort of religious affiliation. Of the remainder, no information was available on 8 per cent, and only 6 per cent claimed no religious affiliation (25). The 96 per cent of the North Carolina psychiatric nurses who reported religion were nearly all "church-going."

Sex. Obviously, nursing is at present a woman's world, and there is not much indication of a change in the near future. That men comprise a minority, both numerically and socially, in nursing is apparent from various sources. Interviews conducted in Kansas City, although they indicate little racial prejudice on the part of graduate nurses, reflect a great deal of sex prejudice. Some nurses spoke of men derogatorily, and stated that they should "stay in their place" (27). It would seem that that place is, by and large, *not* in nursing, the exceptions being nursing which requires physical strength or calls for certain treatments for male patients. Men nursing students interviewed in Kansas City (26) generally state that they do not have career aspirations in nursing but rather use their nursing education as a steppingstone toward another career such as medicine or hospital administration. There is a large reservoir of manpower which conceivably could be recruited to help mitigate the shortage of nurses, but until public attitudes and the attitudes of nurses themselves change radically, there is little probability of men flocking into nursing.

In the six hospitals studied in North Carolina, only two men nurses were encountered, and these were not included in the study. Of the 182 R.N.'s who filled out personal data sheets in the central Missouri study, only one was a man (9). Seven men were found among the 2,441 graduate nurses in the Kansas City Survey (25). None of the graduate nurses in the New Orleans study were men (18). It is safe to assume that these figures are typical of all the studies and of nursing. In spite of a loosening of sex restriction by nursing schools and the recent concession of the military to provide commissions for men nurses, there seem to be few men entering the profession.

leisure time and participation in the community

What are nurses like off the job? How do they occupy their time when they are not working? How would the nurse prefer to spend her off-duty hours if she were free to choose? To what extent do nurses participate in the organized activities of the community in which they live and work?

Two studies, one conducted in the Kansas City metropolitan area (25) and that of the Arkansas general duty nurse (17), make a start at answering such questions as these. According to the Kansas City report, nurses prefer more than anything else to spend their leisure time in activities related to the home or the family: over a third of the working nurses in the sample said so. After home and family activities came "reading," named by 20 per cent of the nurses. "Social Activities" were preferred by only 14 per cent and, interestingly enough, 5 per cent of the nurses stated that what they would most like to do in their leisure time is "just rest and relax."

A curious fact is that housekeeping, care of children and other home and family activities are not an unmixed blessing. Those nurses who stated that they did not manage to do the things they would most like to do in their leisure time indicated that the major reason was that this time was consumed by home and family. In this respect, the unmarried nurse seems to have somewhat more freedom than her married colleague; she is more likely to spend her leisure hours engaged in kinds of activities which she would prefer. For the most part, little difference appears between single and married nurses in their off-duty aspirations. The only difference worthy of note is the married nurses' interest in activities related to the home, over twice as many of them stating such preference as did single nurses. On the other hand, single nurses express more interest than the married in group activities, reading, spectator sports and "cultural" activities.

Of course, it is true that one's notions about how best to spend leisure time are bound to be modified with the passage of years. Forty-one per cent of all working nurses in the Kansas City sample are 40 years of age or over, and it is hardly surprising that only 27 per cent of them prefer active sports. At the other extreme, over half of those nurses who like individual activities such as hobbies, shopping and walking are 40 or over. It is the nurses between 30 and 39 who most prefer to spend their time on home and family activities; although only 28 per cent of all of the working nurses are in that age group, they represent 35 per cent of those who prefer household and family activities. This is the only age group which is overrepresented in preference for this kind of activity and is the only age group which has a larger proportion interested in housework and family than in any other kind of activity.

To what extent do nurses take part in the life of the community in which they work? A rough index of participation in the affairs of the local community is the extent of membership in nonprofessional clubs and organizations. As might be expected, the working nurse is not as frequent a participant in clubs and organizations as is her nonworking colleague. The Kansas City data indicate that over half the working nurses do not belong to any clubs, as compared with only 34 per cent of those who are not working. Among the Arkansas general duty nurses, about half belonged to clubs, and of these, half did not go to meetings or engage in the activities of the clubs to which they did belong (17). Of course, work consumes time, and it could be anticipated that working nurses would have less time for clubs and organizations than would those who were not working, or for that matter, than would any women who were not working. Also, it might be anticipated that, because marriage and family take time, married nurses would have less time for club activities. However, this is *not* true: in Kansas City more of the married working nurses than of the unmarried nurses belong to clubs or organizations.

Table 10. Nurses Who Do Not Belong to Any Clubs or Organizations

Kind of Position	Number of Nurses	Per Cent Who Are Not Members
Head nurse or supervisor	290	61
General duty	501	60
Miscellaneous nursing positions*	90	60
Office nurse	132	57
Private duty	237	52
Industrial nurse	79	44
Administrative position	91	38
Not working**	810	36
Nursing educator	60	35
Public health	60	35
School nurse	78	23
Unknown	13	77

Source: (25).
* One-half of this group consists of nurse anesthetists, surgical assistants and clinic nurses; one sixth of them, although they remain in the health field and are registered nurses, are not actually nursing; these include such persons as medical librarians, physical therapists, laboratory technicians, X-ray technicians, etc. The remaining one third is composed of nurses who are employed by nursing organizations, registered nurses in school, and nurses in the armed forces.
** Includes housewives, new graduates, retired nurses, etc.

As age influences leisure activities in general, so would it be expected to enter into organizational participation. It is in the age range of 40 to 49 that most nurses—both working and nonworking—belong to at least one club; 56 per cent of working nurses and 77 per cent of nonworking nurses are members. The biggest proportion of nonmembers appears in the youngest group of working nurses—those between 20 and 29; 65 per cent of them belong to no clubs in contrast with only 43 per cent of the nonworking nurses of the same age.

The Arkansas report on general duty nurses suggests that nurses in other branches of the profession play a greater part in community affairs than do general duty nurses. This is documented by the Kansas City study. The proportion of nurses who do not belong to any clubs or organizations is listed by field in Table 10. Apparently, there is a difference in the extent to which nurses in the different fields partici- pate in community affairs. School nurses appear to be by far the most active in community life. Actually 45 per cent of them belong to three or more nonprofessional clubs or organizations. Nursing educators, public health nurses and administrators also appear to have relatively high rates of participation—in fact, about as high as those nurses who are not working at all. Approximately 60 per cent of the head nurses and supervisors, those in general duty, miscellaneous nursing positions and in offices, do not belong to any clubs or organizations.

It should be remembered that in this chapter we have been dis- cussing only nonprofessional organizations. Membership in profes- sional organizations will be discussed in Chapter 10. We will antici- pate that discussion only by pointing out that the Kansas City data indicate that in general the nurses who belong to nonprofessional organizations also belong to professional organizations or by implica- tion, nurses who participate in the affairs of the community are, by and large, those who are most professionally committed.

labor force status and income

Not all women who are entitled to call themselves graduate nurses are working. This is an obvious point but important in so far as it bears on what is thought to be a shortage of nursing personnel. In any occupation constant job turnover may be expected. People leave old jobs for new; they retire for reasons of age or health; they tem- porarily or permanently leave the particular occupation or the labor force in general. The Kansas City survey reports on the labor force status of its 2,441 graduate nurses on one particular day in 1954, which is referred to as the "complement date." They found that 31 per cent of the nurses were not employed at all on that date; 1 per cent of the complement were employed in work unrelated to their nurses' training, and another 1 per cent had retired because of health or age. Those who were working were distributed among a variety of kinds of positions. The nature of this distribution and its characteristics will be discussed at other places in this volume.

This is not the whole picture of the participation of nurses in the labor force. To say that 31 per cent of all nurses in a metropolitan area are not employed does not imply that the remainder are fully employed. Only about half of the local complement of graduate nurses were working full time. Nine per cent had regular jobs at which they worked on a part-time basis, while eight per cent did part-time nursing occasionally (25).

As might be expected, both age and marital status have something to do with the nurses' participation in the labor force. Between the ages of 30 and 39, the smallest proportion of nurses is working full time (in the Kansas City area). Of course, this is the period when children are likely to require a mother's fullest attention; thus it is also the decade when the largest percentage of nurses is not working at all and, along with the over-60 group, is the age-span in which the largest percentage of part-time nurses is found.

Nurses between the ages of 50 and 59 are not only more likely to be working than any other group of nurses but also more likely to be working full time; only 21 per cent of them were not employed, and 65 per cent were working full time. With the growing concern for the shortage of nurses, it is important to note that in the decade approximately following graduation (20 to 29 years), 30 per cent of the nurses are not working at all, and only 54 per cent of them are employed full time. This is the decade in which young women can be expected to marry and begin to bear children; however, it is hardly conducive to high morale among nursing educators to have to expect 30 per cent of their graduates not to enter the labor force during the decade following their graduation.

What effect does marriage have on the nurse's participation in the labor force? Only six per cent of the nurses who are not working at all are unmarried, as contrasted with 52 per cent of those working full time. It is also true that those in the part-time categories predominantly are married—especially the part-time, occasional worker. A careful analysis of the effect of marriage and children on nurses' participation in the labor force was conducted in the Pennsylvania study (19) and will be reviewed in Chapter 10. Those nurses in

Kansas City who are engaged in only part-time occasional work are seldom hired by hospitals, as compared with part-time, regular and full-time nurses. Only 16 per cent of the occasional workers were employed by hospitals, as compared with 62 per cent of the full-time nurses. In this respect, nurses who work at regular, part-time jobs do not differ from those who work full time.

In addition to age and marital status, is there any relationship between the nurse's labor-force status and other personal attributes? Comparing those who work full time with those who do not work at all, it appears that over half of the full-time nurses do not belong to any clubs or nonprofessional organizations, while 63 per cent of those who do not work belong to one or more. Although this is a reasonable observation, the distribution of the part-time, occasional nurses is not so easily explainable. Why is it that these nurses, who work only occasionally, have a higher percentage of membership in clubs than any other group, including those who do not work at all? This is not the only difference between the part-time, occasional worker and other nurses. In spite of the fact that they appear to participate in community life more than do other nurses, the data also show that they do not succeed in spending their time doing what they would like to be doing to the extent that other nurses do; only 40 per cent of the occasional workers do what they would most like to do with their off-duty hours as compared with 46 per cent of those who work full time and to about half of those who do not work at all. Also this group spends far more unwilling (in that they would prefer to be doing something else) hours at housework and family duties than does any other. Another relationship seems to appear in the area of social mobility. The biggest contrast in mobility is between the part-time, occasional nurse and the one who does not work at all. There is evidence in Kansas City of a tendency for nurses who marry men of higher occupational status than their fathers to leave the labor force.

The salary question in nursing is of persistent interest. How much money do nurses make? How does this vary in different parts of the country and in different fields of nursing? How does it compare with other occupations in this respect? These questions cannot be answered fully on the basis of the available data, but some clues do exist.

The distribution of annual (1954) income for the Kansas City nurse complement, according to position, is found in Figure 1. Obviously, it is incorrect to assume that all nurses' salaries can be discussed in a single breath. The income distribution varies from one field to another. The largest proportion of poorly paid nurses appears in general duty, with 35 per cent making less than $3,000 a year, and only 8 per cent making more than $4,000. The best-paid nurses are those in administrative positions, where about 30 per cent make over $5,000 a year and only 5 per cent earn $3,000 or less. Industrial nurses are also relatively well off as compared with most others; only 10 per cent of them make less than $3,000 a year.

School nurses present an interesting picture, salarywise, as seen in Kansas City. About 30 per cent of them earn less than $3,000—a larger percentage than any other group except general duty nurses, office nurses and those in miscellaneous positions. On the other hand, 40 per cent of them earn over $4,000—a larger percentage than any other group except administrators. This strange distribution of salaries is explained in part by the fact that the local school nurses are part of the school system and work under the same salary schedule as do school teachers.

Because there is probably some regional variation in nurses' salaries and because the figures cited here are for 1954, one needs to be careful in generalizing the absolute figures and applying them to other parts of the United States and to later years. However, it is safe to say that the relative income of various groups of nurses as compared with one another probably remains constant. In other words, administrators may make more money in Los Angeles than in Kansas City, and in both places they may earn more in 1958 than they did in 1954, but regardless of the place or the time, administrators make more than nurses in other fields. Thus, in Arkansas (17) it was found that the sample of general duty nurses had an average income in 1955 of $229 a month, while their supervisors and directors earned $289. Another Arkansas report (16) reveals that operating room nurses averaged $247 a month.

A hint at rural-urban differences is obtained by comparing the income of central Missouri institutional nurses (9) and Kansas City general duty nurses. Although this is the poorest paid group of Kansas City nurses, they are better off financially than those in nonmetropolitan Missouri. Eighty-four per cent of the latter group were earning

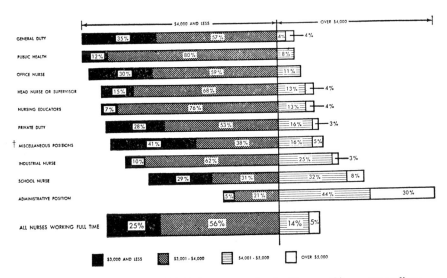

FIG. 1. Annual income of full-time nurses in the Kansas City metropolitan area. Source (25). Sample is from Kansas City area.

Because administrators in the fields of public health, industry, school, and nursing education are included in the administrative category rather than in their own fields, the lack of high-paying positions in these fields is more apparent than real.

† One-half of this group consists of nurse anesthetists, surgical assistants, and clinic nurses. One-sixth of them, although they remain in the health field and are registered nurses, are not actually nursing. These include such persons as medical librarians, physical therapists, laboratory technicians, x-ray technicians, etc. The remaining one-third of this group is composed of nurses who are employed by nursing organizations, registered nurses who are in school, and those who are in the armed forces.

$3,000 or less in 1954, in contrast with the Kansas City general duty nurses, 35 per cent of whom were earning that amount or less. The central Missouri nurses had an average monthly salary of $233, which makes them somewhat better off than the Arkansas general duty nurses.

In order to arrive at a more comprehensive understanding of income distribution, it is necessary to observe the effects of both marital status and age. The Kansas City survey shows that as one moves into higher income brackets, the proportion of single nurses increases considerably. Well over half of those who earn less than $3,000 are married, while fewer than a quarter of those who earn over $5,000 are married. It is also true that older nurses are found in higher proportions in the higher salary brackets. As in most occupations, it takes years and experience to work up into the better-paying positions.

However, there are some deviations from this general pattern. For example, nurses 60 years of age or older appear in about the same proportions in all income categories, while those between the ages of 30 and 39 provide a peculiar picture: about a fifth of the nurses in the highest and the lowest income groups are within those ages, while they account for nearly a third of the middle income group. This phenomenon is partially explained by a previous observation, that this is the age group in which the greatest proportion of nurses is out of the labor force. It may be assumed that as they return during the next decade, they will move largely into better paying positions and thus provide the same kind of income distribution we see for those who are now 40 to 49 years old.

Kansas City nurses were compared as to income with several other groups in the United States. There is a larger proportion of nurses earning $3,000 a year or more than women college graduates in the United States as a whole, but men college graduates earn more than nurses.[6] However, nurses earn more than the category, "Professional, Technical and Kindred Workers" in the United States. Of course, income data become rapidly obsolete, and it may be assumed that nurses are currently earning more than they were in 1954, when these data were gathered. It is true though, as we mentioned earlier, that income comparisons between nurses and other groups and among the various nursing fields remain relatively constant. It is also true that the effects of age and marital status on income probably remain relatively constant; so the advice given to the young nurse by the Kansas City report, with tongue in cheek, is: if you are interested in increasing your earnings, stay single and get older!

---

[6] Havemann, Earnest, and West, Patricia Salter: They Went to College, chart 17, p. 74, New York, Harcourt, 1952.

student nurses

The findings reported in this chapter are drawn almost entirely from a single sample surveyed in the only research monograph devoted to the subject of students of nursing. Other surveys now in progress will soon enlarge our picture of the student nurse. In the meantime, the present data bear on an important problem: the conceptions with which young women enter training and the fate of their ideas as they progress through school. While it is true that many kinds of schools were not represented in the study, those which were included are all of familiar types.

whither from?

Where do students of nursing come from? We know relatively little about the styles of life followed in their homes, but the research monographs yield facts about the size of home town, father's occupation and the like. The data are drawn from small samples which no doubt are locally representative, but generalizations drawn from them must be applied to other places with the greatest caution.

The proportion of students with rural backgrounds, as of nurses, is large in states which are largely rural, and small in states which are largely urban. A Kansas City study (26) reports that the fathers of 30 per cent of student nurses were farmers. This figure corresponds closely to the proportion of people in the general population who live in the country and leads one to conclude that nursing students are probably representative of the population at large.

When we look directly at a group of 227 student nurses from the Kansas City metropolitan region, the assumption that nurses originate in the middle ranges of American society is supported. Excluding farmers, whose occupation is hard to compare with others, 26 per cent came from families in which the fathers followed occupations above the average in prestige; 26 per cent were daughters of men whose occupations fall at the middle of the range; and 48 per cent had fathers whose occupations were below the middle rank in prestige and presumably in income.

The Kansas City study established that nearly half of the student body of a collegiate school (47 per cent) came from families *above* the middle of the socioeconomic range, while far more than half of the students in two publicly supported three-year programs of nursing education (61 per cent) came from families *below* the middle of the range. The student bodies of three-year schools supported by religious groups fell between the two. Obviously, the degree program involves a long and rather costly period of education attainable to students whose families can bear the expense or at least forego the lost earning power. On the other hand, the publicly maintained schools offer less expensive instruction, a shorter schooling and, frequently, stipends or allowances ranging from a small sum for beginning students to nearly twice as much for seniors. Most of the differences in class origins in the student bodies must be attributed to variation among freshman students. On the other hand, senior students in the various schools are much alike in socioeconomic background. Thus, students who come from families in the middle and higher socioeconomic positions are more likely to complete their schooling in nursing than are students from the lower social classes, while students who come from families below the middle range are less likely than others to complete their nursing education. However, it is unlikely that an able student would be forced to leave for financial reasons; loan programs, scholarships and stipends make this an infrequent occurrence.

Students who have dropped out of school offer evidence that socioeconomic origins enter into the successful completion of nursing education. Forty-four per cent of senior students approaching graduation came from families where the fathers' occupations were below the middle range of prestige, as compared with 51 per cent of freshmen and 65 per cent of those who dropped out. Plainly, nursing education (like most other types of formal education) selects students of relatively high socioeconomic background and eliminates those from families toward the lower end of the scale. More than half of all who failed to finish reported that they left school to be married.

why nursing?

The question, "Why do students choose to enter nursing?" may be broken down into two components: "What are the reasons for choosing nursing?" and "What alternatives were rejected?" Of course, this will tell nothing of the presumably large group of persons, mostly young women, who consider nursing and then reject it in favor of some other vocation. But the data do shed light on the complex of vocational choices of which, in the minds of potential students, nursing is one.

The idea of nursing is cherished at an early age. The study of psychiatric nurses in North Carolina reveals that of 67 nurses, 24 had considered no other occupations, 17 had thought of teaching, and 11 of clerical work (29). In Kansas City, teaching and office work together made up 61 per cent of all alternatives reported by freshmen (52 out of 85) and 62 per cent of those reported by seniors (26 out of 42). Rejected possibilities included creative and performing arts, 13; medical specialties such as physical therapy and laboratory work, 12; various service occupations, 6; journalism, 5. Thus, students of nursing choose from a group of occupations often followed by women, which involve skill and education, usually of a technical sort (but not prolonged) and which yield moderate incomes.

The students in a collegiate program in the Kansas City sample chose from the widest gamut of occupations; those in church-sponsored, diploma courses from the narrowest, and the students in public and voluntary three-year programs from in between.

When the Kansas City students were asked why they decided to become nurses, 49 seniors and 50 freshmen said that they had "always wanted to be a nurse" (see Table 11). Theriault, studying nurses in New Hampshire, found that this was very common (22). The students from small home towns gave, in addition, reasons which

Table 11. Reasons Given for Choosing Nursing

Reasons	Total	Reasons Given By Seniors	Reasons Given By Freshmen
Total number of replies	497[a]	259[a]	236[a]
Always wanted to be a nurse	115	55	60
To help people	90	45	45
Previous work in medical field	61	30	31
Relatives in field	57	28	27
Interested me	56	36	20
Friend a nurse	38	18	20
Job security	31	15	16
Glamorous	16	11	5
To get education	15	12	3
Miscellaneous	18	9	9

Source: (26). Sample is from Kansas City Area.
a. These totals include up to 3 responses from each student. The mean frequency per student is 2.2.

included a desire "to help sick people," an unexplained "interest in nursing" and the appeal of its "glamor."

Students from large towns and urban areas gave these and still other reasons, chiefly of expediency: job security, the desire for education and the availability of a nursing course, and the fact that it could lead to something else, such as being a missionary or an airline stewardess. The girls from the city gave, on the whole, more concrete grounds for their choice and appear to be more realistic.

The psychiatric nurses surveyed in North Carolina gave reasons for having chosen nursing which agree only in part with the Kansas City findings: they say that they were influenced by friends and relatives and not by mass appeals or by strangers (29). In Kansas City this is less true of the students' choice of vocation than it is of their choice of school.

which school?

Why do students choose one school rather than another? This is a matter of considerable concern to those interested in recruitment. A prospective student, given the means to pay for an education and having a given vocational aspiration, may be as likely to choose an occupation because schooling is available on convenient terms as to choose a school because it offers preparation for a vocation already selected. That is to say, students may choose school first and profes-

Table 12. Reasons for Choice of School

Reasons	Total	Reasons Given By Seniors	Reasons Given By Freshmen
Scholarship awarded	13	5	8
Special features	25	21	4
Near home	31	16	15
Good school	22	5	17
Pay	4	3	1
Relatives go (went) there	27	17	10
Friend goes (went) there	26	11	15
Advice	41	20	21
Worked there	5	3	2
Far from home	5	5	0
Right size	12	5	7

Source: (26). Sample is from Kansas City Area.

sion later as often as the reverse. In any case, their replies to the question disclose only two notable differences between the responses of freshmen and of seniors (Table 12). Freshmen are more likely to say they chose their school because it was "good"; seniors, as a rule, refer to a specific advantage. Here again, as in the case of reasons for choosing nursing in the first place, there are significant differences between the replies of students of rural background and those of urban.

The distribution of reasons for choosing nursing provides an interesting contrast with the reasons for choosing a given school. Whereas rural students place emphasis on their wish to help the sick, or on an "interest" or on "glamor" in talking about choice of *vocation,* they focus on the advice or example of intimates in talking of choice of *school.* When urban students describe why they chose nursing, they speak mostly of the influence of friends and relatives. But, in describing why they selected a particular school, the focus shifts to such factors as scholarships, convenience, and other special features of the particular school. It is generally true that the city girls offer more objective and less personal explanation than do the country girls.

attitudes and expectations

The remainder of this discussion draws almost exclusively on the Kansas City study (26), it being the only one in the research program which traces changes in the attitudes and the expectations of students as they progress through school.

Conceptions of the Ideal Nurse. Students of the eight schools surveyed were asked to tell what kind of person would, in their opinion,
make the ideal nurse.

To 51 per cent of all who replied (two did not), she is a person
with such qualities as sympathy, energy, mental stability and an incli-
nation to help people. The remaining 49 per cent of students not only
emphasized these desirable personal attributes but also technical
facility, knowledge of nursing procedures and interest in nursing as a
profession. Very few failed to mention personal characteristics, but
only one half included technical and professional standards.

Freshmen were more likely to describe their ideal without mentioning skills and tasks; seniors were more likely to include them.
Although all seniors agree on their picture of the ideal nurse, freshmen
in the various schools differ significantly on this point. Therefore, it
can be concluded that nursing education, in whatever kind of school,
eventually brings about similarity in the students' ideals.

Changes in Conceptions of the Nurse. Students were asked in the
course of the Kansas City survey to report what changes, if any, had
occurred in their conceptions of nursing and of the nurse during their
time in school; that is to say, to compare their current images with
what they were when they first entered school.

There were unfavorable responses in some cases. These included
the ideas of "hard work," "menial work," "immorality," and a variety
of disliked personal attributes. But other replies included agreeable
personal qualities, references to "easy work" and "glamor." A third
type of reply focused not on pro and con judgments but rather on
descriptions of the nurse's work, her skill, knowledge, responsibilities,
aid to the sick, and so on.

The accounts of seniors of their pre-school notion of the nurse were
distributed much as were those of the freshmen: The unfavorable
impressions were reported by 9 per cent of seniors and 10 per cent of
freshmen; favorable descriptions came from 77 per cent of seniors
and 66 per cent of freshmen; the third, or task-centered image was
reported by 14 per cent of seniors and 24 per cent of freshmen (the
differences are not of statistical significance).

When the current version (in contrast to the original or pre-school
version) of the nurse in the minds of freshmen is compared with that
of seniors, dramatic differences appear. Larger proportions of the

first-year students described nursing in favorable or unfavorable terms, and only 34 per cent built their notions of nurses on what nurses do (the third type of reply). But the latter is reported by 62 per cent of the *seniors*.

When the original pictures of the nurse presented by students of both years are compared with their current images, similar significant shifts appear. Freshmen students, currently conceive of nurses in either task-centered or unfavorable terms to a significantly greater degree than they did originally, i.e., before they had committed themselves to nursing school.

The same shift occurs in the minds of senior students, except that it is even more marked than with the freshmen. This is a common experience; the initiate in time abandons her idealized picture of her new occupation for one more realistic perhaps and, in any case, less glamorous. No differences were found in this respect among the different types of schools.

Students' Conceptions of the Public's Image of the Nurse. Students were asked their estimate of the lay public's idea of the nurse. Seniors were the most likely to report the public's impression as one of "glamor" and agreeable personal characteristics. Freshmen, for the most part, think that laymen look upon nurses in the light of what they do. Now it may be that as, with the passage of years, the students become better informed and more sophisticated, they magnify the distinctions between themselves and the general public, attributing to laymen misconceptions under which they themselves once labored. Perhaps, too, the laymen in dealing with students of nursing put the latter's chosen profession in a good light. As to this, we can only conjecture. Be that as it may, it will be found (Chap. 8) that women on the whole cherish favorable opinions of nurses, and on this point the student nurses guessed accurately. However, they understated the male public's emphasis upon the nurse's technical skill and knowledge.

The Place of "Tender, Loving Care" in Nursing. Next, the Kansas City sample of nursing students was asked to give a judgment of the importance of "tender, loving care" as a technique of the good nurse.

One style of reply referred to tender, loving care as therapy or as a means of making the patient more manageable. Some thought it "ought not to be overdone" or that it "ought to be given to some patients but not to others." But in a second type of reply no reasons were given for its importance, though it was admitted to be so, and some expressed satisfaction in rendering it or said that it was "good" for patients. The majority (62 per cent) of freshmen gave the first sort of reply, although only those in the three-year programs in publicly and voluntarily supported schools actually offered more replies of this type than of the second. In the church-sponsored schools, they stressed humanitarian themes as found in the second class of reply. However, the first-year students in the other three-year programs were more impressed by the uses of tender, loving care in therapy. In the collegiate school, 75 per cent of the beginners offered the second class of reply, which represents tender, loving care in personal and sentimental terms. The curious thing is that the last-named school is one which, judged by the prospectus it sends out in recruiting, presents the nurse's work as technical rather than personal service. Thus, again, as in the case of the notions of the ideal nurse, freshmen differ as between the schools but not in ways which could be predicted from the school's own bulletin.

While only 35 per cent of freshmen thought of tender, loving care as a therapeutic technique, 55 per cent of seniors shared their view. Once again, the outlook of senior students was task-centered; the outlook of freshmen humanitarian and personal.

Conceptions of Professional Behavior. The student nurses in Kansas City were shown a newspaper advertisement depicting a uniformed nurse. Below her appeared the line: "Nurse Praises Mountain Valley Water." The text of the advertisement stated that she was a registered nurse and gave her initials. The students were asked what they thought of it and if this was "a good way for a nurse to make a little extra money."

Only one freshman—and no senior—gave unqualified approval of the endorsement as a "good way to make money." Five freshmen and one senior expressed conditional approval—"if she really needed the money," or, "if she really believes what it says." The remaining 216 students (3 freshmen and 1 senior did not reply) condemned it as unbefitting a nurse. Of these, 45 per cent called her conduct "unprofessional," pointed out that registered nurses ought not to prescribe, feared lest laymen be misled, or gave other rational grounds for objection. On the other hand, 55 per cent of those who disapproved thought the endorser's behavior "ridiculous," "bad" or "silly." Some of them said that a registered nurse "should not" give endorsements without giving reasons, or declared that "she could not really be a nurse," and that the advertisement was fraudulent. These replies betrayed awareness of professional conduct but without explaining or justifying the code of ethics.

As might be supposed, freshmen and seniors differed in their opinions. The former rejected the nurse's behavior on rational grounds in 37 out of 99 cases. This relatively sophisticated view was shared by 51 per cent of 117 seniors. Of the seniors, 49 per cent simply condemned the endorsement without reference to professional conduct. This raises the question as to whether a large block of the seniors may not be basing ethical judgments on rote learning rather than on a mature and intelligent grasp of the professional code.

Assessment of Education. The freshmen were asked what they liked best in their schooling and what they liked least. The seniors were asked what changes they would make in education for nursing, if they were free to do so, and whether or not they would repeat their course if they had it to do over again.

The net impression given by their replies is that of unequivocal approval. Only 4 seniors out of 119 said that they would not take the course if they had it to do again; 80 seniors and 75 freshmen said that there were no better schools than their own; and 20 out of 227 failed to name a school or a feature of any school which was "better" than their own.

Theriault found much the same thing when he asked 127 graduate nurses in New Hampshire to look back over their training:

86.4 per cent expressed a deep loyalty for the basic education they received in hospital schools of nursing and look back upon their years in training with satisfaction and pleasure. We found only five nurses who had disliked their training, only one who claimed to have no feelings either way, seven who disliked it at first but learned to like it, and ninety who either liked it or liked it very much. (22).

The changes which seniors say that they would like to make in schools of nursing reflect a certain maturity. Concern with hours of ward work looms large in the replies: 28 students mentioned it. They complained that it interferes with instruction and study. Thirty-three students wished that formal instruction were made to bear more directly upon ward experience. As it happens, the nursing educators, too, are worried over the load of ward duty, over evening and night shifts and the connection between ward experience and formal instruction. Supervisors in New Hampshire hospitals also are concerned about the problem of a healthy balance between theory and practice in student's programs (22).

Expectations of First Jobs in Nursing. The nebulous character of the freshmen's expectations is shown by the fact that 76 had no idea as to what their first job might be. Because so many gave no reply, only senior students are discussed here. Of 119 of them, only 14 did not answer the question. After all, graduation and the first job are near realities in the final year.

Of 105 seniors, 56 (or more than half) expected to work as staff nurses; 17 expected to work in operating rooms; 11 in the pediatrics service; 4 in psychiatric units; 3 on obstetric floors; 5 planned to apply for jobs in physicians' offices; and 6 seniors expected their first job to be outside of nursing. Students in their last year of school appear to have clear cut plans for their immediate future. No matter how the pie is cut—by kind of school, size of home town, etc.—no deviation from this pattern can be found.

Ultimate Aspirations. When asked their long term ambitions senior students usually had an answer, most freshmen did not.

Nineteen seniors—that is, about 20 per cent of those replying—had ambitions which would take them out of nursing and indeed out of gainful employment altogether, and into marriage and motherhood.

Of the 80 remaining, 17 aspired to positions in schools of nursing, 12 hoped to enter administrative and supervisory nursing, 10 wished to work in surgery, 9 in public health, and 1 in a physician's office. Thus the aspirations of 49 students are toward instructional, administrative and technical services—all in the world of nursing.

Thirty-one seniors (40 per cent of those who hoped to remain in nursing), expect to devote themselves to the direct care of patients; 10 would like to stay in general duty on hospital staffs; pediatrics nursing is the goal of 9; psychiatric nursing of 7 and obstetric nursing of 5.

Direct patient care was named as their ultimate objective by over half of the seniors in church-connected schools; only 28 per cent of the seniors in other schools named direct patient care. Of the seniors in the other schools, the great majority aimed at nursing specialties where bedside duties play a small part or no part at all. It is interesting that this division of ambitions as between the schools corresponds to the emphasis on types of nursing to be found in the school's bulletins.

Nursing education, administration, public health nursing and work in physicians' offices comprise about 50 per cent of the aspirations expressed by students. These positions, as it happens, make up just over 20 per cent of the posts actually occupied by local nurses. Therefore, their aspirations cannot be realized quickly—unless they move away. Some will certainly do exactly that if they stay in nursing long enough. (Cf. Chap. 11) While the aspirations of others will be revised and modified.

Conceptions of Relations with Practical Nurses. On being queried, some students said that the relations between registered nurses and practical nurses were "good," without going into details. Some said that the two groups formed a team; others said that the practical nurse "helps" the registered nurse. Less favorable was a second group of opinions. These came from students who thought that relations between the two were "fair," who pointed to "confusion" about the division of labor or merely said that there was "some trouble." Some were specific in describing unfriendliness: they spoke of the practical nurse as having "a chip on her shoulder" and thought that she should "help more" or that she "assumes too much." Others thought that the registered nurse "pushes the practical nurse around."

It turns out that the freshmen are likely to take a bright view of this vexatious problem; 44 per cent thought that relations between the 2 groups of nurses were "good," in contrast with 27 per cent who noted that there is conflict. However, of the seniors, only 25 per cent declared that relations were "good," as against 40 per cent who mentioned trouble between them. These differences, statistically reliable, probably can be attributed to the seniors' more extensive experience in the wards and to their closer association with graduate registered nurses, many of whom hold opinions just like these. This is a matter on which the seniors differ significantly, depending on what schools they attend; but this is not true of the freshmen, whose views, one must conclude, reflect their lack of experience.

Now, a majority of students in the church-sponsored schools, which are conducted in small hospitals for the most part, spoke of conflict between registered nurses and practical nurses; but those in schools with public or voluntary support, which are generally conducted in larger hospitals, spoke, on the whole, of "good" relations or of possible problems but not of conflict. Why?

We will see (Chap. 6) that in smaller hospitals the organization of work is less formal and clear-cut than it is in larger institutions and that this leaves room for disputes over responsibilities and prerogatives. This appears, in general, less true of larger institutions. However, there is another possible explanation.

The practical nurse, as the time studies show (Chap. 6), often takes over most of the care of the patient, and the registered nurse is responsible, as a rule, for the more technical services. It may be that students in church-sponsored schools, whose aspirations are centered on bedside care, see the practical nurse as a competitor. Students who hope for technical and administrative positions will view the practical nurse as a necessary complement of their work.

The two explanations do not contradict each other; both could be valid at the same time. Also, it should be kept in mind that the students' opinions as presented here are averages. No student body was unanimous. Moreover, this is a local sample; the case may be quite different in other schools and hospitals and in other parts of the country.

Conceptions of Relations with Physicians. When asked to describe the relations between doctors and nurses, 63 per cent of the freshmen replied "good," without elaborating. This was the opinion of 44 per cent of the seniors. The remaining students in each class (38 freshmen and 65 seniors) held various opinions. Some described the nurse as the physician's assistant, or as wholly dependent on him for the directing of her work. Others thought that the nurse had, or should have, some autonomy in organizing her work. Some said that the relationship was "co-operative" or that the nurse and the doctor were "a team." Others said that the physicians "should be more friendly"; that they "abused the relationship"; and that relations were "only fair."

About 75 per cent of those who went into detail described the nurse as dependent on the doctor. This was the view of 92 per cent of the students in church-sponsored schools but of only about 60 per cent of those in the other schools. Why?

It might be that students in the church-sponsored schools, who plan to engage in bedside care and at the same time see the practical and the professional nurse as competitors, are the most strongly imbued with the "traditional" values. If so, then they would see the nurse as the physician's "right-hand man" and not as a relatively autonomous professional. However, another explanation might be offered. Most of the church-sponsored schools are in small hospitals, as remarked above, a large proportion of which have patients under the care of private practitioners, socially remote and personally powerful. On the other hand, students in larger hospitals, which are staffed mainly by interns and residents and accept charity cases, might be expected to conceive of the nurse as enjoying some measure of independence. The Kansas City findings strongly suggest that just such differences in work experience, rather than the orientation of the schools, are at the root of the divergencies in opinion.

Conceptions of Tactics for Professional Advancement. Students were asked to tell what they thought could be done to improve the status of nurses in general. One hundred and four seniors (87 per cent) reported ideas on the subject, as did 84 freshmen (77 per cent). The percentages probably reflect differences in experience. About one third of each class (30 per cent of seniors, 33 per cent of freshmen) had in mind the personal advancement of the individual nurse. They mentioned improved hours of work, higher pay, better standards of conduct and, in a few cases, more time for bedside duties. The remaining two thirds of the students in both classes advocated higher levels of professional education, improved recruitment of students, the education of the public on the subject of nursing and changes in the relationships between nursing and allied occupations. Thus, 2 students in 3 talked about improvement in the status of their profession, as a whole; and 1 in 3 spoke of individual betterment as the road to professional advancement.

On this question, no significant differences were found between seniors and freshmen, among schools, or among students classified by any of the other variables under consideration.

Marriage. Although marriage in itself may not have much effect on the nurse's career, children are a powerful force in removing her from professional work. Of course, this force weakens as the youngest child reaches school age.

Nearly every student interviewed in Kansas City reported that she was either married or wished to be. Of freshmen, 101 said that they were married or definitely planned to get married, 2 said "maybe," 3 "didn't know," and 2 expected to stay single. Of seniors, 108 planned definitely to marry or were already married, 2 "might get married," 3 "didn't know," and 6 expected to remain single.

Marriage immediately upon graduating was either desired or planned by 43 students; 11 were either already married or expected to marry before graduation; 10 expected to marry within 6 months after it. Thus, of 227 students, 28 per cent expected or hoped to be married 6 months after graduating. At the other extreme, 74 students (32 per cent) did not specify the interval before marriage. Seniors spoke of intervals averaging about 18 months; for the freshman it averaged about 11 months. If they all get their wish, 58 per cent will be married within 2 years of graduation.

They described the husbands whom they have in mind, frequently but not always by occupation: 54 students stated the occupations that they would prefer them to be in; 74 specified a college education; 24 wished to marry men in the professions, of whom 10 stipulated physicians. Nearly as many students expect to marry men in the "blue-collar" occupations as hope to marry men in the professions.

More students have definite notions about the number of children they want, than have pronounced hopes of marriage. Only 2, both freshmen, say that they have no desire for children. The others plan on families which range from one child, to "as many as possible." The commonest number named is 4 (73 students); then 3 (41 students); the third number is 6 (32 students) then 5 (26 students). "Many" is the goal of 18. The mean number of children desired by those who name a number is about 4.

summary

On the basis of these strictly limited and local data, we may come now to the following conclusions:

Students enter schools of nursing with ideas and ideals about nursing much like those of any group of laymen, even though the idea of becoming a nurse may have been with them since childhood. They chose nursing from a pool of "womanly" vocations which require some special skill and education but not a great deal of either. Young women choose their school on the basis of information provided by the press, the radio, the movies and by impersonal contacts, in the case of the country girls; others are drawn into it by more intimate associations in the city. Students are drawn from the urban and the rural parts of the region in proportions that correspond to the general distribution of population. Large schools and small, diploma and degree programs, provide characteristic experiences which lead to certain important differences in the graduate's orientation to her work and her attitudes toward colleagues and associates.

The senior student at graduation entertains expectations, aspirations and intentions which, if realized, will lead into and sometimes out of, a career much like that of her older sisters in the profession, and which will bring her face to face with the same problems as plague them.

A piece of evidence is offered in the research monographs on the subject of vocational tests for student nurses. In the Pennsylvania survey of the nearly 2,500 registered nurses in the sample, it was found that the beginning student's score on aptitude tests is a real indication of what her standing will be in the graduating class. Moreover, her test scores as a student are in the same way borne out by her performance at the state board examinations. Useful—and startling—is the correlation established in the survey between the scores and "professional longevity," that is, how long the young nurse may be expected to remain active in her profession may be predicted from how she acquits herself on tests given her on entering nursing school (19).

chapter four

in the hospital

deference

More than most institutions of civil life, the hospital with its array of titles, uniforms and graded quarters and facilities makes it quite clear that the people who work there are not thought of as all alike or equal in power and importance but are sorted into publicly acknowledged ranks. As in the army or the navy, with which it is so often compared, those who belong follow a variety of careers.

In all hospitals, doctors are accorded more deference than nurses, graduate nurses more than practical nurses, and nurses more than orderlies. All hospitals insist upon certain forms which impress upon the personnel the hierarchy—always autocratic to some degree—in which they live and work. For the special thing about a hospital is that the decisions made within its walls are often desperate, none the less so because they are made daily, even hourly. Therefore, if its organization is almost military, it is precisely for the reason that, like the army, it deals in danger and death.

It is said that when a nurse stands in the presence of a physician she is giving "the hospital salute." The ranks and the titles, the prerogatives and the modes of deference, the uniforms, the caps and the badges are constant reminders of the imperatives: duty, subservience, obedience. In fact, if a Pennsylvania hospital is representative, most of these distinctions are accepted without resentment by all strata of the personnel (19), evidently not because the distinctions are considered as serving medical ends but as symbols of the part which each in his own station assumes of the work of the whole hospital. To the doctors, then, who assume the greatest responsibility for the healing of the sick, most of the honor and the glory are given—on the whole, willingly—and if other levels are accorded smaller portions of deference, it is approximately in the measure of their contribution.

Conventions and formally prescribed behavior arise in the first place, one supposes, to reflect some sort of relationship, and once set up, they save the individual the burden of conscious judgment and become more or less automatic. The nurse who respects the rules and the forms is rewarded by a certain ease in encounters with superiors and subordinates, but if she flouts them she may pay a heavy price; the loss of a hard-won cap, for example, is a symbolic punishment— now rather out of date—which, like degradation in the army, is a hard blow at status and personal pride.

One is apt to think of the formalities of hospital life as unquestioned, blanket conventions; but there are, it seems, some fine distinctions. Bressler and Kephart, seeking to discover the opinions on the matter of deference of registered nurses licensed to practice in Pennsylvania, asked them three questions: (1) In hospital situations, should nurses rise when the doctor enters the room? (2) Should nurses and doctors have separate dining facilities? (3) Should nurses rise in the presence of doctors in a social situation? (19). To the first question, 77 per cent of the 2,425 nurses said "yes," 19 per cent said "no" and 4 per cent were undecided; to the second, 50 per cent said "yes," 37 per cent said "no" and 14 per cent were undecided; and to the third, the figures were respectively 16, 80, and 4 per cent. Thus, nearly four fifths of the state's graduate nurses think that a gesture acknowledging the doctor's superiority is proper *on the job;* but only half of them are willing to defer to the doctor on the less urgent occasions of dining and entertaining, not from disloyalty but from the sentiment that the pyramid of authority belongs strictly in a place and for a purpose.

Complementing their acceptance of authority, the graduate nurses studied in Pennsylvania in turn were disposed to insist on deference from those below them (19). They were asked: "In a hospital situation, do you believe that student nurses should be required to rise when a graduate nurse enters the room?" Half of the nurses who graduated in 1950 said "Yes." Of those who were graduated in 1940, 55 per cent, and of those of the class of 1930, 60 per cent, said "Yes." Thus symbols of deference are still demanded, even if not to the extent that they once were. The authors suggest the explanation that democratic behavior is everywhere increasingly acceptable today, but they think, too, that the newer graduates being closer to their own student days, hesitate to "set themselves up."

The distinctions between graduate and practical nurses parallel those between graduates and students. For when asked, "Do you think that practical nurses should be permitted to wear the same uniform (including caps) as registered nurses?," the 2,425 graduate nurses in the sample were solidly opposed. The class of 1950 said "No" in 96.6 per cent of replies; and their predecessors in the classes of 1940 and 1930 held an identical view—97.2 and 97.4 per cent, respectively (19). These sentiments were corroborated in New Orleans in Charity Hospital of Louisiana, where the professional nurses are reported as cordial in their bearing toward the nonprofessionals "as long as the latter stay in their place" (18, pp. 197-8). At the same time, the professional nurses look upon the use of nonprofessionals as a temporary expedient that will go when the shortage of nurses is over—a curious attitude when one remembers that here and elsewhere the newer variety of nurse makes up a large fraction of hospital personnel and has done so for more than 20 years. None the less, the supposed transitoriness of nonprofessional nurses is taken into account even in formal measures. (One wonders if this unrealistic attitude makes it easier to be hospitable.)

chain of command

These studies are mentioned here as establishing the prevalence of attitudes which attest to the formal side of hospital organization. The organizational charts of the larger hospitals, with their boxes and connecting lines, show the division of labor and the chain of command which these gestures symbolize. These charts report the official organizational setup in the hospital as a guide to smooth working. But when one looks into the details of hospital life, there appear to be other siftings and sortings: the lines of caste or class or clique—

whichever name one wishes to call it—and the points of authority are blurred in some hospitals and in others, while distinct, assume a pattern of their own. The research workers who gained an intimate knowledge of the hospitals they studied found clusterings which did not correspond with what is "supposed" to be but give the individual hospital its character. Whatever it is, this character is created by the habits and the manners of the staff and the patients, and then, once established, it pervades the institution and more or less compels newcomers to conform.

All this amounts to saying that, while some features of hospital organization appear to be fairly standardized and general, there is in each an informal laying down of the lines that is peculiar, and more vital, and may even determine who does what work and with whom. The organizational charts may be a fairly true picture, but they are always a deliberate intellectual construction, and in all hospitals, as in all human society, human whim and perversity, expressing itself in the unofficial connections and divisions, will qualify, at times even nullify, logic.

When the chain of command breaks and prerogatives are disputed, one should look to the two structures, the formal and the informal. The first, the deliberate creation, is usually shown on charts on the board-room walls of the large hospitals. The second exists in the minds and the habits of the personnel, and the investigators whose work is reported here sought to discover it by observation and sympathetic inquiry.[1] To one who has mastered the second system, the inconsistencies between it and the first may be identified immediately as the ground for boundary disputes and uncertainties of all sorts. At the same time, it must be admitted that the incompatibilities sometimes serve to make an unrealistic framework tolerable. In fact, insistence upon the deliberate plan of control may rarely solve conflict; it can always be circumvented in quiet ways.

A classic case of the undermining of the official chain of command by the logic of the workaday world is that of an Alabama hospital—though it might have been anywhere else—in which occurred a situation like a Gilbert and Sullivan plot. The head of the central supply

---

[1] Walker and Stone present a diagram of the informal organization of the Premature Center, which is contrasted with the diagram of the formal organization drawn up by the Louisiana State Department of Health (18, pp. 183, 186).

department there is also head of surgery. But the director of nursing service considers herself to be the superior of the head of surgery, and in consequence—and almost inevitably—she assumes authority over the head of supply, that is, over the one individual serving in two capacities. Now, at the same time, the administrator regards himself as the superior of the head of central supply, and the latter concurs in this opinion and refers problems to him. Of course, this angers the director of nursing service, who thinks it is she who should be consulted. Furthermore, as the central supply department and the surgery are closely related, the administrator, in assuming direction over central supply, in effect also makes himself director of operating room policy. As a result of all this, the unhappy head of central supply and of surgery is, in reality, head of neither, no matter what the organizational chart may say (10, p. 33).

Of course, this travesty on authority could occur only in a small hospital where one functionary must fill more than one administrative office, and, indeed, the authors cite it to show this particular vulnerability of the small institution. Where the administrative staff is larger, duties in the Alabama hospitals are not overlapping and on the whole are more clearly understood; each worker knows who her immediate superior is and what are the proper channels through which decisions should be transmitted. However, the large hospital has its own susceptibilities, as will appear.

To the nurse at work, the informal social system is the true face of the hospital. She senses it constantly in the facts of working together and in her awareness of a "we" feeling. In Utopia's hospitals, no doubt all personnel work together smoothly to ease and heal the sick, and no inharmonious obsession with personal dignity or professional pride obtrudes. Here below, we hear of some approximations to the ideal but always imperfect and never simple. In a small proprietary hospital in Missouri, for example, the "we" feeling in the nursing staff extends to all shifts and all services. But the myriad sick cannot be accommodated in small proprietary hospitals, even should the nursing teamwork prove to be perfect. In an immense metropolitan institution, the "we" feeling cannot be inclusive, and the nurses will attach themselves primarily to their colleagues and superiors in the same department or service or unit, on the same shift (9, p. 150; 18, Pt. I, Chap. 5).

the home guard

The clearest expression of the "we" feeling is what has been called the *home guard*.[2] This phenomenon may turn up in almost any type of institution—hospitals, schools, universities, the army, government agencies, business offices, and so on, where there are some itinerants whose term of service is brief and where there are others, the Old Faithfuls, who stay on year after year, sometimes sacrificing professional advancement for the comfortable berth which they have built for themselves in their long stay on the spot (9, p. 48). The latter form the home guard. They go far to give the institution its special character. They set its tone and its public opinion and they can make or break authority.

Nothing is more revealing about a hospital's social system than its home guard. In the great Charity Hospital of Louisiana, in New Orleans, a form of home guard—there called "the care group"—was identified as among nurses concerned with bedside care (in this case, of infants) as contrasted with administrative or "paper" work. Here, as it happens, caring for the babies in the premature center will gain a nurse admittance to the home guard established there, whereas mere length of service will not—a parallel of which is found in the navy, where the sea-going officer enjoys more prestige than the desk man, even a desk man of comparable rank and greater seniority. The home guard will "adopt" a new nurse assigned to bedside care, initiate her into the local ways and protect her when necessary. But if she shows what is considered an insufficient interest in her infant patients or an undue attachment to "the front office," they reject her (18, p. 198). Fortified by very high morale, the home guard may openly resist an innovation or, on occasion, defeat it silently, while appearing to acquiesce. Uncommonly able nurses, they stand together like members of a lodge or a sisterhood.

Indeed, the good bedside nurse is in many hospitals the nurse who will be respected by her fellow nurses and the students, and by the practical nurses and the aides who are subordinate to her. In some hospitals, the admired supervisor is the one who "isn't afraid to get her hands in it," while the story is told that one who failed to "pitch

---

[2] Everett C. Hughes, "Discussion of the Bryan Report," in A Forum of the Public Library Inquiry, Lester Asheim (ed.), pp. 106-14, New York, Columbia University Press, 1950.

in and help when we were in a jam," lost standing and eventually had to be transferred to another department (18, p. 201). Yet this criterion is not admitted on the organizational chart; as a matter of fact, the organizational chart may attribute power to the very class of administrators and "paper workers" whom the home guard rejects, while the home guard itself, a very forceful reality, is not even shown. (Of course, this is natural, for the home guard exists in the *informal* structure of the hospital.) All the while, it is the more fateful fact, for it sets the climate of opinion which surrounds the nurses and their patients—even the doctors.

Where would one look for the home guard? Why, for example, is it located in the premature center of 3,200-bed Charity Hospital of Louisiana? The authors of the Louisiana report argue that the skilled nurses in the Center are a unique group (18, p. 199). There are few places in the country where a nurse can get specific training in the special problems of keeping alive the spark of life in the baby born before its time. Too fragile to handle, the infant must be judged often by observation alone, and the fine line between healthy responses and behavior that means danger and justifies handling is hard for even the experienced to detect. The skill and the intuition of the nurse who works year after year among such delicate patients give her an advantage over the physicians. The doctors are known to swallow their pride and watch without protest—loud protest, that is—the overriding of their own judgment (18, p. 201). The young medical men depend upon the nurses for advice, and the more experienced openly consult them. What might appear to be insurrection is tolerated by the doctors because they want the babies to live; the cost of winning an argument with a wise nurse may be one which no doctor would care to pay—the loss of his patient. These women command power because they are excellent bedside nurses, and their reputation shields them against being dislodged. Furthermore, they are set apart in their own section of the institution.

"Homeguardism" quite often flourishes in the operating room. Like the premature center, the surgery is relatively isolated. Moreover, here highly specialized nurses and doctors stand in close dependence upon one another, and their mutual reliance may continue for years in an arena where, more than in any other part of the hospital, the drama of life and death is sharp and sudden, and crisis is common.

One of the studies in Missouri (9) points out that the operating room nurse is very likely to live in the nurses' home, where she may be reached on short notice. The nurses' residence, they find, is another focus of homeguardism. The old-timers—they speak of one nurse who lived there for a quarter of a century and of many who had lived there for more than a decade—form a close group which wields great influence in the hospital. Long residence in the home, more than long tenure in the hospital, seems to be the ticket to a place in the home guard. Now it is obvious that the experienced nurse in the premature center may be both a long-standing employee of the hospital and a permanent resident of the nurses' home who has no family ties or competing responsibilities. Thus, several circumstances conspire to entrench and fortify the older nurse in the home guard. Yet it cannot be said that the home guard must consist of older nurses, or of unmarried nurses, or of residents of the nurses' home, or of those in a special department. The basic condition for the growth of such a power group is the simple fact already mentioned, that a hospital is one of those institutions where many pass through and a few stay on.

This few, all too human, is likely to develop a fondness for things as they are, a dislike of innovation, and suspicion of the front office and the newcomer. Indeed, Habenstein and Christ saw its formidable potentialities. They describe a home guard in Missouri which, by intrigue, self-arrogation of authority and courting of board members and physicians, created impossible situations for their superiors and their peers, while they bent every effort toward the building up of their own power. Its members refused an opportunity for promotion if it would mean losing touch with their clique and identifying themselves with "outsiders, newcomers and innovators" (9, p. 48). No doubt, they are quite sincere in claiming that all this is done for the good of the hospital. Yet one cannot say categorically that homeguardism is a bad thing. If, in the Missouri institution, it perverted means to ends, it is equally true that in the premature center in Louisiana it used influence in the interests of the patients. It is not always possible to foresee what direction its energy will take, but we do know that it is a common human phenomenon and an important element in the hospital environment. Once one understands it, one must see that a home guard is an inevitability.

In a Catholic hospital in Missouri, Habenstein and Christ note that the religious community of the sisters is the seat of a home guard. One may question if this is quite the same thing. After all, there members of the religious community are *officially* in the saddle; they have not achieved ascendancy over the lay personnel by informal, spontaneous and private strategy. None the less, there may be and probably is such a thing as a home guard of powerful sisters within the religious community itself, which may make itself felt in the hospital.

What types of nurse are members of the home guard? Speaking of nurses in general, Habenstein and Christ distinguish three classes (of which more will be said shortly): the "professionalizer" ("stiff and starched"), the "traditionalizer" ("the lady with the lamp") and the "utilizer," to whom nursing is only a means to a livelihood. They state that the home guard usually begins as a nucleus of traditionalizers. If benign, they continue in the true fashion of traditionalizers to put patients' interests first. But where it hankers for power, the home guard may admit utilizers; the utilizer, being something of an opportunist, willingly allies herself with so effective a group, and the home guard welcomes her because it adds to their numbers (9, pp. 52-3).

and other spheres of influence

Whether or not there is a home guard and no matter who is in it, there will always be little groups of special friends, but the basis of the "we" feeling may differ from one institution to another. It may unite those who work on a shift or in a unit. In small-town Missouri hospitals, observers learned that professional personnel sat apart from the nonprofessionals in the dining room; that surgical nurses did not mix freely with those in other departments; that the young nurses were separate from the older, and the married from the single (9, p. 64). These lines cut across other possible divisions. For example, they saw no disposition for supervisory nurses to sit at a table of their own. Among the married, the younger nurses seemed likely to ally themselves with each other; however, among older nurses age rather than marital status seemed the basis of attraction. The groupings in Charity Hospital in New Orleans are: the home guard as distinguished from the newcomer; Negroes from whites; professional from nonprofessional; and those involved in bedside care from supervisory, administrative and teaching personnel (18, pp. 197-8). (The division along racial lines is less stringent than in institutions outside of the hospital. Negro nurses are paid the same salaries as whites and may become head nurses. That they are not made supervisors is explained as due not to lack of qualification but to doubts as to whether "the white nurses would accept them." As yet, the hospital authorities seem not to have put the assumption to the test.)

In the Arkansas hospitals, the research teams found the usual separation between professional and auxiliary nurses. They also found degrees of prestige among the latter: the practical nurses were at the top, the students in the middle, and the aides were at the bottom (15, p. 12). These distinctions are based on education and are confirmed in the scale of salaries but—and this is a cause of resentment—not so clearly in duties. For example, the aides complain that though paid much less than practical nurses they do much the same work with similar responsibilities. The lines between auxiliaries and the housekeeping staff, too, always were drawn strictly in both pay and prestige; yet, again, many of their tasks—cleaning patient units, for example and replacing supplies of linen—were identical. (Who does what will be gone into at greater length in Chap. 6.)

It is fashionable to deplore cliques and divisions, but they are based on realistic conceptions, commonly shared, of how people stand toward each other, and it may be that they are irrepressible social growths. Hospital administrators may find it hard to enact work teams that override these natural, unofficial affinities—in other words, to set up a formal organization that runs counter to the informal. Yet they cannot discover the latter except by diplomatic observation and certainly not by intellectual exercise, for it differs from one institution to another as the features of the human face differ from one person to another. It may be proof against deliberate control.

However, there is always one class of hospital personnel which violates the established rules and ignores the spontaneous social patterns with impunity—the doctors. Like the army "brass," the doctors have no superiors. Because they are charged with the greatest responsibility, they are given a free hand, and everyone else understands that almost any order they think to be necessary—it is always presumed that they act for the good of the hospital and the patient—must be obeyed. Actually, the doctors command more power than they ordinarily exert.

Yet, inevitably, the occasion will arise when a doctor's orders will do violence to other rules, and then the subordinate, most often a nurse, must follow them, transgress the conflicting rules and pay the price. For the nurse sometimes has to assume more power than she has. This kind of trouble is endemic in hierarchies of every sort. The administration has to expect it and to be merciful to the victim. At best, the cause of conflict is not mismanagement but the uncontrollable facts of life and fate: accident, emergency, Acts of God; at worst, it is a physician's fatigue, vanity or arbitrariness. In either case the hospital, from top to bottom, has to live with it. An urban hospital of 285 beds in Alabama offers a classic instance: The doctor, who had asked for some laboratory tests on a patient, noticed that the reports were not on the chart when he made the rounds and remarked on it to the charge nurse. She immediately telephoned the laboratory to ask the technician to telephone the report if it happened to be ready before the doctor left the floor, and to have it delivered later. Yet the nurse knows full well that the technicians fill requests in the order in which they are received and that if one is made out of turn, others will be delayed, and other doctors may be annoyed. "Physicians," conclude the authors, "seem to cause the few disputes between the nurses and the lab." (10, p. 52). They tell, too, of a doctor who stepped into the x-ray department and asked for a roentgenogram of his patient. The aides immediately fetched the patient. Then the nurses noticed that the patient's bed was empty. The doctor had made no note on the patient's chart of the order for a roentgenogram, and the nurses had no clues whatever as to the patient's whereabouts. They had to drop everything and try to find the patient, and their fright and misery increased—until the aides suddenly appeared, bringing the patient back (10, pp. 52-3).

When someone must break one law to obey another, the administration must make some gesture to reassert authority—or may think it must—and it is all too easy to make a scapegoat of the luckless offender. The supervisors may mete out punishment. In other cases, peers and co-workers in endless, unobtrusive ways can make the unhappy nurse's life unbearable. But the almost impregnable home guards, who are heard of from time to time, set themselves above or, more exactly, in place of the doctors and are not easy to discipline. They act, as do the doctors, "for the good of the patient," and if this is outrageous, it is because nurses are not supposed to be competent judges. In any case, it is not for them to make the judgment. To illustrate: in the premature center in Charity Hospital in New Orleans, the nurses, a powerful home guard, were told by the doctors in staff meeting that some of the babies should be laid on their abdomens to promote drainage from the chest. A supervisor and a nurse, in turn, remarked respectfully that some babies in that position turn blue and have difficulty in breathing. Nonetheless, the meeting ended with the request from the physicians that the nurses try it. But at the next meeting, the medical director observed that it was not being done. Again a nurse told of an infant that had shown distress. Asked a resident, "Did you suction it out?" The nurse replied, "Of course. We suction them out all the time, but I'll tell you one thing—the babies don't like being on their stomachs!" (18, pp. 200-201.)

These stories, familiar to every hospital administrator and to every nurse who has been as long as a week in nursing school, demonstrate a very important fact: that, no matter how the Board members and the superintendent plan the organization of the institution, the web of attachments and loyalties formed at work—what we have spoken of as the informal structure—provides, in reality, a government whose rewards and punishments are no less effective for being unofficial. The parallel systems, the planned and the spontaneous, and their inevitable dislocations and the boundary disputes, are vital elements in the hospital climate or, as the sociologists call it, the hospital culture, within which the nurses pursue their careers. Yet, inside each institution, the quality, the location and the balance of power will differ, while gross likenesses remain.

big and little hospitals

It is assumed that the institutions surveyed in the American Nurses' Association's research are representative and that the findings will hold true of all American hospitals, type for type. But what are the types? The more one sees, the greater is the range of types and the more difficult does it become to make reliable statements about "the" hospital. Thus Theriault, speaking only of the 11 hospitals he studied in New Hampshire, remarks:

The nurse at the nurses' station in a 400-bed hospital that is a medical center with a medical staff of fifty doctors and that employs over eight hundred people in various capacities faces different problems at a faster pace and with far greater complexity than her counterpart in a small rural hospital of 25 beds. The nurse in a hospital serving a resort and recreation area has different types and classes of people as patients than the nurse in a hospital in a textile center. The nurse working under the supervision and control of a religious order of nursing sisters lives and works in an atmosphere that may be quite different from that found in a hospital under secular control and administration. Thus, differences and variations may be quite as marked as similarities and must figure prominently in systematic studies of nursing functions and nursing personnel (22).

Looking over the completed research, presented in more than 30 monographs, one is struck first with the enormous difference in the size of the institutions. The largest of all is one of the largest in the world: Charity Hospital in New Orleans, which has 3,200 beds that are always filled and serves 5,000 patients a day in the outpatient clinics. Its regular medical staff numbers 424, with a visiting staff of 682 more. At the other extreme, is an 18-bed hospital in a small town in central Missouri, and a 30-bed hospital, staffed by 51 employees, in a town of 6,000 in Alabama.

What difference does size make to the nurse and how she does her work? How do the nurses in the nation sort themselves out and find their places among the array of hospitals?

In the first place, a hospital, by its very bigness, may attract a certain sort of woman from among nurses. However, this is difficult to show, since most very large hospitals are in large cities, and city life may be the attraction. In any case, the reports of research have only a few suggestions. Theriault, for one, found that in all but one of his New Hampshire hospitals the percentage of younger nurses grew with the size of the institution (22, Chap. 3), implying that the new graduates seek employment in the big hospitals. Likewise, the younger general duty nurses in Arkansas are not attracted to the small hospital in the small town; and any who are, usually turn out to be from local families (17, pp. 19-20). This holds true of general duty nurses of central Missouri but not of auxiliary personnel (9, Chap. 12). Vacancies in these small hospitals were often filled by women who came to town from elsewhere with their husbands and found it convenient to take employment locally. (It has been pointed out already in Chap. 2 that nurses come in disproportionately large numbers from the cities.) Since the older nurses go to the small-town hospitals, it follows that the married nurse is likely to be the rule there; in Arkansas, for instance, the percentage of women who had never married was only 15 in smaller institutions, but 30 in the larger (17, pp. 19-20).

The nurse who works in a small hospital is certain to know every employee within its walls in a very short time. This makes for informality and blurs distinctions. All who are directly concerned with the patients—and indeed it may be the whole personnel—develop the "we" feeling. Especially in the small proprietary hospital, the sense of being part of a working team includes everyone—doctors, nurses, housekeeping staff and patients. In the Catholic hospitals in small-town Missouri, this sentiment seems to extend even to the people on the outside (9). Obviously, this cannot be the case in 19-storied Charity Hospital in New Orleans, with its elevators and public-address system, where a whole department is devoted to the maintenance of locks and the duplicating of keys. Here, intimacy among work-mates, the "we" feeling, can reach no further than a small cell within a service or a shift (18, p. 150) or a tightly knit clique like the home guard off by itself in the premature center.

How this enters into the nurse's working day can be inferred from statistics gathered—to take only one example—in the study of the operating room nurse in Arkansas. There, in hospitals of over 100 beds, 19 per cent of her time is spent in conferences and consultation, but the percentage drops to 6 where there are fewer than 100 beds (16, p. 17). Not that there is less talk between nurses or between nurses and doctors, in smaller institutions: this simply means that where there are not many of them, anyway, and where they work closely together, there is many a chance for conversation and no need for formal appointments.

As in industry, so in the hospital bigness is in itself a divisive force: supervisory personnel must be multiplied, but the more there are, the harder it is to accomplish anything. Planning may not be more difficult in an enormous institution, but communicating plans becomes formidable, despite telepage and other devices—possibly even because of them. There is some evidence that the change in hospital climate sets in at about the 100-bed size, for by then some explicit and fairly complicated formal organization is necessary, including a departmentalized medical staff; moreover, a hospital is usually at least of this size before it undertakes a training school for nurses or medical students (4, p. 399). So, too, modern architecture may help destroy the sense of a common life by the liberal provision of nursing stations and classified lounges, and by providing a variety of built-in space-dividers that take the place of those makeshift common rooms that get established somehow in linen closets and odd nooks and corners (9, pp. 30-31). Distinctions of rank are impossible to maintain at a coffee-break in cramped quarters.

In the little hospital in "Noah," Alabama, there is a cozy, folksy climate in dramatic contrast with the hospital of middle-sized "Crestville" and even more so to metropolitan "Alabama City." For Noah takes its color from the surrounding countryside. Visiting hours are any time at all, and there is no limit to the number of kinfolk and friends who may perch on the bed or spend the night curled up on the floor in a hospital blanket (10, Chap. 3). Their behavior, in fact, falls not far short of those South Pacific Islanders' who, as described by Margaret Mead, take turns in holding the sick in their arms and see to it that they are never left alone. Much the same thing is found in country hospitals in Missouri. However, what might be attributed to rural ways or the intimacy which smallness engenders may sometimes be regional and independent of size. Despite its vast dimensions, Charity Hospital in New Orleans, regards the swarming of kin in time of sickness as natural. In this immense modern plant, relatives camp next to the patient and settle there amid quantities of personal belongings. Early ambulation is the rule, and the convalescents with their retinues of visitors stray in and out of the wards, making friends and seeing the sights. Far from discouraging these folkways, the hospital enlists the families' help, not only in watching over their own sick but also in giving a hand with other patients, doing errands, attending to simple wants and, if need be, calling the nurse. They are given the title of "visiting attendants." Horrifying as this may be to some nurses, doctors and patients, it struck the investigators as a great comfort and solace to the sick. It is easy to imagine that to be ill in a big city hospital with modern facilities and yet not to be anonymous and among strangers may be a very good combination.

Southern though it is, Alabama City, the largest of the three hospitals studied in Alabama, permits no such laxity. Nursing there is professional, visitors are visitors, and visiting hours are enforced. In Crestville, the conventions are midway between it and rural Noah. These differences are continued in the language between hospital personnel and patient. In the two larger institutions, the doctors and the nurses are said often to annoy and confuse patients and their relatives by their "town talk" and their incomprehensible technical phrases. Moreover, the patient, identified by bed and room number, sees not more than two or three: doctor, graduate or student nurse, and aide. In Noah, on the other hand, intercourse is chatty and easy, and often the patients and their relatives, as in small towns everywhere, have friends on the staff. They understand answers to their questions because they are colloquial. Noting this, Ford and Stephenson venture a promising generalization: the more formal the relationships of hospital employees and patients, the more technical is the former's vocabulary (10, p. 24).

Not only is their talk understandable, but also the nurses and others in the little hospital are more inclined to chat about affairs within its walls with the townsfolk. In a city hospital an employee may say, "We do not give such information over the phone." But it is well-nigh impossible to take such a tone in a hamlet where everyone knows who answers the phone and assumes that a natural concern for the sick will be respected. For the hospital, and all that goes on in it, is a subject of great local interest in the small town; in fact, the interest runs in both directions, for the nurses know local families from having cared for various members as time passes, and they keep up the connection long afterward (9).

On the date when research workers were to begin their survey in an 18-bed hospital, it had only 2 patients, and their 20-bed hospital was staggering under a load of 34 (5, p. 8). Violent fluctuations in patient census, such as these, are to be expected only in the small hospital, and they strongly affect the nurse's working day. If the hospital is nearly empty, naturally she will keep busy at tasks which she might not ordinarily think of as her duty, like cleaning and some kinds of clerical work. The same thing will happen if the patient load is too big: she may be a supervisor but she will find herself doubling as everything else, all within the day's work, as need arises. In only one of a sample of 16 small-town or country hospitals in Missouri was the director of nursing service occupied solely with executive work. In the 15 others, she was at times also an operating room head nurse, a floating supervisor, or a head nurse in charge of pediatrics, a scrub nurse, an x-ray technician, or an assistant head nurse; that is, she was "all over the house!"

In the smallest hospital surveyed in Alabama, there were departments with only one member or with no head, while at the same time individuals filled a variety of places which in larger institutions are the work of several. It does not make for a smooth life for the nurse; strain and irritation are inevitable under such conditions (as will be shown in Chaps. 6 and 7). Technical specialists, pharmacists, x-ray technicians and the like may be employed part-time or only occasionally, and while it complicates her work load, to step into the breach brings the nurse a variety of professional experience which she might never gain in a great hospital. However, a surgical nurse may never see, for example, some of the rarer operations on the chest or the skull if she remains in the small place. All-around competent as she may become, this woman may then be unhappy in the thought that she cannot claim to be a nursing specialist, for that requires, if not postgraduate work, at least a period of concentrated experience in a big city hospital.

As, through force of circumstances, her job expands upward, downward and sideways (as, that is, the small-town nurse from time to time undertakes tasks that are considered beyond her, or beneath her, or out of her department), she may not be able to avoid accepting greater responsibilities than her professional education anticipated, or the law allows; and hence greater risks. Incidentally, Habenstein and Christ point out that today's nursing schools, which are so often in metropolitan hospitals, for the most part inculcate a strict view of the nurse's proper duties which ill prepares her for the realities of nursing in the small hospital. Because she must face the possibility of making grave mistakes she may live in a state of constant anxiety (9, pp. 72, 146) which the specialized nurse in the big hospital is spared. At the same time, often she must work without supervision. In many of the little institutions, no one is specifically assigned to supervise and instruct; in many others, the director of nursing service is the supervisor, but she is on hand only in the morning shift. And, of course, "Everything has to happen at night!" On the evening shift, in five of the six small Arkansas hospitals, the general duty nurse was the only professional unless a doctor had been called. The operating room nurse under the same roof always has the support and the guidance of the surgeon, and this freedom from responsibility is said to be one of the attractions of her job: "operating room nursing is nursing without nursing responsibilities."

One thing the nurse in the little hospital must face is living in a women's world. There will be no resident doctor, unless it is a proprietary hospital, no internes, unless it is a small osteopathic training school as in central Missouri, no male nurses and rarely an orderly, no chefs and perhaps not even porters and maintenance men. The laboratory technicians will be women. The sociologists who draw attention to this (9, p. 71) do not claim that it enters into the nurse's work, but it is bound to color her life as time goes on, and some will find that it takes the zest from work, and they will avoid employment there.

other hospital classifications

Apart from size, the hospitals covered in the ANA and American Nurses' Foundation research programs can be classified in a half dozen ways. For one thing, there are the tax-supported hospitals, federal, state and municipal; the proprietary hospitals which are controlled by one doctor or a group of doctors, either medical or osteopathic; the osteopathic hospitals; the teaching hospitals whose nursing schools are directed in some cases by a university; the psychopathic hospitals; and the denominational hospitals. The investigators have hazarded some general statements about each type as an environment for the nurse—statements which, it must be understood, apply to the institutions surveyed; in varying degrees, they will fit other places.

The small proprietary hospitals, which are not uncommon in the Middle West, have a particular atmosphere. The nurse works very closely with the doctor-owner and often develops a conception of herself as a partner in a team of healers. Yet, she may be very conscious of the fact that the doctor is her employer and that she holds her job at his pleasure. It has been remarked that such a nurse is apt to play the old-fashioned role of devoted bedside comforter and in her bearing toward the doctor to be "womanly" in the traditional sense.

If the doctor is an osteopath, his social position will not be much above the nurse's; certainly he does not attain the exalted position of the medical man. He is described as a "big brother" to his nurses, while the conventional doctor is more apt to be called "fatherly." (Cf. Chap. 7, "Nurses and Doctors.")

The psychopathic hospital is unlike the general hospital much as the psychiatrist is unlike the medical man—similar in having therapy as the goal but vastly different in outlook and method. Many psychopathic hospitals—excluding recently established modern installations—are currently in the process of changing their orientation from custodial to therapeutic, and these are trying times for the nurse who is not specially trained.

In the study of psychopathic wards in hospitals in North Carolina, the research team quotes a doctor as remarking that trouble arises when a doctor and a nurse must work together, one of whom is committed to "organic" medicine while the other has the psychiatric point of view. Because therapy so often follows a doctrinaire school of thought, some institutions think it imperative for their nurses to be given in-service training (29, p. 144). The problems, after all, of psychiatric nursing are basically not medical but of human relations, and this sets the atmosphere of the institution.

Fortunately, we have a vivid account of a hospital of 98 beds in northern New Hampshire which is run by sisters of a French-Canadian order. They have survived adversity in the form of declining local population, of a growing preference of young nurse-candidates for basic schools under secular auspices, of the scarcity of personnel that afflicts hospitals generally today and of a meager budget. Everyone there works hard. "Ward H" has as head nurse a sister who is on duty 15 hours a day and expects—and not in vain—almost sacrificial devotion to duty from the others. Heroic performance makes it possible to run the ward with very little professional help and a handful of auxiliaries, including three extraordinarily competent and hard-working orderlies. The building, though antiquated, is immaculately clean. The research report states:

An atmosphere of authority, discipline and austerity, tempered by a religious faith shared by nearly all personnel, pervades this hospital and its work. These qualities are accompanied by three principal practical consequences for nursing personnel, namely, high work expectations, a certain penuriousness in compensation and the acceptance of the many constraints upon the individual that a rigid hierarchical organization imposes (22, "Ward H").

These Spartan virtues combine to produce nursing of a very high quality. Said a nurse who had had extensive experience elsewhere:

If anything, I think our patients here are spoiled, because from what I know of hospitals in the city and from what I hear of larger hospitals today, the patients aren't getting the attention that we used to give them in my training days. . . . I have had patients come to us that have had to go out of town, to Boston and other places, and they've said that they haven't had care like they've had here . . . just attention. Yes; frequent baths and backrubs and nourishment offered them at intervals; all the things that they like. I think the sisters have a lot to do with that. I think it's the old-fashioned type of nursing that still clings. *(ibid.)*

The staff complain of being permitted little independence of action. But the sisters are clearly convinced that in their circumstances it is only with the strictest supervision that high standards can be maintained. This hospital may not be representative, but some measure of the spirit of authority, sacrifice and devotion found here in such exalted degree probably will characterize, by and large, the Catholic hospital.

The Catholic hospitals are peculiar in that many of the positions commanding prestige and power are filled by sisters. Thus there may be a limit to advancement for the layman nurse, no matter how competent she may prove to be. This is not the case, apparently, in institutions affiliated with Protestant bodies, where the denomination's only role may be financial and administrative. In some Catholic hospitals in rural Missouri, the sisters supervise lay personnel even though, as occasionally happens, the latter are better qualified, the reason given being that secular employees must be kept subordinate for the sake of the order's morale. Yet in those where assignments are made solely on the basis of professional ability, whether the nurse is a sister or not, relations between the two seem to be healthier (9, p. 22). We have no data on how all this affects the patient, if at all.

Repeatedly in this research, the hospitals have been classified on the basis of how they are controlled: governmental or public, voluntary, or proprietary. But, in the end, this or that peculiar feature of one or other of the types turns out to be really due to its size or to the fact that it is in a small town or in a city, or to some other condition. However, one striking characteristic of its nurses has been attributed to the tax-supported hospital *because it is* tax-supported, namely, that they are the most likely of all nurses to belong to professional organizations. We are offered an explanation: that the nurses there sense the authority of some inaccessible "board" which is responsible to an intangible "public," and they grasp at the professional organization as a means of making themselves heard and of safeguarding their rights (9, p. 103).

Whether or not the secular nurse in a Catholic hospital will join a nurses' association depends upon the institution. In Missouri, some sisters have discouraged membership; others insist upon it. Thus one can expect either no nurses or all nurses in the hospital to belong. This is true also in the proprietary hospitals. Perhaps working on close terms with their associates and the doctor gives these nurses the sense of security which others find in joining. In any case, some doctor-owners are unlikely to welcome what might smack to them of a challenge to free enterprise. Nor do the religious orders tend to favor what might compete with the authority of the church.

nursing specialties

In study after study, differences are reported between the nurse's career in one part of the hospital and in another, or between one nursing job and another. If the hospitals themselves vary from one another, it may be scarcely more so than the intramural variation to be found within one institution. The nursing specialties—surgical, obstetric, pediatric and the like—in their turn, provide a subclimate of work. Inevitably, to review them here entails the repeating of matter covered elsewhere in this book in greater detail, but this, one hopes, is justified to complete the picture of hospital nursing.

Nursing today is not the diffuse and generalized business it was until not many years ago. In the large hospitals, the graduate nurse is likely to be, first of all, an administrator and a teacher. She will direct a team of student nurses, practical nurses and student practical nurses, and aides. Not only has her work become managerial on ward and floor, but also that part which is strictly nursing has become specialized. In large hospitals, the general duty nurse is on the way to becoming a specialist by default. Like the general practitioner among physicians, she is a residuary legatee, and her inheritance is the nursing which is left over from the operating room nurse, the obstetric nurse, the nurse in pediatrics, in psychiatry, and so on; and she is growing more specialized as the specialties keep breaking away. Then, too, under our very eyes, the nurse who used to carry on in comparative obscurity in the old people's homes is blooming into a respected new professional known as the geriatrics nurse. She matches a new branch of medicine, geriatrics. This new character carries on in what we are now calling institutions for the chronically ill—since so many are surviving the acute illnesses and living on into old age with the ailments that have still defied cure.

Detailed findings about the work of nurses in specialties in the hospital will be presented in Chap 6. Here we will consider the research workers' general statements to characterize special types of nursing, seen as a milieu rather than as a bundle of tasks.

The Surgical Nurse. In the smallest hospitals, there are no specialized nurses, but if a hospital is large enough to have any departments, the operating room nurse will be the first specialist and may remain the only one. This sets her apart from the general duty or floor nurses, and she is spoken of as "the operating room nurse," even though surgical work takes up only part of her day and she fills her time with general duties.

Operating room nurses are admired and envied. Floor nurses are apt to scold and grumble that "they" seem to have a lot of spare time, to which the operating room nurses may reply, "Those on the floor don't know what we go through standing on our feet all day having to please the surgeons" (10, p. 60). Yet, they know full well that the others envy them their close association—more supposed than real, in many cases—with the lords of the medical profession. In fact, one may suspect that the prestige of the surgical nurse is high exactly because she shares in the work of the most revered class of physician. The supervisor or head nurse in the operating room, for one, is likely to be described by both surgeons and nurses as a prima donna.

Surgical work is thought of as more varied than general duty nursing and so as being more interesting. For one thing, there is less record-keeping—which nurses say they do not like—and less of the dull routine jobs. On the other hand, the operating room nurse is on call more than the others; but she may have more free time on weekends. Some nurses say that they do not like surgical nursing because the patients are asleep, but general duty nurses in New Orleans declare that for that reason it is easier than is work in the medical wards where the patients are supposed to be excessively demanding—yet time studies in their own hospital show that the surgical nurses are giving more bedside care than they (18, p. 52).

Operating room nurses, it turns out, are in many respects a special class. Put another way, surgical nursing attracts a particular group from among the women who nurse. To repeat facts reported in Chapter 2, they are younger; there is a constant draining away from surgery of the older nurses, and so, while many floor nurses were at one time operating room nurses, few of the latter have had floor experience. As might be expected, the operating room nurses' average period of professional experience was the shorter: six years as contrasted with the nine years of the floor nurses. Being younger, they have had fewer periods of unemployment such as family responsibilities and ill health bring upon their older colleagues. At the same time, the surgical nurses appear to be better paid. In any hospital, they are the most likely to have taken postgraduate work.

Their relatively autonomous life off in the surgical wing or on the surgical floor favors, as mentioned earlier, the forming of a home guard (9, pp. 49-50); and being on call, they are the more likely to live in the nurses' residence, which strengthens them further as a power group. Beyond these considerations which promote coteries anywhere, research does not show surgical nursing as intrinsically conducive to homeguardism. Still, they are thought of as a "they" group, younger, better paid and on the whole better educated, a distinctive set in the hospital world.

The Obstetric Nurse. Nursing in the maternity division of a general hospital is naturally divided into antepartum care, delivery-room and postpartum care, and work in the nursery. In big hospitals these are three departments, separately staffed; in very small hospitals the same nurses do it all.

Care before delivery, to the extent that it is given in the hospital, is typically carried on in the outpatient clinic where the obstetricians examine women at regular intervals throughout pregnancy. The visits are matters of routine, and to be on duty there is spoken of as hardly nursing at all. Typical comments are: "It's just boring routine!" and

"It's just getting a bunch of people in and out in a hurry" (20, pp. 84-5). Since aides and volunteers are capable of giving excellent assistance in the examining booths, nurses commonly remark that there is no need there for professional service, and many of them will not accept assignments in such unchallenging work.

Where this attitude prevails, the nurse, as found in a study in New York, is likely to consider herself as "the doctor's assistant" (20, pp. 95-6). The obstetrician, and the job of getting his work done, then becomes the focus; and the patient, sensing that no one has much time for her, may be unhappy, though receiving impeccable scientific care. (This point is enlarged on in Chap. 7, "Nurses and Patients.")

Some nurses speak disparagingly of working in the delivery room: "After all, it used to be the job of the midwife." The patients are not ill; their care is not challenging. Some comments are: "Of all places in the hospital, it is the most *routine* place to work," "Crying babies get on my nerves and mothers do, too," and "It is inconvenient; there are days when you have nothing to do but twiddle and then there are times when every baby in the country decides to get born, whether it's time to be born or not" (9, pp. 27-28). To such a nurse, obstetrics grows interesting only when that rather pedestrian character, the obstetrician, turns over a complicated delivery to the glamorous surgeon; it is as though the nurses formed their tastes after Hollywood's picture of the hospital's *dramatis personae;* or did theirs come first? Yet, a nurse in obstetric service in New York City said, "Here it's a bit like the operating room—things keep moving, and you keep moving—especially in the delivery room. They're in, and they're out —but meanwhile anything can happen" (20, p. 133).

With these opposed views of the repetitiousness of obstetric nursing, it is interesting to see how much the work actually is a routine. On this point we have some facts: the research teams which observed in 10 Arkansas hospitals found that the labor and delivery room nurses in the 4 larger institutions used 42 nursing techniques and procedures in an 8-hour shift, as compared with 85 used by operating room nurses, which is simply a statistical way of showing that the former do relatively few things and do them over and over all through the working day (16, p. 26).

The Nursery Nurse. Among the most specialized nurses seen in the whole research program are those in the premature center in New

Orleans' Charity Hospital. From them has come a picture of marked identification with the infants:

An attendant may go to the formula cart and state that she is "going to feed *her* baby first, before anyone else gets him." A nurse may choose a formula from the cart and as she feeds the baby, call "Come over here and look at my baby. Isn't she cute. I always try to get her." Attendants tease one another by saying "I'm going to get Jane's baby before she gets to him" to which another attendant answers, "You better not, that's my baby. If you do I'm going to see that somebody feeds yours next time." Attendants tease head nurses by saying, "Miss Blank, I'll bet I can pick out your baby," and then remarking to the group, "I can always tell" (18, p. 206).

Now it may be that this type of nursing, focused on a particularly dependent patient, attracts the sort of woman who easily becomes emotionally involved. In any case, this account takes on interest and importance as illustrating one sort of relationship of nurse to patient that conceivably can develop in other parts of the hospital.

Remarking on the nurses' patience and tenderness, the authors go on to point out the other side of such possessiveness: that it can be a wall against "interference" and changes in treatment. Thus, a professional nurse may insist on feeding a big healthy crib baby who, she claims, "has been mine all along," while attendants deal with the frail incubator babies (18, pp. 206-7).

This Louisiana group seems to be an extreme case of fiercely devoted care, but its unquestionable success suggests that such practice may be a very good thing for institutionalized infants. In any case there is an atmosphere which it may be the nursery nurse always engenders in some measure, something which she enjoys.

The Psychiatric Nurse. Something has been said already about the psychiatric ward as an environment in which to pursue a nursing career. We have no facts to show whether or not the nurses in a special psychiatric hospital lead professional lives that are unlike those of nurses in the psychiatric wards of a general hospital.

As found in psychiatric wards in North Carolina, psychiatric nurses are younger than the floor nurses, 75 per cent of the sample were under 39 (29, p. 12). They may turn out to be the Cinderellas among nurses, for only one quarter of them said that they went into their work for its own sake. Others entered it because it was convenient, or the only job available at the time, or better-paid, as it often is. However, once in it, 44 per cent said that they planned to spend the remainder of their professional lives in it, while only 8 per cent said that they did not; 49 per cent were undecided.

It was found quite common for the psychiatric nurses in the North Carolina study to be the wives of attendants in the same institution. Thus, there are families of mental hospital workers. The presence of kinfolk may give such nurses moral support which may be very important, for both nurses and attendants are described repeatedly as accepting their first positions apprehensively, with alarmist friends confirming their doubts and misconceptions (29, pp. 50, 69).

One great source of difference between psychiatric and medical nursing lies in the difference between the ailments: psychiatric nurses have to learn to operate on a deeper level of experience. Thus, one of them remarks that the patient's physical needs are easily met, but that it takes time to recognize his emotional needs—and this is not only in withdrawn cases: "He may act like he needs to depend on you when he actually needs you to depend on him" (29, p. 103).

Yet, where emotional relationships are primary, there are special hazards, not the least of which are the dangers of playing favorites. The "right" balance of closeness and distance calls for great sophistication. This may be too much to expect of attendants, as a class, and not all nurses can cope with it. Much of the graduate nurse's day is spent in supervision and record-keeping, while the group that spends the most time with the patients is the attendants, a class of personnel with little theoretical training, great turnover and relatively short careers. Perhaps it is inevitable that the nurses who recognize the problem of emotional involvement are the very ones who complain that they do not have enough time. One gets the impression that, with mental illness on the increase and with the growing disposition to hospitalize patients, the problem of time will be more and more serious for both nurses and doctors and that anxiety over it pervades psychiatric nursing.

In trying to learn what is peculiar to this type of nursing, Martin and Simpson discovered that the doctors in North Carolina are more in agreement than the nurses as to what basic skills it calls for (29, pp. 92-8). One quarter of the doctors put skill and understanding in dealing with the patient's behavior first; the next highest consensus

(19 per cent) was that it takes general nursing skills. But of the nurses themselves, 22 per cent put personality characteristics first, and only 8 per cent thought that the most important thing was the skill and the understanding which had loomed so large in the doctors' view. The nurses, too, placed less value on psychiatric knowledge. In these and related opinions, the nurses in psychiatry disagreed both among themselves and with the doctors. All this points to the likelihood of strain and frustration. In fact, psychiatric nursing may be reflecting the controversial character of psychotherapy itself.

The Private Duty Nurse. The private duty nurse was once the ministering angel who entered the house of the sick, tended the patient and comforted and reassured him and his whole family; but that is a thing of the past. Today, she has followed her patient into the hospital, and many a "special" has never nursed in a private home. Thus, her work has become one of the specialties in the hospital, where, if Georgia hospitals are representative, she does from 12 to 49 per cent —that is, an average of about one third—of all the nursing by professionals (7, p. 178).

In discussing her occupation as a professional environment, one should first ask who goes into private duty nursing and why. The private duty nurses studied in Washington, D. C., averaged 47 years of age. The average age for those studied in Georgia is 45, as it is also for the profession throughout the nation. Thus, it is a group of older women, for the median age of American nurses in general is 35. The Washington nurses on the average had nursed for 20 years, 13 years in private duty; in Georgia the corresponding figures are 17 years in nursing and 13 years in private duty; and for the whole profession, 20 and 11. Private duty nursing, then, is not just nursing that is accepted when there is nothing else, or because it is convenient to pick up and drop when one has a growing family, but is regarded as a career in itself (7, pp. 115-6). In Georgia and Kansas City, nurses are disclosed as long-time residents in their state and often living in their own birthplaces (7, p. 98; 25, p. 42). In Georgia, half of them are married, and two thirds have dependents.

Whether by choice or not, these nurses often are not at work. In 1954, the Washington sample worked on an average of 142 days; in 1953, in Georgia, it was 167 days; and the Spohn national survey reports that the median of the specialty is 200 days (34). If a normal working year totals 210 days, then 37 per cent of Georgia's private duty nurses worked a full year in 1954. Of those in Kansas City, 47 per cent worked full time; but the figure for Kansas City nurses as a whole was 79 per cent (25, p. 64). The older nurses work on more days in the year than do the younger, and the single work more than the married (30, Technical Supplement III, p. 6; 7, p. 110, table 4).

Why do nurses go into private duty? Some say that they like to be able to control their own working time. Some declare that it pays better than general duty; in Kansas City, 19 per cent of the private duty nurses made over $4,000 in 1954, as compared with 8 per cent of the general duty nurses (25, p. 64), but general duty nursing often brings fringe benefits, compensation, unemployment payments, paid vacations and the like, which reduce the difference. Almost half of the Georgia nurses said that they preferred it because it involves more complete bedside care than any other branch of the profession does (see Chap. 10).

As practical nurses and aides take responsibility for innumerable personal attentions to the patient, the private duty nurse looks like the last bulwark of "professional" tender, loving care; and even it is threatened. As a matter of fact, the licensed practical nurse is invading her field also, providing care adequate for many types of cases at lower fees. Moreover, many of her former duties are passing into the hands of regular staff personnel, such as the surgical and the recovery room nurses and the dietitian, so that she is now, only relatively speaking, in complete charge. However, isolated with her patient, she can still feel that his recovery devolves upon her. As one nurse summed it up: "Private duty nursing enables me to give the required time for the patient's comforts and needs, to observe the progress the patient makes and his recovery and [permits] time off between cases for rest, recreation, and for work in the home" (7, p. 145).

Unspecialized as to patient, the private duty nurse is supposed to be able to take any kind of case. But some find themselves turning into specialists without planning it: the doctor who finds one who is good with alcoholics will keep recommending her; or he may call to mind a certain placid, confident nurse every time that he has a neurotic on his hands. Getting her patients one at a time, she has less varied work than the general duty nurse, and the latter may deride it as uninteresting and slow, but in the end it is, of course, more varied than the work of the surgical nurse or the obstetric nurse. Nursing directors and educators and, more especially, senior medical students, complain that, with her diverse experience, she does not keep up with medical advances, but the nurses themselves do not speak of that as a professional problem.

When the Georgia private duty nurses were asked to rank cases in the order of their preference, and their answers were compared with the rankings of the cases which they actually got, there was almost perfect correspondence, i.e., they got what they wanted. The conspicuous exception was chest surgery, their fourth choice, which was their eighth most frequent type of case (7, pp. 152-3. See also the rankings which we have introduced in this book in Table 22, Chap. 9). As 82 per cent named general surgery first, and 54 per cent named medical cases, it is clear that they think of themselves largely as surgical and medical nurses.

When the individual nurse is asked to state her problems, she dwells upon personal relations with the physician, the patient and his family, the hospital staff, and with other private duty nurses with whom she may from time to time share a case (7, pp. 286-288; 30, p. 9 and Technical Supplement III, pp. 10-11). More than any other type of nurse, one concludes, she lives and moves in a world where all depends upon her tact and adaptability (see Chap. 7). It begins with the registry through which she is called on her cases.

The registry, on request of the patient, calls the nurse at the top of the list at the time. In theory, a nurse does not decline capriciously, once called, but there are many grounds apart from illness or family reasons which may prevent her from accepting or cause someone actually lower on the list to be called in her stead. For one thing, the doctors intervene; they recommend to their patients a certain nurse whom they know, or a doctor or a hospital may blackball a nurse; or the nurse herself, on learning what doctor or what hospital is involved, may decline. She can exercise a fair degree of choice and she may also be the victim of choice. In short, rotation of calls from the registry is never quite perfect. There are, in reality, all sorts of taboos and priorities, as a registrar confessed: "I would not last two days at this job if I didn't know everything that's going on up at the hospitals. I make it my business to find out" (7, pp. 163-4).

The registry is the broker for the private nurse's services, but the collecting of her fees rests with her, though a few hospitals collect for her as a convenience. Sometimes her claims are tied up in an estate, and sometimes there is unpleasantness because the patient was under the impression that her bills were included in the hospital bill. The system entails possibilities for trouble, though the nurses say that on the whole it works well.

Entering one hospital after another, nursing one patient after another, the private duty nurse deals with a parade of personalities, but the doctors are the abiding figures in her world. They can keep her busy or out of work. She will know each physician's standing in the local medical world and his temperament, and she does not forget that the impression she makes on him is fateful. The Washington physicians appear to be well satisfied with the private duty nurses whom they encounter. But the fact that some of them think of her as caring for patients under their direct supervision may bring about a situation between her and the supervising nurse, if it happens to be in a hospital which expects the latter to keep an eye on her.

Also, the private duty nurse has to get along with the patient, a stranger met when he is not at his best. Shut in with him for eight hours a day—some hospitals like the "specials" to keep to their rooms —she becomes a comforter and adviser, explaining the doctor's wishes, and teaching the patient how to behave as a sick person, while preparing him to return to normal life. The intense concentration upon the sick charge is relieved only when she goes on errands or to meals, or when he sleeps, and it is not surprising to learn that on the rare occasions when a nurse is dismissed from a case, "clash of personalities" is the commonest ground (30, p. 11).

She must make endless daily decisions. In short, her work, as the authors of the Georgia report put it, is to manipulate the climate of feeling surrounding the sick person in the way that best promotes his recovery. And since the patient's family is a vital part of his world —and sure to be right there!—she must make sound and rapid judgments about how to use the family in restoring the patient to health and how to get on peaceably with it herself (see Chap. 7, "Visitors and Patients' Relatives").

Of course, any nurse recognizes that promoting the patient's recovery is her job. But there is this difference, that the private duty nurse is in charge by herself. She may have trouble precisely on that score. She is the patient's private employee, yet is employed inside the hospital and draws on its facilities and, inevitably, has dealings with all ranks of its personnel.

The nursing office and the hospital staff are apt to regard the private duty nurse as one who is there to help the general duty nurse (30, p. 9). The general duty nurse, a fellow professional, sharing the same hospital facilities, may take it hard that she has to divide her time between so many sick people while the private duty nurse "has plenty of spare time," "hoards linen," "makes too many phone calls" and is "just a companion on luxury cases!" (30, p. 13). The aides and the private duty nurse both have duties to the patient, and if the patient's private nurse calls upon aides or orderlies for help, they are bound to give it, though they have no responsibility to *her*. There may be complaints on both sides of un-co-operativeness or shirking and boundary disputes that never get settled. For instance: should the private duty nurse carry on, in the hospital, the scores of small housekeeping jobs she formerly used to undertake for the patient in his home? Or is she in the right if she passes them on to the auxiliary staff, after the manner of the general duty nurses?

However, the aspect of her work which the private duty nurse finds the hardest is how to "maintain case continuity," that is, how to work harmoniously with the private duty nurses who may care for her patient on the other two shifts (7, p. 288). Who is to arbitrate if they have differences? In all likelihood, they will not let it come to the ear of the doctor, and positively not to the ear of the patient or his family. The nurses involved speak of this as calling for "flexibility."

Fortunately, the private duty nurse *is* flexible. With all these personages to please and appease, she has to work under very different conditions from those she knew when she was a "doer of all things in the home." Yet, she impresses the research workers as adaptable and as usually very successful in her dealings. If the reports seem to present her as forever seeking a narrow course between Scylla and Charybdis, it is not because she herself puts it that way; on the whole, she seems to be in confident command. Rather, the pitfalls are described as a way of showing how skilled she is.

The General Duty Nurse. Amid all these specialties, what is left for the general duty nurse? When the contributions of all the specialists are subtracted from the total field of hospital nursing, there remains a great deal for her. She has not only diverse kinds of patients to care for—and often too many of them—but she often has more responsibility than for example the surgical nurse. She is in charge of perhaps critically ill patients, and if the hospital is small, she may have complete responsibility for them. Head nurses and supervisors may be on duty only in the morning. Even in a large hospital, her superiors are not always at hand, and she has to know what to do and see that it is done. She is, after all, a specialist who undertakes not only direct care of patients and of other duties but also the direction of a team of nonprofessionals who share the work with her (17, p. 99).

She is not always happy under this burden of responsibility, if one may project the findings in Arkansas to other places. There, 87 out of 107 (about 80 per cent) general duty nurses said that they would not like to be promoted to be supervisors or directors of nursing services. Eighteen of these had already had a fling at it.

The graduate who enters general duty finds herself usually in a group of young married women. For example, the general duty nurses in Kansas City were younger than the whole group of nurses in the city: 73 per cent of them were under 40, as compared with 63 per cent of the local nurses, as a whole; 63 per cent of them were married, but only 56 per cent of all the working nurses were married. While 66 per cent of all working nurses in Kansas City had had no postgraduate education, the general duty complement contained 78 per cent who had had none; and while 19 per cent of the local private duty nurses and 19 per cent of *all* the nurses in Kansas City who worked full time, had made over $4,000 in 1954, the general duty nurses could show only 8 per cent who had made that much (25, pp. 56, 57, 64, 111).

Being one who is more concerned than her superiors with the direct care of patients, and being less occupied than her superiors with teaching and record-keeping, she is in a position to develop a special relationship with the patients. This is particularly true of those in smaller hospitals or the afternoon and the evening shifts, or on those shifts in larger hospitals in the special services such as orthopedics or pediatrics, where there may not be an overlarge patient census. This is the feature of their work which these nurses claim that they enjoy most of all, and they speak of the voluminous records most of them must keep as an unwelcome competitor for their time.

a tool for analysis

This discussion has not exhausted the roster of nursing specialties carried on in hospitals, not to mention the supervisors and the teachers and the administrators among the graduate nurses or the several categories of auxiliary personnel. Chapter 6, where nursing is analyzed as a bundle of tasks divided between all varieties of nurse, offers some implications about the general atmosphere of their work, but we have no research monographs specifically on them as we have, for example, on the private duty nurse. But the specialties we have presented should be enough to make the point that the hospital is like a continent where climate varies dramatically from one part to another. We turn now to an entirely new way of describing nursing: by analyzing nurses.

Now it is quite clear that there are kinds of nurses—more accurately, of professional women who are in nursing—who may turn up anywhere in the hospital. Everyone knows nurses who behave like those in the premature center in New Orleans, but who happen to be in, say, the psychiatric or the maternity ward. If we look at nurses classified not according to where they work or whom they nurse, but in the light of their attitude toward nursing, i.e., how they conceive of their work, we arrive at a more fundamental set of types. This sociological typing is extraordinarily illuminating. Habenstein and Christ developed it in the course of their inquiries in Missouri and made a basic contribution to research which makes possible a complete reinterpretation of nursing as a profession and of its dilemmas and leads to some solutions. (Two similar analytical devices from two other studies are discussed in Chap. 9.)

Sorting nurses on the basis of their orientation to nursing, Habenstein and Christ arrived at three types to whom they gave the not too happy names *professionalizer, traditionalizer* and *utilizer*. They describe them as follows:

The professionalizer type of nurse is not motivated by any blanket dedication to an ideal. Accepting the principle that good health is better than bad, her focus is not specifically upon the patient to be healed but upon the special things that must be done and the special modes of operations that must be evolved if the problem of healing is to be more adequately and intelligently met. Her case rests with *knowledge,* and knowledge in this case represents the application of rational faculties to experience. Furthermore, it should be applied in such a way that, at the same time, better knowledge can be achieved. She is directly attuned, therefore, to medical science; . . . (9, p. 41).

The professionalizing nurse operates, then, on the assumption that she has been given a general mandate to produce and preserve better health. In turn, she asks for trust, not from the individual patient in particular but from society at large. The trust she receives implies her use of judgment; but the judgment of the professionalizing nurse is not felt by her to be subject to public review; her function, through the use of such judgment based on training, accrued medical and clinical experience, she believes, *is to create appropriate therapeutic* (healing) *situations* (9, pp. 41-2).

The traditionalizer type of nurse is motivated by an ideal long since recognized and venerated in the society, personified in the name Florence Nightingale. The basis of the motivation consists in a sense of dedication, the components or terms of which are so taken for granted as seldom to be examined. It is expressed in a philosophy that present success is based upon the successes and the lessons of the past. The traditionalizing nurse does not rest her case with knowledge as something tentative, hypothetical and modifiable in use; rather her basis of action is the wisdom of accumulated experience from the previous generations. Having cast her lot thus, her stance in the nursing occupation necessarily must be defensive and negative. Her only orientation to the future is in terms of reform, i.e., bringing *back* a situation under the control of values long since legitimated. . . . The new is suspect and the old is always preferable on the grounds that it could not have existed long had it not been worthwhile. . . . Her function within a pattern of complete and unquestioning deference to the doctor, is simply to bring into force all her nursing skills in the healing of the patient. . . . Ideally, to the community she is a cloistered, dedicated "saint of mercy"; to the doctor, a selfless adjunct to his work; and to the patient, a personality resource. To a fellow traditionalizer she is one of the same identity, i.e., she "belongs" . . . (9, p. 42).

The utilizer type of nurse is motivated in terms of no goals that transcend her particular short-run needs. Likewise, there is no particular dedication to an ideal, and no life philosophy in which the work occupies a central role. Rather, the work role begins with the work-day, and with her entrance into the institution. It ends with the change of shifts. The stance of such a nurse toward her work is one of relative indifference since it provides only minimally a focal point of personal organization. Innovations and changes are accepted or resisted in terms of their immediate practicality, or "sense," and the amount of immediate return in the form of time, labor, or personal effort saved. . . . Her commitment consists only in an agreement to do her job when her job is specified. Competence of performance to her means getting the job done. Her work philosophy can be summed up in 3 short words, "it's a job." Thus her functions are discharged in a set of discrete events, strung together to make out the day's work. The ego-involvement, or self-involvement in the occupation as a collective image is minimal. In this sense, finally, she is in the work, but not of it (9, pp. 42-3).

The language of the traditionalizer is spoken by nurses of all three types: that nursing is an art, and its concern is the whole person. True, in the past, the traditionalizer was probably the predominant, if not the only type of nurse. But medical advance and specialization and the new habits of hospitalizing virtually every sick person and treating him to innumerable scientific tests have given rise to changes in nursing which, in turn, promote the development of the other types, the professionalizer and the utilizer. Obviously, if there were no practical nurses and no aides, and few or no technicians to share in the nurse's work, the nurse would do everything herself for her patient, for one thing—and fewer sorts of things would be done—and, secondly, she would not have to direct teams of auxiliaries. For while the graduate nurse, in theory, might have been freed by the auxiliaries to give more of her time to patients, in actuality she often has to give that time to directing the auxiliaries in what was once her own work and in helping to run the institution (Chap. 6).

The situation may not be exactly as it is stated here, but the point is that the three different attitudes to work have come into existence when nursing is undergoing great changes, and it is anachronistic to look upon it as purely or typically bedside care and comforting. Today, there is a vast amount of record-keeping, supervising and teaching to be done, and it is easy to see that there will be nurses whose idea of the good nurse is one who does this type of work well and finds that the reward for work well done is the satisfaction of efficient mobilization of the resources in the hospital to heal the sick. However, to the traditionalizer, tender, loving care and personal devotion remain, as throughout nursing history, their own reward. To the utilizer, declare Habenstein and Christ, it is "another day, another dollar"; if it seems to some shocking in a nurse, is it shocking in other occupations?

A story is told of Charity Hospital, New Orleans, which is cited here not to show the professionalizer in an unfavorable light but to demonstrate that the hospital climates which we have already described may be described again by reference to type of nurse:

> . . . an orderly came to take a patient to the operating room. The woman in bed appeared anxious, tense and disturbed. A man who apparently was her husband was with her. A colored male orderly from the operating room rolled a stretcher into the ward and handed a junior student nurse (who was responsible for the ward at that time) a slip on which the patient's name was written. The student accepted the slip, went to the chart rack and pulled a chart, and read the order sheet. She then took a bedpan to the woman's bedside; the woman raised her hips, and the nurse placed the pan under her. The nurse did not speak to the patient or her husband. In a short time she returned and removed the bedpan and went to prepare a hyperdermic for the patient, which she administered with technical precision. After this she went back to the chart and recorded the nursing care. The orderly waited a few minutes and then rolled the stretcher up to the bed and the woman slid onto it. The orderly rolled the stretcher to the entrance of the chart room and the nurse came out and placed the chart on the stretcher. Not a word had been exchanged. The woman was crying soundlessly in fear and apprehension. The husband stood by helplessly a companion to his wife's fear and to their shared ignorance of what was going on. As the orderly started to roll the stretcher out of the ward, a nurse aide came into the ward. She stopped by the woman, patted her on the arm and said, "Now, you'll be all right, and hurry back, because we'll be waiting for you" (18, pp. 44-45).

But one is not to conclude from this that all or most student nurses are professionalizers and that aides are traditionalizers. The types cut across the ranks. Thus, in the following story a young head nurse in the same institution is cast in the role of traditionalizer:

> . . . She came into a ward of obviously depressed patients, and in 20 minutes had completely changed the atmosphere by asking three of them to help her fold paper cups. She began by rolling a brooding old man from his bedside to an open window and suggesting that he sit where he could see what was happening outside and help her at the same time by folding cups. His shoulders straightened and he was soon describing the people passing to a patient confined to his bed. The head nurse then asked another patient to help with the cups, and suggested that he take them over to the bed of a boy who had recently been admitted and who appeared timid and dejected, and show him how to make them. Ten minutes later she told the old man "what a help he was." Complimented the second patient for being a good teacher, and told the new patient that he had learned to fold cups more quickly than anyone she had ever seen. They

all responded with childlike pride and she hurried across the hall to her other duties (18, pp. 46-7).

When it comes to making studies of the allocation of nursing tasks among the grades of personnel, the 3-fold classification of types brings some order into the mass of conflicting opinions. Thus, Habenstein and Christ found that the professionalizers were quite willing to entrust to auxiliaries unpopular tasks customarily done by professional nurses. On the other hand, the traditionalizer would consent to pass down these very duties only if there were no professional at hand; and if an aide or practical nurse had to do them without supervision, then she must have had appropriate training (9, p. 57).

To the three questions about a given task—Who does it? Who is supposed to do it? Who is expected to do it?—all grades of hospital personnel differ among themselves and from grade to grade, both as to fact and opinion (see Chap. 6). But it now appears that the disparities may merely reflect the balance in which the three conceptions of nursing are to be found among the nurses interrogated. In other words, to get consensus on who does and who should do a given task, one would first sort the respondents into professionalizers, traditionalizers and utilizers.

As a matter of fact, it is the balance of the three orientations that determines the climate of work. Now that we have this tool of analysis, it would be instructive to discover such things as whether, as we might suspect, obstetric and private duty nurses are on the whole traditionalizers, and operating room nurses professionalizers. Do the specialties attract certain types of the three? What are the psychiatric nurses? The head nurses? The spirit of the home guard in the premature center in New Orleans is probably traditionalizing; which prompts the question: which type is most prone to homeguardism? It is suggested that the nursing schools in large cities tend to produce professionalizers and that they have a hard time settling into rural hospitals (9, p. 146). What type thrives in small institutions? Finally, seeing that good nursing is the eventual intention of research, do these attitudes in any way enter into the patient's progress? In short, this new theoretical framework has opened up very promising avenues of research and meanwhile provided some convincing data.

chapter five

outside the hospital

The residue of work settings in which graduate nurses are found is discussed in this chapter. In the preceding chapter, hospital nurses were analyzed, and it was discovered that there are important ways in which they differ as well as important ways in which they are alike.

The array of positions in which nurses are found to be employed in the Kansas City area is shown in Table 13, as an example. That distribution does not clearly distinguish between those who work in hospitals and those who do not. There is a category called "administrative position" which includes, in addition to directors of nursing service and of education and their assistants, administrators in public health agencies and in industrial nursing. Nurses who are clinic supervisors are included with the hospital head nurses and supervisors. Finally, the private duty nurses are all included in a single category and, although some of them probably do not work in hospitals, the extent to which this is the case cannot be determined from the Kansas City data. However, the Georgia study indicates that by and large private duty nursing has moved from the home to the hospital (7). Two thirds of the private duty nurses in the Georgia sample did less than five days work in homes in the year preceding the study; only

Table 13. Positions Held by Active Graduate Nurses

Position	Number	Percentage
Total	1,682[a]	100.0
General duty	501	29.7
Head and supervising	290	17.2
Private duty	237	14.1
Office nursing	132	7.8
Administrative nursing	91	5.4
Industrial nursing	79	4.7
School nursing[b]	78	4.6
Nursing education[b]	60	3.6
Public health[b]	60	3.6
Recently graduated, not yet employed	36	2.1
Anesthetist	16	1.0
Clinic nurse[c]	16	1.0
Surgical assistant	15	0.9
Nonnursing in the health field[d]	15	0.9
Nonnursing outside the health field[e]	15	0.9
Miscellaneous nursing[f]	28	1.7
Insufficient information	13	0.8

Source: (25). Sample is from Kansas City area.

a. Excluded from this analysis are the 759 nurses who are retired for reasons of health or age, housewives (not employed), and nurses on leave of absence for reasons other than educational.

b. Administrators excluded; administrators in this field are included in "Administrative positions."

c. Clinic supervisors are included in "Head nurses and supervisors."

d. Includes nurses who are now employed as dietitians, X-ray technicians, medical librarians, physicians, etc.

e. Includes nurses now employed as clerks, salesladies, restaurant operators, etc.

f. Includes registered nurses who are currently in school, employed by nursing organizations, in the armed forces, and missionary nurses.

seven per cent of them did all of their work in homes and none of it in hospitals; and so it is unfortunate that the Kansas City investigators in making their distinction between hospital nurses and nonhospital nurses chose to classify their 237 private duty nurses in with the nonhospital group. This distinction was on the basis of "employment *by* a hospital," and of course the private duty nurse is rarely a hospital employee, even though most of her work is carried on in a hospital setting. We cannot say exactly to what extent Kansas City's nurses are representative of their colleagues elsewhere in the nation.

Fields in which the settings are primarily outside of the hospital are discussed below. More specific findings related to career lines leading into and out of these fields are analyzed further in Chapter 11. In this chapter, we shall describe, so far as it is possible to do so on the basis of the available data, the office nurse, the industrial nurse, the school nurse, the nursing educator and the public health nurse.

the nurse in the doctor's office

According to the Kansas City survey, the largest single group of nurses employed outside of the hospital setting are office nurses (25). They comprise eight per cent of the local complement of working nurses. Unlike the industrial nurse whose work has been examined in some detail (21, 31), little attention has been paid to the office nurse. However, as will be seen, the office nurse and the industrial nurse have many problems and characteristics in common. Because there is no other research specifically on the office nurse, the material in this section is derived almost wholly from the Kansas City survey.

The nurse in the doctor's office is subject to a set of expectations and is judged by criteria which differentiate her sharply from her counterpart in general duty. In the first place, in the hospital the graduate nurse is the one fixed staff person so far as the patient is concerned. Certainly the doctor is important, but the patient knows that it is not his hospital—that in effect he only "visits." From the patient's vantage point, the hospital nurse appears to be the person who runs things; apparently she is there all the time and is in control. Almost the reverse is the situation in the doctor's office. The patient comes to see the doctor in *his* office. The nurse is relegated clearly to the status of an assistant of sorts, and it is probable that often the patient is not even aware of the fact that she is a nurse (and, indeed, the office "nurse" may not be a graduate nurse at all). She may be expected to act as combination receptionist, bookkeeper, clerk and medical technician. A study of what the doctor thinks of nurses (11) indicates that he judges the office nurse according to how much "help" she is around his office, and "help" is defined quite broadly. One physician dourly reports that "nurses are no help around the office; they don't know bookkeeping or how to meet the public." Clearly, this criterion for judging a nurse's capability is not what would be applied in the hospital.

The Kansas City survey indicates that, like general duty nurses and head nurses, office nurses do not participate widely in the organized social life of their community. Nearly 60 per cent of the office nurses in Kansas City belong to no nonprofessional clubs or organizations; in contrast, three quarters of the school nurses belong to one or more. This characteristic is associated with the office nurses' socioeconomic background. Of all the fields of nursing, it is in that of office nursing that the smallest proportion of fathers was engaged in higher status occupations—only 13 per cent. With the public health nurses, they have the highest proportion of fathers who are engaging in lower-status occupational pursuits. Another relevant characteristic (one which, not unexpectedly, goes along with low rates of participation in formal organizations and low socioeconomic background) is low income. The office nurses are the only group in which the top income bracket is completely cut off: in 1954, not a single office nurse in the Kansas City area was found to be earning over $5,000 a year. In addition, only 11 per cent of them were making over $4,000. Only general duty nurses were worse off, eight per cent of them earning over $4,000 or more, but in the case of the general duty nurses, half of those making over $4,000 were in the $5,000 or over bracket.

A seeming contradiction found in the analysis of the Kansas City office nurses was that, on the one hand, they were the most stable of all groups geographically, i.e., they tend to spend their entire careers in the same locality. On the other hand, they ranked among the top three fields in the frequency of job changes. In other words, although they remain in Kansas City, they do not remain with the same job. When we add to this their age (as indicated in Table 14 nearly half are under 30, and 90 per cent are under 50 years of age), an interesting hypothesis is suggested: that office nursing becomes the final resting place for many nurses who, for one reason or another, cannot or will not leave the vicinity, yet cannot find a job which satisfies them. Because office nurses are relatively young, it appears that their careers involve geographic stability, job mobility and an early exit from nursing. Incidentally, they are among the most married of all groups of nurses, being surpassed in this respect only by those in general duty and industry.

Table 14. Kansas City Nurses Under 30 Years of Age by Field

Field	Total Number in Field*	Per Cent Under 30
General duty	489	47
Office nursing	131	46
Miscellaneous†	88	36
Nursing education	60	32
Head nurse and supervisor	282	32
Housewives (former nurses)	708	27
Industrial nursing	77	21
Private duty	220	14
Public health	59	8
School nursing	76	4
Nursing administration	83	4

Source: (25). Sample is from Kansas City area.
* These figures exclude nurses for whom age was unknown, retired nurses, recent graduates, and nurses on educational leave.
† One half consist of nurse anesthetists, surgical assistants, and clinic nurses; one sixth, although they remain in the health field and are registered nurses, are not actually nursing. These include medical librarians, physical therapists, laboratory technicians, etc. The remaining one third are employed by nursing organizations, registered nurses in schools, and in the armed forces.

Just as her participation in the organized life of the community is limited, so too the office nurse does not appear to be highly committed to or involved in her profession. Over a third of them do not belong to professional organizations at all, and over half do not belong to their state nurses' association: office nurses have the smallest proportion of ANA members of any field of nursing in the Kansas City nurse complement. Their opinions about professional organizations also indicate lack of interest. They are the only group in which less than half of the members checked the favorable response: "I think every registered nurse should hold membership in some professional organization." They are second only to the industrial nurses in the proportion of those who checked the unfavorable response: "I don't think that professional organizations do enough good to make them worth the money or time they take." Although extreme, as compared with other groups of nurses, these proportions remain small. Perhaps more significant is the fact that the office nurse far exceeds any others in the proportion of people checking the neutral category. It is this "neutrality" which leads us to suspect that the field attracts the "utilizer" type discussed in the preceding chapter. This is a different sort of attitude from that of the industrial nurse, who, more than any others, can be described as "hostile" or "antagonistic" to professional organizations.

Like industrial nurses, relatively few office nurses are graduates of governmentally supported schools of nursing, and they stand out among all others in that over 80 per cent have obtained no further education, either clinical or academic, since graduating from school. As might be anticipated, theirs is among the four fields of nursing in which college degrees are rarely found in Kansas City; the others are industrial, private duty and general duty.

the nurse in industry

Unlike the office nurse, considerable material is available on the industrial nurse, thanks to two highly suggestive exploratory pieces of research, one conducted in the Ohio Valley by Erna Barschak (21), and the other in Pennsylvania by Wendell Smith (31). Other than the comparative data derived from the Kansas City nurses (25), this section is based almost exclusively on Barschak's findings.[1] The latter are not intended to be conclusive or necessarily applicable to all industrial nurses. They provide valuable ideas and hypotheses for further research and were the best material available at the time of writing.

The Kansas City survey indicates that about one in every five of the local nurses is employed by industry. More than those in any other field of nursing, they are concentrated in early middle age; nearly half of them are between 30 and 39 years old, over two thirds are under 40; and only 14 per cent are over 50. But in private duty, school nursing, nursing administration and public health, over half of the nurses are over 40, and more than 30 per cent are over 50. On the other hand, in general duty, office nursing, nursing education, and head nursing, the proportion of women between the ages of 20 and 29 exceeds that found among industrial nurses. That most industrial nurses become established in their careers during their second decade in the profession is probably because by then their children have reached school age.

---

[1] The monograph by Smith (31) did not become available in time for its findings to be fully incorporated into this chapter. However, some of Smith's more salient findings have been added at the end of this analysis of the nurse in industry. The careful reader will note close parallels between the Smith and the Barschak findings.

Industrial nurses are the most-married group of all of those examined in Kansas City; 56 per cent of all of the working nurses there were married at the time of the study, as compared with 70 per cent of the industrial nurses. This is in contrast with nursing educators and administrators, only about one third of whom were married; but this, of course, does not mean that if a nurse wants to find a husband she should go into industrial nursing. It more likely reflects the attractiveness of the work for married women; and no doubt, many husbands find it pleasanter for their wives to be in it than in other kinds of nursing. Barschak asked 36 of her respondents, all of whom worked in "one-nurse" units, why they had looked for a job in industry. The typical answer to this question was, "I liked the hours and the good pay."

According to the Kansas City data, it is true that the industrial nurse does well as to salary; 28 per cent of them earned over $4,000 a year in 1954 as compared with only 19 per cent of all working nurses in Kansas City. Thus, a higher percentage earns over $4,000 than in any other field except school nursing and administration. Only 10 per cent of the industrial nurses made $3,000 or less as compared with 25 per cent of all full-time working nurses.

Other personal characteristics of the industrial nurse are that over half belong to nonprofessional clubs and organizations—a higher rate of community participation than is found among head nurses, and among general duty, office and private duty nurses and a lower rate than that found among administrators, educators, school nurses and public health nurses. Of all the fields of nursing, industry interestingly contains the fewest persons who identify a member of their family with a minority—only three per cent as compared with eight per cent of all working nurses and with 18 per cent of public health nurses; and few women of the minorities themselves are found in industry or in the doctor's office. One possible explanation would lie in the ways in which people are selected for these positions and the powers of those doing the selecting. The industrial nurse or the office nurse is usually hired by a businessman or by a physician who uses his own judgment and is influenced by his personal likes or dislikes and impressions. On the other hand, public health positions are most often filled by competitive public examinations, and the policy of the examining and selecting body is not to discriminate against members of minorities.

Knowing this, nurses are attracted who feel that they might suffer discrimination at the hands of private employers. Although this is a convenient explanation, it has not been demonstrated and is offered here only as a hypothesis which awaits testing.

The industrial nurse, like the office nurse, appears to be one of the least committed to her profession as reflected by her opinion of and membership in professional organizations. Of all the Kansas City nurse complement, the industrial nurses cherish the most unfavorable opinions about professional organizations "such as the League and the ANA"; 13 per cent of them indicated that they did not think that professional organizations "do enough good to make them worth the money or time they take." Less than half that proportion of all working nurses were so minded. Forty per cent of the industrial nurses do not hold membership in any professional organizations—a record which is surpassed only by general duty nurses, 46 per cent of whom belong to no professional groups. Contrast these figures with the 29 per cent of all working nurses in Kansas City who do not hold such memberships. Less than half of those in industry hold membership in the ANA through their state nurses' associations. Along with general duty and office nurses, they have among the lowest records in this respect. Nearly two thirds of all working nurses belong to the ANA, membership ranging as high as 92 per cent for public health nurses.

Also, the industrial nurse is often isolated from her colleagues and the medical world. When in "one-nurse" industries, she must use initiative and ingenuity to keep from developing a parochial mentality (21, pp. 22-3). Of course, in industries which maintain health units staffed by more than one nurse, she is less likely to be shut off. Industries large enough to maintain a multiple-nurse unit usually can afford a physician, if not on a full-time basis, at least on a regular part-time basis. Then, too, the nurse in such a plant does have colleagues who speak her own language and share her professional values.

Isolation may be exactly what the industrial nurse is seeking. There is evidence that jobs outside of the hospital are frequently filled by nurses who "don't like the responsibility of life and death" or who "don't like to wait on patients all day" (27). However, industrial nurses in the Ohio Valley complain occasionally that too little recognition is given to them and their work by their colleagues in other fields of nursing as well as by their superiors. In point of fact, about a third of these nurses were listed on the organizational tables in various industries as executives or supervisors; and among the head nurses, all of whom might be expected to be given supervisory status, only two thirds were actually accorded it.

Another indicator of the nurse's status in the industrial situation is whether she receives a salary or an hourly rate of compensation. Customarily, labor receives the hourly rate while management, including executive and administrative personnel, is on a salary; 78 per cent of the Ohio Valley industrial nurses are salaried. In the one-nurse units 81 per cent are salaried, while in the multiple units there is a difference between the head nurses and the staff nurses, 90 per cent of the former being salaried as contrasted with 71 per cent of the latter. The type of supervision which the nurse experiences is also indicative of the position she occupies among other professional employees in the plant. We will return to this point in a moment. Meanwhile, let us examine a few of the ways in which industrial nurses express anxiety about their status.

The following is a typical complaint: "I think that one of the important phases being neglected in our plant is that our opinions are not asked when there are problems in our plant dealing with nursing procedures and that we are never asked to sit in on safety meetings or health conferences." Here are other examples of complaints involving assaults upon status: "We nurses are not being fully recognized in the personnel organization; there is not very much real interest in the nurse and first aid." "My pet peeve is noncooperation of management; professional nurses are treated as laborers, not as professional workers." "Monthly salary instead of being paid on an hourly basis; wage scale is low in comparison to clerks or typists."

Barschak observes that "Experience and personality of the nurse are intangibles but they largely determine her performance, as education alone cannot account for the competence of the professional nurse" (21, p. 9). The interviews with the Ohio Valley industrial nurses and others who work with them reveal a wide range in the ability of the nurse to adapt to the situation and carve out a niche for herself. At one extreme, we have the kind of nurse to whom the personnel director in a plant is referring:

I haven't found a nurse so far who wants to go out in the plant and look for her own work. My last nurse turned me down when I asked her to inspect the women's locker room and take charge of sanitation. She wanted to work only in the medical department and refused to leave it. Another nurse, although technically well trained and efficient, antagonized the workers by her unfriendly attitude. The workers refused to go to see her, so I had to discharge her. I think nurses go into industrial nursing work only because they want an eight-hour job and a closely defined set of responsibilities which don't tax their brains too much.

The personal relationship between management and the nurse, says Barschak, is important—the tact, the timing and the manner in which suggestions are presented. When the nurse does not show an interest which the management feels she should, she finds her professional attitude, or lack of it under attack. Under some circumstances, the opposite extreme develops: the nurse becomes a really important figure in the plant both in the eyes of management and of labor. Such a nurse is described as follows:

Although the plant is in a rather dilapidated area in the town, the nurse has done, as the personnel director points out, excellent work in making the worker safety-conscious. She tours the plant twice a day. The author went with her through the plant and observed her talking to the women on the production line. The nurse was treated as a friend and advisor, and the author could fully understand why the workers turned to her on different occasions for advice as well as for the bandaging of a cut finger or to get an aspirin. In her capacity as welfare director, she also makes use of the various denominational welfare services in the community.

Apparently most of the employees in the small plant in which this nurse works are women. They described changes she brought about in the plant and how she built and developed her department. She uses effectively a complex referral system and instituted pre-employment examinations. Among other things, she gives advice on "women's troubles."

The industrial nurse, perhaps more than any other, finds herself in a largely undefined position. Her responsibilities and her functions may be very broad or very narrow. In the Ohio sample, her functions depend on four conditions: (1) the size and the scope of the medical department, (2) the type and the availability of medical supervision, (3) the type of other supervision and (4) the experience and the personality of the nurse.

The most unquestioned and common function is first aid, which

99 per cent of all these Ohio industrial nurses reported they gave. Other activities of a very different nature were mentioned frequently, such as visiting retired workers, participating in planning plant recreation, preparing lists for Christmas baskets for needy families, referring employees or their dependents to local welfare agencies, making home visits, touring the plant and counseling. Especially in the one-nurse units with no doctor on the payroll, nurses frequently report that they purchase supplies of medications.

A task which the hospital nurse traditionally feels that she ought to complain about is "paper work." However, what she has to contend with is as nothing compared with some of the functions expected of the industrial nurse. Every nurse in the Ohio sample reported that she had to fulfill certain office duties. Although record-keeping and report-writing were the most frequent, 39 per cent of the nurses did part-time secretarial work and over two thirds mentioned that they did typing. Like the general duty nurse, the industrial nurse responds to queries about the least important parts of her work by mentioning such things as record-keeping and paper work.

The nurse in industry is frequently placed in a peculiar position ethically. The American Medical Association Council on Industrial Health does not endorse a nurse in a plant without medical supervision. Their position is:

> Industrial physicians should be responsible for the proper instruction and subsequent activities of nurses and other assistants. Their functions should be described in clear and comprehensive written orders posted in the medical department. There should be no delegation of services requiring expert medical attention.[2]

As is true of most such edicts, this is unrealistic; it bears no resemblance to what actually happens in industrial plants. Barschak expresses "surprise to find out in the course of the investigation that there exist a considerable number of plants which provide nursing services but with no written orders available" (21, p. 62). She discovered that in 19 per cent of the one-nurse units there were no doctors' written orders, and even in the larger multiple-nurse units, 14 per cent had none.

The nurse in industry seems to have far more administrative re-

---

[2] Medical service in industry, J.A.M.A., p. 895, March 14, 1942. Cited by Barschak, op. cit., p. 61.

sponsibility than her colleague in general duty. This is particularly true in the one-nurse unit. For example, 74 per cent of those in the one-nurse units share responsibility for planning the plant's health program, but only 38 per cent of those in multiple units. Not even the head nurses in the multiple units perform as many administrative functions as a rule, as does the nurse who is on her own. The explanation is the presence of a medical director. When the nurse works under him, she checks questions regarding administrative duties by writing, "the medical director takes care of that." It is apparent from the Ohio study that one of the most pervasive complaints of the industrial nurse is that of being left out of administrative and policy-making decisions and programs.

The author of the Ohio Valley study is convinced that the nurse's role in industry will shift more and more toward preventive medicine and health education. Her work, it appears, will become more that of the health counselor and less that of the first-aider, gradually shifting from work traditionally associated with nursing to knowledge and skills more closely related to social case work and health counseling. Yet, in spite of this presumed trend—and it is one which has the strong approval of nursing educators—the study in Ohio illustrates over and over again the predominance in her daily agenda of first aid.

Closely related both to the diversity of her functions and to her problems of status is the industrial nurse's place in the formal power and authority structure of the institution in which she is employed. Supervision and work assignments do not always come from the same source, and there are wide variations between one-nurse and multiple-nurse units. In the one-nurse unit, a fifth of the respondents receive their work assignments from personnel, that being the largest single source. Only 11 per cent of them receive assignments from physicians. Nearly 40 per cent receive assignments from no one. In the multiple-nurse units, on the other hand, the largest source of assignments is the physician—25 per cent, followed closely by assignments from the head nurse, 21 per cent. Another 10 per cent receive assignments from the safety department.

In the one-nurse units, the biggest percentage of supervision again comes from the personnel department. In the multiple units where the primary sources of assignments were the physician or the head nurse, the major source of supervision is the personnel department.

Barschak points out, as has been remarked elsewhere in this book, that the nurse resents working under the safety department largely because the directors of safety often are not professional engineers and she, as a professional person, feels that she should not be supervised by a nonprofessional man and consequently prefers it to be the personnel department. In discussing the trend in industrial medicine with production managers, vice-presidents in charge of industrial relations, and personnel directors, Barschak noted a keen awareness of new trends in medical services and also, with progressive management, a sincere desire to abide by those tendencies. "It is only fair to say," she continues, "that management at its different levels, especially personnel directors, seem to be more aware of these trends than are some medical doctors." Of course, it is generally conceded in the medical profession that at present the industrial physician does not stand high in this fraternity, and it is possible that he does not always keep up with medical developments in his field. The nurses' preference for personnel department supervision seems to be an implicit recognition of the fact that sometimes medical supervision in the industrial setting may be inferior.[3]

Being in a nonmedical setting and without colleague or medical support as the industrial nurse often is, she is likely to find herself on occasion in difficult ethical positions. The safety department with its engineering orientation and the industrial management with its business orientation cannot always understand her dilemma when, as sometimes happens, they insist that she violate the confidences of her patients or even, for their own reasons, exert pressure on her to slant medical reports one way or another. Personnel departments may be more understanding. Certainly, an important function of a medical director in the industrial setting is to provide the nurse professional protection against unethical demands, when, for instance, the boss demands a medical record. Often the nurse does not have the authority or the prestige to refuse, but if she can turn to the plant physician, the responsibility then becomes his, and he is much more likely to be able to resist.[4] Industrial nurses in Kansas City indicate concern over

---

[3] Data gathered by Joe L. Spaeth for a doctoral dissertation on the industrial physician and his work, appears to substantiate this observation (Dept. of Sociology, University of Chicago).

[4] This is the role of the doctor which is formally recommended by the American Association of Industrial Nurses in their "Principles to Govern the Relationship between Physician and Nurse Working Within Industry," cited in 21, p. 30.

this becoming involved in legal affairs, when, say, their treatment of an injury involves the company in compensation claims or affects the legal status of the workman seeking compensation. This legal aspect of their work, and the paper work connected with insurance matters, loom large in their opinions about their work (27).

The nurse's relationship to the doctor in the larger industrial health units is often like the pattern of the hospital; and so, working as she does in industry in isolation from colleagues and medical supervision, sometimes under pressure from engineers or businessmen and confronted with emergencies and undefined situations of one sort or another, it is little wonder that the nurse is not infrequently accused by the plant physicians of going far beyond her training and ability. "They practice medicine!" is the accusation heard now and then. But the hard thing is that the nurses are never fully in control.

The Ohio Valley industrial nurses say that they are performing functions some of which are quite different from those learned in the hospital schools of nursing and that they lack certain skills essential in the industrial setting. For example, nearly 60 per cent of them report counseling as one of their main duties (21, p. 74). They may be asked for advice about childrearing, marital difficulties or financial impasses. Few are trained to cope with such problems nor are many familiar with modern techniques of counseling. Perhaps it is more feasible not to attempt to make them into social caseworkers or guidance counselors but to familiarize them with community resources so that they may make intelligent referrals. Indeed, some of the more resourceful nurses have managed to educate themselves along these lines.

Four per cent of the Ohio industrial nurses have obtained a college degree and five per cent of those in the Kansas City metropolitan area where, with their sisters in private duty, they are the least well educated of nurses. (Thirteen per cent of all working nurses in Kansas City have college degrees; the figures range from the five per cent of industrial and private duty nurses to 53 per cent for nursing educators.) Over two thirds of the industrial nurses have no further education, clinical or otherwise, after graduation, which is twice the proportion found in school nursing, nursing education, nursing administration and public health.

The industrial nurse resembles private duty, office, general duty and head nurses in that about a quarter of them agreed with the statement: "I think that registered nurses are educating themselves right out of nursing" in a series of alternative opinions about nursing education. Only 23 per cent of the industrial nurses checked the alternative: "Registered nurses need more formal education than most of them are now getting," which is not nearly as large as the percentage of educators, administrators, public health and school nurses who thought so. It is of incidental interest that of all fields, industrial nursing has the highest percentage of graduates from religious schools (72 per cent), and the lowest percentage from governmentally supported or controlled schools (15 per cent) (25, p. 97).

It would appear that industrial nursing has a hold on those nurses who enter the field. As Barschak points out, people do not become industrial nurses right after graduation; 70 per cent of the Ohio sample had had experience in general duty. This is not unusual, but the 61 per cent of them who had had experience in private duty and the quarter who had been office nurses at one time or another are more than are found in other branches of nursing. The fact that 95 per cent of the Ohio Valley industrial nurses had held jobs previously in industry lends support to the notion that industrial nurses stay in it. Thus, the career of the industrial nurse can be characterized by early entry into the field and tenacity after entering it. Although the nature of the work itself is quite different, there is close resemblance between office nursing and industrial nursing both in basic problems and in the characteristics of the nurses who go into them.[5]

The Pennsylvania Industrial Nurse.[6] The industrial nurse's role is decisively affected by her position in the plant. She finds her working environment is more congenial and her supervision of employees' health more effective and extensive when she is called a "Head Nurse" and when her unit is known as the "Medical Health Department" rather than the "Dispensary," or the "Hospital," or "First Aid" (31, Chap. 8). The distinctions of status implied by the titles pervade all her relations with the plant, her superiors and the employees, her patients. Of the sample of 163 industrial nurses in Pennsylvania about

[5] Chapter 8 in Barschak's book (21) contains a series of vignettes describing a particular industrial setting and its nurse or nursing team.
[6] This addendum consists of findings by Wendell Smith (31) whose monograph was completed too late to be incorporated into the preceding section.

whom this statement is made, 44 per cent direct all suggestions to the personnel director, 22 per cent to the medical director and the rest to others.

However, we are warned that the "purposes" covered here are stated purposes; performance, of course, may not quite coincide with them. Further inquiry brought to light the fact that nurses who report to the personnel director actually have more responsibility for the health of employees and more representation on committees; they have more voice in the conduct of their own department and are more familiar with the environment in which employees work (31, pp. 40-41).

Finally, a circumstance of great importance for the industrial nurses' morale is the fact that when their immediate superior is the personnel director, they have the gratification of feeling that they belong with management rather than with the workers—in short, that they are professional people and treated as such. Nonetheless, 56 per cent consider themselves employees rather than members of management (31, pp. 28-30), and 86 per cent of the "management nurses" state that they meet supervisory and executive personnel socially, while of the "employee" nurses only 49 per cent do so. The relations on the job between the first-named and management itself are reported to be the more co-operative.

the school nurse

Is the school nurse a schoolteacher or is she a nurse? How does she think of herself, and how do others think of her?

The only research available on this group is again from the Kansas City survey (25), and this hardly delves deeply enough to uncover much in the way of social-psychological processes and problems. Interviews with school nurses in Kansas City do indicate their tendency to identify themselves primarily as members of a school faculty. For example, they heavily emphasize "health education" and "teacher training" (27). Like the industrial nurses, school nurses comprise five per cent of the local nurse complement.

As was seen in Table 15, school nurses and administrators were the oldest group, only four per cent of them being under 30 years of age; 10 per cent were over 60, a proportion exceeded only in private duty and public health nursing. School nurses in Kansas City were more active in the affairs of their community, as reflected by their membership in nonprofessional clubs, than any other group of nurses; 45 per cent of these nurses belonged to three or more such clubs or organizations, and they had the smallest proportion of any group of those who belonged to no clubs (23 per cent). The percentage of *all* nurses in the complement who belonged to three or more clubs was only 17, and 48 per cent belonged to no clubs at all. To make another comparison, of housewives who were former graduate nurses and were not employed, only 26 per cent belonged to three or more clubs or organizations, while 36 per cent belonged to none. Thus, by almost any standard, the school nurse is very active in her community. One reason for this may be that she stays for the most part in one place. With the exception of office nurses, school nurses tend more than any other group to have worked always in Kansas City. However, that geographic stability does not account automatically for high rates of participation in the community is illustrated by the office nurse who shared the stability but not the high rate of community participation.

Several outstanding characteristics of the school nurse appear to be derived directly from her participation in the world of public education. She is not only fixed in one place but also does not change jobs nearly so often as her colleagues in other fields. About 90 per cent of the Kansas City school nurses average at least two years on each job they have had during their career in nursing. This is true of only half of the whole local complement. In addition, school nurses are the only group reported in the Kansas City survey without any nurses who averaged less than a year on a job. Every other field has at least a small proportion of highly mobile nurses: 18 per cent of those among general duty nurses fall in this category. Of course, the high job stability among school nurses is, at least in part, a result of the fact that school nurses, like school teachers, are often employed by annual contracts. Even if there is no formal contract, it seems that the nurse feels herself committed to remain in a position for the duration of the school year, once she has accepted employment.

The school nurse is not only committed to her work but also becomes deeply involved. At least this is true in the Kansas City area where, for the most part, she is subject to the same requirements and enjoys the same privileges and incentives as the teachers. She is administratively a part of the public school system there, which means that she must meet its educational requirements. It is not surprising then to discover that school nurses obtain more education after graduating from nursing school than do any other group of nurses: 35 per cent have over two years of additional education, in contrast with only seven per cent of all the local working nurses; 37 per cent of them have college degrees, a proportion exceeded only by nursing educators and administrators and certainly significantly greater than the 13 per cent of all working nurses who are college graduates.

In one sense, school nurses are, with the exception of administrators, in the best paid field of nursing. In 1954, at the time of the Kansas city survey, 40 per cent of school nurses were earning over $4,000 a year; only 10 per cent of all nurses working full time there were in that bracket, but,—to repeat a point mentioned elsewhere— they present a peculiar picture because a large proportion of them are both poorly paid and well paid in comparison with other nurses. About 30 per cent of the school nurses were earning less than $3,000 —a larger percentage than in any other group except general duty, office nurses, and those holding miscellaneous positions. This rather odd distribution of salaries is explained in part by the fact that school nurses in Kansas City, as a part of the school system, work under the same salary schedule as do school teachers.

Just as school nurses have a high rate of membership in non-professional clubs and organizations, so do they also have high rates of membership in professional organizations. They are exceeded only by administrators and equaled only by educators in the proportion of them who belong to three or more professional organizations. School nurses, with their double professional identity, are eligible for both teachers' and nurses' organizations. The Kansas City survey does not report the extent of membership in their state teachers' association compared with membership in the state nurses' association. The facts, if we had them, would signalize the professional priorities, as they see them.

the nursing educator

Although nursing educators may often find themselves working within hospital walls, obviously they are not there to nurse the sick. The important relationship of the educators is with students, and few nurses are as isolated from patients as they. This is documented by a study by the faculty of the school of nursing at Vanderbilt University of their own activities (13). They show that even the clinical instructors spend an average of only three hours a week in activities classified as "nursing service"—and not all nursing service involves contacts with patients. The nonclinical instructors spend an average of one tenth of 1 hour a week at nursing service. From the Vanderbilt study, one gets the impression that the educators are academic people who differ little, if at all, from other college professors. In this respect, the survey probably does not reflect the life or the activities of the educator in the *hospital* school of nursing.

As is the case with most of the other specialties in nursing, our data on those who teach nursing are largely limited to the descriptions in the Kansas City survey (25). Findings discussed in Chapter 3 were related more directly to student nurses and their education than to their instructors, but it was impossible to consider the one without the other. However, here we are interested in the educator as a nurse in a special field and how she is like and unlike others.

Four per cent of the nurses in the Kansas City metropolitan area are primarily educators. It should be remembered that that study has a separate classification of nurses called "administrators," in which educational administrators are included. Actually, the data on educators reported in Kansas City are concerned only with educators who are not holding administrative positions. This is important when we consider such things as income, for example, because it means that the top income group has been cut out.

To a certain degree, this is probably true of age also. The nursing educators show no unusual age characteristics. Although a third of them are under 30 years of age, another third are over 40. Slightly under half are married, as compared with 56 per cent of all working nurses and with the extremes of 70 per cent for industrial nurses and only 33 per cent for nursing administrators. Like public health nurses, they spring in relatively high proportions from national or religious minorities: whereas only eight per cent of all nurses and only three per cent of industrial nurses belong to minorities, 17 per cent of the nursing educators identify members of their family as such. A high proportion are members of nonprofessional clubs or organizations, although the figure is not as high as that for school and public health nurses.

Along with administrators, nursing educators have the smallest proportion in the lowest pay bracket. Only seven per cent were earning

$3,000 or less as compared with 25 per cent of all full-time working nurses in Kansas City. However, this does not imply that they are concentrated in the high pay brackets. They are not; in 1954, over three fourths were earning between $3,000 and $4,000. The odd distribution is due in part to the fact that many of the highest paid were classified as administrators rather than as educators. The nurse educators, like the administrators, are the only groups of Kansas City nurses in which over half have worked outside of the two states in which the metropolitan area is located. In addition, educators are second only to administrators in the proportion who have been registered in two or more states. Thus, educators are a highly mobile group geographically. But they are also highly mobile as to jobs, like general duty nurses. Those two are the only fields in which over half of the nurses do not average at least two years on a job.

How do the teachers of nurses stand in relation to their professional organizations? Theirs was the only group in Kansas City in which there were no unfavorable opinions regarding professional organizations, and only nine per cent of the group expressed neutral opinions. That 91 per cent of the nursing educators checked, "I think every registered nurse should hold membership in some professional organization," is in sharp contrast with, for example, the office nurses, less than half of whom think so.

Turning from opinion to behavior, we find that 87 per cent of nursing educators belong to one or more professional organizations. Although high, this is not as high a percentage of membership as is found among private duty and public health nurses and among nursing administrators. One might ask why, of a group which is primarily responsible for instilling a professional attitude in students, do 13 per cent belong to no professional organizations? Although over 80 per cent of the educators belong to their state nurses' association, this percentage is exceeded in the three fields mentioned above. On the other hand, it also is true that over half of the office, industrial and general duty nurses do not belong to their state nurses' association.

As might be expected, nursing educators have some distinctive educational characteristics. For one thing, they are five times more likely to be graduates of degree programs than of diploma programs. The great majority of nurses are graduates of diploma programs, and four per cent of the nurse complement are in nursing education, but the Kansas City data show that only three per cent of the diploma graduates are educators, in contrast with 15 per cent of those with degrees. It is not surprising then that nursing education should be the only field in which over half hold college degrees. The educators rank after school nurses in the percentage of them who seek additional education after graduation from nurses' school.

Also, it could be anticipated that they would have the most favorable attitude toward current trends in nursing education, and they did: 45 per cent of them state that "registered nurses need more formal education than most of them are now getting." What is surprising is that 15 per cent thought that "nurses are educating themselves right out of nursing," and 40 per cent checked a neutral category.

the public health nurse

Public health nursing, which according to the Kansas City survey occupies four per cent of the local nurses, is a broad concept sometimes large enough to cover any nonhospital nursing services, including such fields as industrial nursing and school nursing. An extensive public health nursing project, uncompleted at this writing, is being conducted by the American Nurses' Foundation, and some fragmentary findings have been reported by Johnson (32). That study includes the school nurse under the rubric of public health nursing. It also includes nurses in specialized agencies such as tuberculosis and health associations. Because the school nurse was considered separately in the preceding section, Johnson's data has been recalculated for purposes of this section, with the school nurses omitted. This also makes his material more comparable with the Kansas City survey data on public health nurses which is composed mainly of nurses employed by health departments and visiting nurses' associations (25).

As the nursing educator is a hybrid teacher-nurse, so the public health nurse is often part social worker and part nurse. In many parts of the world, there is little or no distinction made between public health nursing and social work, and students receive training in both fields.

It is probably true that public health nursing is not a homogeneous field; that it is, in effect, several different fields of nursing. Even when school nurses are eliminated from Johnson's data, important differences appear between health department nurses and those with the Visiting Nurses' Association. For example, the median age for the health department nurses in the New York-New Jersey metropolitan area is 42, but 35 for those in the local Visiting Nurses' Association. However, it is well to point out that of the Kansas City nurses, public health nurses are by far the oldest: three quarters of them are over 40, while 15 per cent are 60 and over as compared with only 5 per cent of all the local nurses. The New York-New Jersey survey indicates a considerably younger age distribution for public health nurses than is found in Kansas City (Table 15).

Table 15. Age Distribution of Public Health Nurses in Metropolitan Areas

Age Group	New York-New Jersey* Percentage	Kansas City Percentage
	N = 2104	N = 60
20 – 29	26	8
30 – 39	23	19
40 – 49	23	41
50 – 59	21	17
60 and over	7	15
Total	100	100

Source: (32) (25).
* School nurses have been excluded from the New York-New Jersey data and are not included in the Kansas City data.

There are several plausible reasons for the discrepancy between observations made of New York and of Kansas City public health nurses. The most obvious would be that the difference is attributable to geography—public health nursing attracts a different group of nurses in New York than in Kansas City. But there are other possibilities which should not be overlooked. The New York sample consists of not only over 2,000 public health nurses in contrast with the mere 60 included in the Kansas City survey, but it also is probably more reliable in that Johnson reports that his data include about 95 per cent of the public health nurses in that area, while the returns from health department and Visiting Nurses' Association lists in the Kansas City survey were 67 per cent. A final explanation for at least part of the discrepancy lies in the difference in definitions of public health nurses used in the two studies. In Kansas City, public health administrators were included in the administrative field rather than in public health, and nurses employed by special agencies such as the American Cancer Society or the American Heart Association were classified in the "miscellaneous nursing position"; in New York, on the other hand, both are included with the public health nurses.

Further discrepancies appear between the two sets of data. One is in marital status. According to the Kansas City survey, 57 per cent of the public health nurses there are currently married. This is about the same percentage as for all nurses in Kansas City. The New York study reports 52 per cent of its public health nurses as ever having been married, and when the Kansas City data are converted from the current marital status to those who ever have been married, the figure there becomes 74 per cent. This is remarkably high by any standards, unless one recalls the age distribution of the Kansas City group. The older nurses are much more likely to have been married at some time than are the younger New York nurses, so that basically the problem remains one of age difference. If the age distributions in the two studies were more alike, it is almost certain that marital status would coincide more closely.

The New York public health nurses are a remarkably stable group geographically; 75 per cent of those working in New York City are graduates of New York City schools, and only 10 per cent come from outside the metropolitan area. Stability even within the metropolitan area is also indicated by the data, which show the Hudson River to be a dividing line, with nurses trained in New Jersey working in New Jersey and those trained in New York working in New York. Along with school nurses and office nurses, public health nurses are the only group reported in Kansas City in which over half always have worked there.

Johnson speaks of high rates of turnover in public health nursing (32) because about a third of the public health nurses in the New York area had been hired in their present positions within the two years preceding the survey. But "high" is a relative concept, and one might suggest that the fact that two thirds of the New York public health nurses have held jobs for over two years indicated a "low" rate. In Kansas City it was found that, with the exception of school nurses, public health nurses had the lowest rates of job mobility of any field of nursing; 81 per cent of them averaged at least two years per job since they had been graduated from nursing school. This is in sharp contrast with less than half of the educators and general duty nurses and the little more than half of the office nurses who had averaged at least two years per job. The point here is not a matter of discrepancy in findings but of interpretation. It is difficult to contend that public health nurses have high rates of turnover without comparing those rates with other fields of nursing and eventually with other occupations.

As has been mentioned previously, the Kansas City survey indicates a disproportionate number of public health nurses from national or religious minorities; 18 per cent of them indentified a member of their family with a minority, in contrast with only eight per cent of all working nurses in that area. Another distinctive characteristic of the Kansas City public health nurses is that none, in 1954, were earning over $5,000 a year. However, it should be remembered that nurses holding administrative positions in public health were not included. This means, in effect, that the top income group was removed and considered in with other administrative nurses. In the group considered, 80 per cent were earning between $3,000 and $4,000 and, along with general duty nurses, theirs was the only field in which over 90 per cent were earning $4,000 or less.

The Kansas City investigators discovered that the kind of education that nurses most frequently seek is in public health, although not necessarily by persons in public health nursing. Public health nursing is among the four fields in which two thirds of the nurses were found to have had additional education; the other three are school nursing, nursing education and administration. In every other, at least two thirds of the nurses did not obtain any further education after graduation from nursing school.

To the extent that membership in and attitudes toward professional organizations can be taken as an index of professionalization, public health nursing would appear to be one of the most professional of all fields. With the exception of educators, public health nurses express the most favorable opinions of organizations, nearly 90 per cent saying that every nurse should hold membership in a professional group. Without exception, public health nurses have the highest percentage of members in professional organizations of any group of nurses in the Kansas City area, as only seven per cent do not belong to one or more. In addition, they have the highest percentage holding membership in their state nurses' association. Only 61 per cent of all working nurses in Kansas City belong to the ANA through their state nurses' association, in contrast with 92 per cent of the public health nurses.

how nurses divide their work

It is now more than two decades since the practical and the professional nurse have been sharing the care of the sick in hospitals. At first, the practical nurses took over the menial and routinized nursing. They filled hot water bottles, bathed the patients, carried trays. To put it brutally, they worked where they could do least harm because their education was minimal. But, with time, more and more duties have been passed over to them as the pressure on nursing heightened with the increase and the aging of the population, with the growing disposition to go to the hospital when ill and with the progress of medical techniques. For modern medical diagnosis alleviates and cures by resort to innumerable technical procedures: electrocardiography, fluoroscopy, bronchoscopy, diathermy, radiation, basal metabolism tests and scores of laboratory analyses of specimens and so on, which require the patient's presence in the hospital. Doctors did many of these things at first, but they are too busy now, and nursing education has come of age and is producing young women capable of taking them over. Thus, there are more patients, but, by the same token, nurses do more for each.

If there are, say, 10 times the number of patients there used to be, there must be 10 times the nursing; but if each patient is to be given only three, say, of the modern tests or treatments, then not 10 times but 30 times the care is needed, not exactly, of course; but the point remains that there are more to nurse, and each needs more nursing. This means more and bigger hospitals and more personnel. Yet, bigness itself, organization itself, takes work merely to keep it going, as is so hilariously depicted in Professor C. Northcote Parkinson's satire, *Parkinson's Law*.[1] Give an overworked bureaucrat a subordinate or two, to relieve him and—as Professor Parkinson demonstrates —he will be busier than ever, while the results achieved remain the same as before, for officials make work for each other.

It is in this situation that we find nursing changing. How are these much multiplied tasks, calling for varying degrees of intelligence and technical sophistication and ranging from the bed bath to lumbar puncture, divided among the large and heterogeneous company of women who are all called nurses?

the time and task studies

Of some 30 studies of the nursing profession in the American Nurses' Association's program, 15 surveyed how the nurses spend their time and who does what (cf. Bibliography). The time studies are, in reality, the core of the whole program, which was conceived of as an inquiry into the nurse's work. Practice varies extraordinarily from hospital to hospital. To anticipate for a moment: in Alabama, for example, the aides are found to prepare and give medications in some hospitals; in others they may not do either! There, too, the aides may serve and remove diet trays in some hospitals; in others they may remove them but not serve, and in still others they have nothing to do with diet trays, for the dietary department takes full charge! Nor does confusion reign only in the world of simple tasks: starting intravenous fluids is sufficiently technical for some nurses to say it should be the physicians' work, and as a rule it is undertaken by professional nurses. Yet, in Minnesota two nurse aides reported that they have done it, and so did a practical nurse in New Hampshire. When pressure of work is great in the premature center of New Orlean's Charity Hospital, where the patients are the most delicate nurses ever have to handle, the attendants are known to do everything the professional nurses do (18, p. 233). It is easy to understand why the compilers of the immense time study in California hospitals wearily concluded

---

[1] Parkinson, C. Northcote: Parkinson's Law (Cambridge, Houghton Mifflin, 1957).

that hospital nursing is *very* unstandardized and that what a nurse does seems to depend on where she is! (4.)

The 15 studies provide an enormous mass of facts about nursing, broken down into small tasks. In nearly all cases, the functions are grouped for convenience into classes, such as "direct patient care," "medications and treatments," "clerical work," and so on, and the headings may number up to as many as 15. The studies are not precisely comparable. For example, where one research team speaks of "direct patient care," another may use the words, "hygiene, safety and comfort" to cover approximately the same bundle of tasks. None the less, the comparisons are very informative and illuminating and for most purposes are adequate.

The tables in the research monographs will give the interested reader the minutiae of nursing functions and how they are divided between the hospital personnel. This chapter will discuss the findings in general terms, beginning, however, with a brief description of each research monograph from which the facts are taken, partly because only a few are in general circulation, but more because one can assess the facts better if acquainted with how they were secured.

The study of 12 hospitals in New York state (1) covers the activities of 50 professional nurses, including students and 22 practical nurses in the medical, surgical and combined services for four days in 1952 and reports what percentage of the time of each category of nurse is spent upon various tasks. The authors divided their 11 areas of activity into Virginia Streeter's categories: the professional, the nonprofessional and the nonnursing. The findings are classified according to the type of control of the hospital (municipal, voluntary, etc.), by bed size and by each of the three shifts. It is only a slight exaggeration of their deductions to say that both professional and practical nurses are doing the same things, and many of those things are not nursing!

The study of two urban and one rural hospital in the state of Washington (2) reports the time spent on several hundred activities sorted under 15 headings, in two weeks in 1952. It includes all personnel on all shifts, even part-time workers who contribute to nursing in the medical and medical-surgical units. The chief aim was to develop an economical standard method, applicable in the analysis of nursing in any hospital, and thus the authors regard their work as a contribution to method rather than as a presentation of explicit findings. Be that as it may, their data, based on almost 900 daily "diaries" in which various personnel report what functions they assumed during a given shift, what percentage of their time each function took and how frequently they performed each, are fairly confirmed by the research done by others.

H. Phoebe Gordon reports activities during five days of 1951 in Charles T. Miller Hospital in St. Paul (3), of 100 persons: head nurses, staff nurses, practical nurses, aides, students, orderlies and secretaries; 11 recorders, most of whom were R.N.'s made the observations in four medical and surgical and one obstetric station. The 87 activities which they witnessed are grouped under seven headings: direct patient care, record-keeping (including checking), oral reports and conversation, care of environment, miscellaneous activities, participation in outside activities, and personal time. The percentage of time given by each class of personnel was calculated. This study, unlike most others, then translates the activities into skills and designates for what proportion of the nurse's time each skill is brought into play. To make sure that the hospital under scrutiny was providing satisfactory care, patients and staff doctors were asked their opinions. (Had they not approved, the investigator might have found herself studying a horrible example!)

The California State Nurses' Association engaged a firm of management consultants which made time studies in 40 hospitals selected so as to be representative of the state (4). Three methods were used. Staff nurses were observed for a day; supervisory nurses were asked to keep diaries reporting how they spent their day; and auxiliaries were interviewed. To make the records comparable, a checklist of 439 tasks was drawn up and eventually sorted into five categories: direct patient care, nondirect patient care, special services, time off and standby. The number of persons surveyed is very large—there were, for example, 690 staff nurses and 782 auxiliaries—and the data on the distribution of their time between 439 tasks are, of course, copious. Two volumes were prepared: one (unpublished) contains the unworked data; the second (4) some 400 pages long, is devoted almost entirely to tabulations with a minimum of generalizations and conclusions. The facts of the nurses' activities are classified by region (North and South), by bed-size, by type of control (government, voluntary or proprietary) and by service. There are tables telling which functions are undertaken exclusively by each category of nurse, which by one but not by another, and which are shared. The conclusions to be drawn have not been published. The facts, when so numerous, cannot "speak for themselves," but the monograph, none the less, is a mine of information.

In Kansas, which has 59 hospitals of 26 beds or less, the small hospital in the small town was studied (5): 90 registered nurses in 23 small general hospitals reported a total of 384 duties and were observed engaged in 98 more which they did not mention! The tasks were grouped as non-nursing activities, nursing activities, personal activities and unreported time, and the percentage of the nurses' time given to each task and to each group of tasks are calculated in various ways, including by shift. About two thirds of the nurse's day in the little hospital goes to nursing the sick, and the remaining third is spent on an unpredictable range of duties, including, sometimes, stoking the furnace and cutting the grass!

One of the studies refers the findings about the distribution of nursing jobs among professional and practical nurses directly to the live issue of the education of the practical nurse and its appropriateness to her eventual work. To judge what she should be taught calls for a survey of what she does. This is the purpose of Helen C. Hanson's and John E. Stecklein's *Study of Nursing Functions in General Hospitals in the State of Minnesota* (8). In 37 hospitals they inquired into 68 tasks, picked because they are disputed, which makes the list interesting in itself. Thus it is not surprising that the 1,284 respondents—head nurses, general duty nurses, licensed practical nurses and nurse aides—disagreed. The questions elicited who did each task sometimes, often, or never and who should do it, and the replies were checked with corresponding answers from 128 supervisory nurses.

Habenstein and Christ developed their suggestive concepts of three kinds of nurse: the professionalizer, the traditionalizer and the utilizer when interviewing nurses of all categories in 24 nonmetropolitan hospitals chosen to represent all those of central Missouri (9). In a follow up study conducted by Christ (28) replies from 133 nursing personnel were obtained as to who does, who is supposed to do and who should do, each task on a list of 233 duties taken from the

Master List of Duties of the Missouri Practical Nurse. This checklist is incidental to the discussion of the three types of nurse, but the replies are useful in themselves and serve to confirm or challenge similar inquiries reported in the other monographs. Their collection of 668 personal data sheets provides, among other things, unique data on little proprietary institutions, some of them osteopathic.

Ford and Stephenson in 1953 reported a study of institutional nurses in three Alabama hospitals: a rural institution of 30 beds, a small-town hospital with 100 beds and a 285-bed city hospital (10). The authors drew up a checklist of 24 functions following systematic observation, then presented it to 230 nurses—head nurses, staff nurses, practical nurses and nurse aides—and asked them what tasks they performed regularly or never. Then they asked a sample of nurses and the hospital doctors who should do each. The authors reveal astonishing differences in opinion and practice which they illuminate by some fine descriptions of the atmosphere of each hospital.

The general duty nurse attracted the attention of Stewart and Needham as a professional whose work is changing before our eyes (17). In 10 general hospitals in Arkansas, ranging from 30 to 330 beds in size, they observed nurses at work and built up a checklist that finally covered 379 tasks; then they asked 107 general duty nurses to check which they do. These checklists show how the nurses' work-load varies according to the size of the hospital, by shift, by service, by patient census and according to the number of auxiliaries whom the nurses supervise. The authors conclude that despite her title the general duty nurse has become a specialist with a characteristic bundle of tasks.

Because the general duty nurse today is much occupied with the supervising of auxiliary personnel, Stewart and Needham undertook a study of the latter to shed light on their earlier research (15). They queried eight categories of auxiliaries, including students of both professional and practical nursing, aides and orderlies, concerning 392 nursing activities. As before, they made up their list chiefly from observation. They calculated the distribution of the work between the supervisory nurses, general duty nurses and the various ranks of auxiliary, the amount of time each class of nurse gave to each task, and the proportion of the nurses' time each claimed.

Stewart and Needham used the same technique again in building a checklist of the functions of the operating room nurse in 10 Arkansas hospitals (16), arriving at a roster that totaled 207. They interviewed 20 surgical nurses, including one man nurse, and learned that they are relatively young and well paid, as compared with floor nurses. Sorting the 207 activities into 10 sets, they reckoned the number of minutes the surgical nurse gives to each, the percentage each task takes of her working day, and they worked over the facts by shift and size of hospital. Finally, the authors learned what are the most time-consuming and the most frequent tasks and gave them special study.

A series of studies by a half dozen individuals, appearing in book form as *Change and Dilemma in the Nursing Profession,* edited by Leonard Reissman and John H. Rohrer, sheds light on who does what in enormous Charity Hospital in New Orleans (18). We are here concerned, first, with the report of Virginia H. Walker of the activities of 11 categories of personnel—including all varieties of nurse, the doctors, visitor-attendants and even of other patients. Her checklist was made empirically, like Stewart and Needham's; it covers 2,983 tasks, classified as direct and indirect patient care, and the contribution of each category of personnel to them is reported. Also, in the same hospital, Sarah Harman Sledge and John H. Rohrer drew up a 112-item checklist of functions specified in the manuals of procedure and policy in the hospital and asked the professional nurses how often they undertook each task and how they liked it. In the premature center of Charity Hospital, C. W. Wing and Virginia H. Walker used a kymograph to record the length of time taken by each nursing task and what category of nurse was doing it: R.N., student nurse or attendant. The data are then rearranged to show how the duties of each nurse vary according to the patient census, an aspect of nursing that is noted in very few of these studies.

The *Master List of Duties of the Practical Nurse in Missouri* is used by Edwin A. Christ as the core of a list of 90 tasks, devised to test the assumptions that the professional nurse is passing some of her traditional work to the practical nurse, and that there is no agreement on where the responsibility for it lies (28). The field work took the form of interviews with 138 nurse educators, 35 supervisors, 42 staff nurses and 89 practical nurses in 8 general hospitals in small Missouri towns. Concerning each function, all were asked: "Who does it?" "Who is supposed to do it?" and "Who should do it?" Suspecting that the practical nurses think that the professional nurses "throw them their dirty work," Christ compiled a list of 50 disparaged tasks and discovered that the two classes disagree most of all on: "Who is expected to do what?" He concludes with a statement of how the professional and the practical nurses are redefining their own and each other's jobs.

The basic difference between the nursing of medical and of psychiatric patients is brought out in the categories of duties devised by Martin and Simpson in their survey of nursing in the psychiatric wards of five hospitals in North Carolina (29). Their interviews with 67 professional nurses, 44 physicians and 144 attendants yielded descriptions of duties which they analyzed and then grouped. The cluster of duties which the other studies call "direct patient care" here becomes "interaction with the patient." They asked all three classes of personnel what tasks are the most important and what the most time-consuming of the nurse's day, then of the attendant's. On a number of points the ideas of nurses and attendants converge substantially, but in so doing they depart from the doctors' opinions.

A study, still unfinished at the time of writing, describes the division of duties in 11 New Hampshire hospitals among all categories of hospital personnel including the ward clerk (22). George F. Theriault, who undertook the research, listed tasks which he observed or learned about in interviews, adding others named in A.N.A. studies which are already on hand and ending with a roster of 58 duties. His tables have not been issued at the time of writing, but he reports that on the whole they confirm the findings of other research workers. In his 249 interviews, of which 132 were with professional nurses and the remainder with the several ranks of auxiliaries, he inquired into the work of each and also into the rewards and the satisfactions that it entails. His report is of particular value for its illuminating stories of how professional activities happen to be provisionally and "temporarily" entrusted to auxiliaries.

Though not strictly a time study, one more piece of research should be mentioned as contributing to our knowledge of how the direct care of the patient is parceled out. This is Harriet M. Kandler's investigation in the Boston Psychopathic Hospital (6). In showing under what circumstances hospital personnel can promote resocialization of mental patients, account was taken by means of "spot-checks," a method of time sampling, of the interaction of patients with personnel, doctors and visitors. Of immediate interest here is the ranking of the staff according to amount of interaction with the patients. In subsequent research in the Metropolitan State Hospital, near Boston, these findings were applied experimentally to chronic mental patients (24), in the course of which the amount of interaction between head nurse and patient was compared with that between attendant and patient.

findings and trends

In the thousands of details in these surveys, some general trends and conditions are discernible. In the first place, they show unanimously that bedside care is no longer the principal occupation of the professional nurse, and the higher the nurse rises in the hospital hierarchy—if she becomes a director of nursing service or a head nurse, for example—the less does she see of the patient.

Thus, in the Arkansas study of auxiliary nurses, for instance (15), it is shown that direct nursing care takes up 18 per cent of the time of directors of nursing service and of supervisors, 22 per cent of the time of general duty nurses and 36 per cent of the time of auxiliary nurses. The same situation is described in another way in the survey made in New Orleans (18); of all the direct care given the sick, head nurses provide 3 per cent, and the nurse aides 35 per cent. To look at it from still another standpoint, in Charity Hospital, bedside attentions claim 43 per cent of all the nursing done by head nurses, 63 per cent of all the nursing done by staff nurses, 61 per cent of that done by students of professional nursing, 69 per cent of that by students of practical nursing, 71 per cent of that by practical nurses, 93 per cent of that by ward aides and 94 per cent of that by nurse aides. Table 16 shows the same sort of balance existing in the hospitals studied in New York state. All the studies tell this story.

The care of the person—the bedside, or "touch" tasks, as they are called—is now largely in the hands of auxiliary nurses; and among the several ranks of the auxiliaries this responsibility is, in turn, passed down so that, as one research worker put it, it is as though education were separating the nurse from her patient, and even among the auxiliaries, the nurse aide is likely to provide a greater proportion of direct patient care than is the licensed practical nurse. Ironically, at the very time when the education of nurses has become more sophisti-

Table 16. Time Spent by R.N.'s and Practicals on Eleven Functions

Function	R.N. (per cent)	Practical (per cent)
Total	100	100
Patient—direct care	23	30
Patient—indirect care	11	14
Medications and treatments	15	15
Administration	17	9
Teaching	2	1
Care of environment	3	5
Clerical	9	6
Equipment and supplies	4	5
Errands	1	1
Professional growth	2	1
Personal*	13	13

Source: (1) Table 1, p. 28. Based on data from 12 New York Hospitals.
* Includes meal times.

cated, technical and thorough, other forces are bringing it about that the better educated the nurse, the less does the patient see of her. This appears, too, in Boston Psychopathic Hospital and is the more significant when one considers that particularly in psychiatric nursing, the professional nurse is expected to manipulate her own behavior and the hospital environment so as to promote recovery:

The attendants interacted most with the patients, the students next, the graduate nurses next, and the supervisors least. . . . Attendants are paid workers who may or may not have received formal training. They work directly with the patients under the direction of head nurses. Graduate nurses function as head nurses and are responsible for supervising the care of patients, educating students and attendants and serving as administrators of a 30-bed unit. Supervisors are administratively responsible for several units. They help with the education program for student nurses and attendants and assist the head nurses in solving problems on the unit and maintaining standards of care for patients. The student nurses come to this hospital from three-year basic nursing programs for a 12-week course in psychiatric nursing (6A, p. 1101).

These statements are confirmed when one turns to the time studies to learn how the professional nurse *does* spend her time. The New York survey shows that she devotes only half her day at work at the "professional level" (1, p. 101). The general duty nurse in Arkansas, who spends 22 per cent of her time on direct patient care, gives an average of 28 per cent of it to record-keeping. If she has one or two auxiliaries under her direction, keeping records will consume a quarter of her time, but if she is in charge of three or four, the time required rises to 28 per cent; if there are no auxiliaries, it drops to nine per cent (17, pp. 69, 78). (Curiously, the figures grow slightly smaller if she directs five or more auxiliaries. This may be because such a nurse is usually in a large hospital which may employ ward clerks or secretaries; we are not told.)

As she sees less of the patient in the flesh, the general duty nurse sees more of him on paper. If she oversees the care of 30 or more patients, she will give 20 per cent of her time to direct patient care, but nearly 31 per cent to the records, while if she has not over nine patients, direct nursing care claims 26 per cent and the records 14 per cent. The patient census sheds light on the findings when the data are classified by service: the general duty nurse in the medical services gives 29 per cent of her time to records (and gives 10 times as much time to patient records as to administrative records), as compared with 27 per cent in surgical units, 20 per cent in pediatrics, 19 per cent in obstetric services, and 14 per cent in orthopedic units—but the patient load is heaviest in the first-named of the services and lightest in the last-named (17, Chap. 3, Table 9 and f.f.). At this point, it should be said that a great merit of Stewart and Needham's work in the Arkansas hospitals is that by classifying their data in innumerable ways they have reinterpreted variables like size of hospital, shift, service unit, and so on, as patient load, or as number of auxiliaries under supervision, so that one can appreciate just what it is that explains the differences.

The California study appears at first sight not to support the foregoing generalizations. There, staff nurses give 60 per cent of their time to direct patient care and auxiliaries 56 per cent; staff nurses give 22 per cent of time to indirect patient care, and the auxiliaries give it 31 per cent (4, pp. 165, 254); but it is impossible to say how much of the difference is accounted for by the way the categories were set up for this study. For example, charts and reports are counted under the heading, direct patient care; and clerical and administrative (including supervision) come under indirect patient care. The picture might be very different if charts and reports were put under indirect care and if supervision were made a separate category.

One should be prepared for the possibility that California's hospitals, like its climate, are different, but to date we have no explanation of it. At least it is not regional, for farther up the coast, in the state of Washington, these things conform to the facts found everywhere else. In the two city hospitals and the small community hospital covered in that survey, the professional nurse spends the greatest proportion of her time at records, reports and acquisitions: 31 per cent in Hospital A, 35 per cent in Hospital B and 30 per cent in Hospital C (2, pp. 41, 62, 69). Now in these institutions, the professional nurse gives to hygiene, safety and comfort—a category which corresponds more or less to the direct patient-care pigeonhole used in most other studies— 16 per cent of her time in Hospital A, 14 per cent in Hospital B and 3 per cent in Hospital C; and the time of the practical nurse is divided in the opposite way, with the greater proportion going to hygiene, safety, and comfort—in Hospital C, for instance, she gives it sixfold the time given it by the R.N.—and a minimal amount to records, reports and requisitions.

Another great competitor for the nurse's time is conferences and consultations. Of all the duties undertaken by directors and supervisors in the Arkansas hospitals, this category is the most time-consuming, using up 22 per cent of their day. The operating room nurse gives it 17 per cent, while the general duty nurse gives it 14 per cent of her time and the auxiliaries 8 per cent (15, Table 2; 16, p. 31). The greater the patient load and the larger the number of auxiliaries in her charge, the more of the professional nurses' time will go to this end (17, p. 93).

Summing up their findings, Stewart and Needham conclude that the general duty nurse, as they observed her day in Arkansas hospitals, gives a greater proportion of her time to bedside nursing if she is in a smaller rather than a larger hospital (making the division at 100 beds) and if she is in a nonprofit rather than a tax-supported institution. If on the evening shift, she gives relatively more time to this set of tasks than if on either of the other two tours of duty. Probably, this is because much of the administrative work, the treatments and the diagnostic procedures, all of which entail record-keeping, are crowded into the daylight hours, and the night gives more time for patients. Then, too, the general duty nurse in the orthopedic service as compared with other services, has highly specialized work with the patients because of the nature of their illness, and gives it relatively large percentages of her time. Finally, bedside nursing looms larger in the day of the general duty nurse the fewer her auxiliaries are, and the fewer her patients.

To generalize very broadly from the reports today, the professional nurse is chiefly an administrator, organizer and teacher, and the practical nurse is the bedside tender. More accurately, this is a statement of trends. What is a fait accompli in some hospitals is the coming thing in others; the frontiers between the work of the various ranks of nurse are shifting lines and the sifting and sorting of tasks is still going on in hospitals all over the country; but it was not planned or foreseen and it proceeds at an uneven pace, differing from one hospital to another, uncontrolled and unpredictable.

It happens piecemeal. One must imagine that in a given institution certain tasks always performed by professional nurses are, now one, now another, pressed upon a reliable practical nurse. Theriault quotes an experienced practical nurse's account of giving colostomy irrigations in a severely shorthanded ward: "Yesterday," she said, "I did it with Mrs. M. [a R.N.] showing me. Today I did it alone. The doctor says, 'You go ahead.'" (22, Pt. II) But in Minnesota hospitals—to pick a comparison—colostomy irrigation is given by 54 per cent of the practical nurses; yet perhaps with trepidation, for only nine per cent of them believe that they should do it alone; and all the while, 45 per cent of nursing service administrators and supervisors think that it is being done by R.N.'s *only* and 57 per cent think that this is as it should be (8, Appendices B-2, C-2, D-1, D-2). Thus, task by task, often by default or almost by accident, practical nurses are finding themselves doing more and more; and while their sphere is expanding, accumulating heritages one by one from the professional nurses, the professional nurses are supervising them, imparting more techniques to them and running their part of the hospital.

The undirected and almost unnoticed division of tasks varies from one institution to another and even by individuals. While a trusted practical nurse may be encouraged to fill in for the graduate nurse in a crisis, a less-experienced practical nurse may be expected to "keep in her place." Yet, in Charity Hospital's premature center, the attendants, who happen to be Negro, are discovered doing virtually all the nursing tasks which the professional nurses do but still are reported as "knowing their place"! (18, pp. 228-233). Nurses who speculate upon the present state of their profession describe it as chaotic because they find it almost impossible to make a valid general statement of the division of nursing tasks between professional nurses and auxiliaries. At the risk of hurting everyone's feelings, one might remark that it is becoming difficult indeed for the layman, from seeing what they *do,* to tell one kind of nurse from another! However, one generalization remains true—that even when they do the same tasks, the line between professional and practical nurse remains inviolate at least at one point: the former teaches the latter, not the reverse; and so, whether she still does them routinely or not, the professional nurse must know *all* the techniques.

Because the division of tasks varies even between individuals within the ranks, the research workers have reported their findings as percentages of categories of nurse which perform a given task. Functions overlap everywhere. For instance, three hospitals were observed in the state of Washington. In Hospital A, the professional nurses contributed 15 per cent of all bedmaking and spent 2 per cent of their time on it; the student professional nurses did half of it and it took 7 per cent of their day. In Hospital B, the graduate nurses undertook 12 per cent of all bedmaking and spent about 9 per cent of their time on it; the nonprofessionals did 58 per cent of bedmaking and it took 30 per cent of their time. In Hospital C, the auxiliaries did all the bedmaking (2, p. 32 *et seq.,* 54, 71 *et seq.*).

A good idea of the jurisdictional disputes is gained from the Minnesota inquiry into nursing functions (8)—to name only one of several appropriate studies. It begins with an inquiry into 68 functions already known to be controversial. Of each of the 68, the general duty and head nurses, the licensed practical nurses and the nurse aides in 37 hospitals were asked: who, of the three categories of nurse, does it? The 1,284 replies disclosed that all 68 activities were performed either often or sometimes by some members of each of the nursing groups. Even the almost symbolic task of starting intravenous fluids was shared by two members of the lowest of the ranks, the nurse aides (8, p. 67). Of the 68 activities, 54 were performed by 50 per cent or more in at least one of each category of nurse and 13 were performed by half or more in all three categories! The 13 tasks included, for example, three of those in the table below:

Table 17. Division of Tasks Performed Among Nurse Categories

Tasks	Performed often or sometimes by:		
	Percentage of Nurse Aides	Percentage of Licensed Practical Nurses	Percentage of General Duty and Head Nurses
Making the bed..............	83	93	76
Recording input and output	72	90	78
Cleaning and maintaining supplies and equipment for service or utility room	78	77	57
Cleaning unit after discharge of patient	65	66	(47)
Charting	(28)	93	91
Checking narcotics	(17)	70	86
Giving penicillin (IM).........	(4)	(46)	89

Source: (8, Table 26, pp. 72-73 and Table 25, pp. 68-70).
Figures below 50 per cent are shown in brackets.

To say that a task is the subject of jurisdictional dispute is to say that some nurses are doing work that they think should be done by other ranks or must see others engaged in activities which they consider properly theirs. Therefore, the investigators asked those who had themselves done a task to state who they think should do it.

Of the professional nurses, i.e., the general duty and the head nurses in the Minnesota sample, more than 75 per cent reported that they had undertaken 45 of the 68 activities; but in respect to only 11 of them were they virtually unanimous in thinking that these are proper responsibilities of the professional nurse alone. For example, 83 per cent of the general duty and head nurses thought that penicillin should be given intramuscularly by R.N.'s only, and another 10 per cent of them thought that it should be "by R.N.'s and others." Yet, this function has in reality been undertaken by 4 per cent of the nurse aides and 46 per cent of the practical nurses; and 73 per cent of the professional nurses thought that narcotics should be checked by R.N.'s only, with an additional 19 per cent saying, by R.N.'s and others; but 17 per cent of the nurse aides and 70 per cent of the licensed practical nurses do it (8, p. 92, Table 34, p. 93, and Table 25, pp. 68-70).

Thus, the general duty and head nurses think of their own proper sphere as containing very few tasks that should be theirs exclusively, but even these have been invaded by the less qualified personnel.

To look at another set of their duties: there were nine tasks which less than half the general duty and head nurses considered should be the work of the professional nurse. One of these was the cleaning and the maintaining of supplies and equipment for the service room (cf. Table 17). This work 57 per cent of them had done, but only 1 per cent thought that it should be exclusively their work and 18 per cent more thought that it should be done by R.N.'s and others (8, Table 35, p. 93). As another example, 76 per cent of the professional group had reported making the bed, as we have seen, but only 7 per cent thought that the job belonged to them and 42 per cent thought that it should be done by R.N.'s and others. The bitter part is that those who think it is their work may not be the ones who are doing it! Thus, only a minority of professional nurses think of certain simple bedside tasks and housekeeping chores as theirs, but the majority actually do them.

In short, then, the general duty and the head nurses are doing work which they believe is more appropriate to the lower echelons and must witness the lower echelons at work which they think should be theirs alone or shared with others.

The practical nurses are in no better position. Of those among them who had performed the tasks in question, 75 per cent considered 47 of the 68 tasks as properly being theirs (8, Table 36, pp. 94-5). Of the greatest interest are those jobs which have just been identified above as the subject of conflict among the professional nurses. Beds, to take one instance, should be made by practical nurses only, according to four per cent of their number. Another 75 per cent thought that they should share bedmaking with other nurses. This comes to 79 per cent. However, it will be remembered that 93 per cent of practical nurses reported that they had done it (Table 17). This means that some licensed practical nurses are making beds who think that the job does not belong to them. Another item of the 47 is charting. Of the practical nurses who had kept charts, seven per cent thought that charting should be their work exclusively, and another 80 per cent thought that it should belong to them and to other ranks as well. Yet, 93 per cent of the licensed practical nurses reported they had done charting. That means that some practical nurses who think of it as someone else's work are undertaking to keep charts.

Then there is the giving of penicillin intramuscularly, which is one more of the 47 activities. This task is thought of by eight per cent of practical nurses as one which should be theirs alone, to which are added 77 per cent more who think that it should be their work, but others', too. This makes a total of 85 per cent; but only 46 per cent of practical nurses say that they have actually done it. Thus, a great many practical nurses feel capable of undertaking a task which is never entrusted to them.

In the same way, the checking of narcotics is claimed by six per cent of the licensed practical nurses in the Minnesota sample as their work alone, and an additional 72 per cent would agree to share it with others, making a total of 78 per cent; but only 70 per cent of them report having done it. So here again, some practical nurses find themselves denied work that they think should be theirs.

The nurse aides, in their turn, feel that the wrong people are doing certain things and that certain people are doing the wrong things. A total of 21 activities were named as their job by over half of the Minnesota sample who had done them and knew whereof they spoke (8, pp. 97-8). One such task is the oft-mentioned item, the cleaning and the maintaining of supplies and equipment for the service room. This, in the estimation of 52 per cent of nurse aides, should be done by themselves only. Another 30 per cent would share the task with others; but this work, to restate, is actually done often or sometimes by 78 per cent of nurse aides and also by 77 per cent of the licensed practical nurses and 57 per cent of the professional nurses.

Then there are nine other activities which only one quarter or fewer of those nurse aides who had done them designated as their functions —in other words, work which on the whole they repudiate. They are all concerned with either specialized techniques like giving narcotics by hypodermic and starting oxygen by nasal catheter, or giving medicines like insulin or penicillin intramuscularly. These they do not think that they should undertake, even in conjunction with their superiors.

Among them is the giving of oral medicines; yet actually 24 per cent of the nurse aides have done so (8, p. 68, Table 25). It would be nice to think that these are exactly the women who regard it as their proper work; but that is highly unlikely.

These findings in the Minnesota hospitals may differ from the data of the other studies in detail and degree, but the general picture and the tendencies are certainly representative. George F. Theriault, whose report (22) is one of the most recent, states that his sample of New Hampshire institutions confirms the conclusions of the earlier investigations. He sums up the situation succinctly: a registered nurse complains that the practical nurses are too ambitious—they even want to give medicines—and a practical nurse reports that she does everything the registered nurses do and adds that she gives medicines, which is not permitted to the aides; and the aides, who learn from the practical nurses, say that they do everything the practical nurses do, plus giving medicines!

The point is made in still another way by the investigators in the 12 hospitals sampled in New York state (1, summary, pp. 101 et seq.). They adopted Virginia Streeter's division of nursing into the professional, the nonprofessional and the nonnursing tasks. The distinctions, very briefly put, are: professional work calls for technical, scientific and social knowledge and judgment, such as is expected of the graduate nurse; nonprofessional work permits a wide margin of safety and is done under supervision, such as, supposedly at least, is the work of the practical nurse; and non-nursing, on the whole, concerns the housekeeping and caretaking of the hospital and its services and may be entrusted to aides, ward maids, orderlies and the like. Applying these definitions to the New York hospitals, the investigators found that the professional nurse devoted under one half of her time to professional nursing and the rest was divided equally between nonprofessional and non-nursing tasks. The practical nurse gives under one fifth of her time to professional work, under one half to nonprofessional work and over one third to non-nursing. Thus, each group spends one half of its time on work supposedly better suited to others and there is a great deal of overlapping.

Surveying the confusion which their research brought to light, the Minnesota team went on to inquire into how much the top levels of hospital administration know of it. They asked the administrators of nursing service and the supervisors (all of whom they call administrators, for convenience) who is doing what (8, pp. 99 *et seq.*).

A total of 10 activities are believed by a majority of the administrators to be done by members of all three groups of nurses. The administrators are substantially right; nine of the activities appeared on the lists of tasks undertaken by half or more of each class of nurse (8, p. 99). Disagreement is minimal between administrators' opinions and both the actual duties and the opinions of general duty and head nurses. Of 20 tasks which 90 per cent of the administrators thought should be done by the professional nurses, the latter disagreed with them significantly on only two (8, p. 107, and Table 41, p. 108). There harmony ends.

The administrators differ consistently from the licensed practical nurses over the latter's responsibilities. On all but five of 37 tasks, the disparity of opinion and fact is significantly great. Consistently, the administrators underestimate the practical nurses. For example, 30 per cent of administrators think that the licensed practical nurses are giving penicillin intramuscularly, but 46 per cent of the latter report that they are doing so; and 37 per cent of administrators think that the practical nurses are checking narcotics, but 70 per cent of these claim to do the task. Thus, only about one third of the administrators are aware of what, in the first instance, almost half and in the second almost three fourths of the practical nurses, are actually doing (8, Table 39, p. 102). Their misunderstanding of the realities of the nurse aides' work is of the same sort: the administrators underestimate the scope of the aides' functions (8, p. 104 and Table 40, p. 105).

It seems fair to say that the administrators' errors are in the direction of conventional and now largely outmoded conceptions. They think of the professional nurses as still undertaking tasks which are now the work of the practical nurses and they consider the practical nurses as having a limited sphere of activity when, in fact, they perform an enormous range of tasks.

Finally, the administrators were asked who *should* do what (8, p. 106, *et seq.*). Their opinions may be summed up by saying that on the whole they believe that a great many activities should belong to the registered nurse—undoubtedly more than she could handle, placed as she is; they believe that a smaller number should be assumed by the practical nurse and that a much smaller number should fall to the aides. The professional nurses and nurse aides were in fair agreement with the administrators; but the practical nurses are disposed to stake out for themselves a considerably larger share and a wider range of work than the administrators would concede. For example, only one per cent of administrators think that licensed practical nurses should start intravenous fluids; but 57 per cent of the practical nurses who have done it think that they should; and 32 per cent of the administrators would be willing to have the practical nurses check narcotics, but of the latter who have done it, 78 per cent think it proper that they should (8, Table 45, p. 113). An inference from the figures is that more than half the administrators agree on 21 items which they think licensed practical nurses should *not* undertake; and the practical nurses dispute them on all 21, in theory and in practice.

Another dimension is added to this aspect of the research by Edwin A. Christ in his survey of country hospitals in central Missouri. He queried 138 registered nurses who teach in hospitals and schools of nursing on the question of who should do what, and learned that the educators, too, have a characteristic cast of thought, though they differ considerably among themselves. Asked "Who should assist with intravenous fluid?" 36 per cent of them said "always the registered nurse." This was the opinion of 32 per cent of the supervisors. These are small fractions, but in each case they represent the largest bloc of opinion, for the replies of the remaining two thirds of each are split up in all sorts of way. To continue, 77 per cent of the registered nurses agreed, and 53 per cent of the practical nurses, but of the practical nurses another 25 per cent thought that it should always be done by themselves (28, Table 66, p. 67). Throughout the questionnaire, the educators are prone to overestimate tasks, that is to say, to assign to superior ranks of nurses tasks which the supervisors were willing to see in the hands of the practical nurses. Undoubtedly, the fact that those who teach nursing have in mind a division of hospital work that is not shared by the supervisors must compound the already too prevalent confusion.

"Who is expected to do it?" is the final question set before the Missouri sample of nurses (28, Chap. 8). Since the hospitals issue no written orders, the answers are only in the heads of the personnel and there are significantly large differences of opinion between the registered nurses, the practical nurses and the ancillaries on well over half the items on the checklist. Here Christ paid particular attention to tasks which the professional nurses are known to disparage and found that the practical nurses claim that these are more often expected of them than they are of the R.N.'s. At the same time, these are tasks which the practical nurses do indeed perform and believe that they *should* perform (28, p. 96).

Most of all, the professional and the practical nurses differ over who is expected to perform tasks which appear on the *Master List of Duties of the Missouri Practical Nurse,* tasks which the practical nurse naturally thinks that she is expected to undertake. Reviewing the replies to the three questions: who does? who should? and who is expected to?, Christ found that the two categories of nurses disagree 77 per cent throughout and that the nearest approach to consensus is agreement by 28 per cent. They concur on one item only: "who is expected to measure and give pills, capsules and powders?". All say that this task is, should be and is expected to be the work of the professional nurse. It is, as Christ remarks, a highly visible duty which signalizes professional standing (28, p. 34). Nevertheless, the Minnesota survey discloses that oral medications are given by 87 per cent of professional nurses, 24 per cent of nurse aides and 72 per cent of licensed practical nurses; and since 89 per cent of the practical nurses think that their own class should give them, there must be 11 per cent who think that others should do it! (8, pp. 68, 94).

In an earlier study of 24 rural Missouri hospitals, Habenstein and Christ asked all three questions: who does? who should? and who is expected to? and they brought the replies to bear upon their concepts of type of nurse. (Cf. Chap. 4.) The professionalizing nurse, they found, is willing to entrust a number of tasks, historically her own but of low status, to auxiliaries. But the traditionalizing nurse clings to them, conceding them to the practical nurse only if there is no professional nurse at hand or if the practical nurse is sufficiently trained to be able to do them without supervision (9, p. 57).

Study after study corroborates the chief point: that today not one but several categories of nurse attend the sick and run the hospitals and that the frontiers of each one's work are all changing at once. Yet, to repeat, it is not as if the work to be done remained the same. We still seek to restore health but of late years have multiplied the techniques of healing enormously. Thus, the work has expanded, the number and the kinds of personnel who divide it between them also have grown, and no one has as yet settled just what is the best division.

The nurses who educate nurses cherish the most consistent opinions as to who does and who should perform given tasks. In the manner of teachers, they are dogmatic. Removed to some degree from reality, they may preach an idealized version of hospital work. In any case, they are distinctly loathe to say that bedside nursing is *not* the professional nurses' work. Probably without realizing it, they tend to assign to professional nurses tasks which, in the end, amount to an impossibly large volume of work. On the other hand, as Christ points out (28, p. 31), they may take it for granted that there will, for instance, be front-office clerks to be responsible for informing the next of kin of a death; or they will assign the duties of tray-carrying and the wheeling of patients to the x-ray room to tray girls, maids, orderlies, messengers or porters; but there are no such employees in small rural hospitals, nor are they always found in city institutions.

The supervisors and administrators, too, like to think of the professional nurse in the traditional way as the bedside comforter and to insist on her status being respected. Like the educators, they are inclined to "upgrade" duties, that is, to pronounce as the professional nurse's responsibility tasks which the latter has for the most part passed on to her subordinates. For example, in Missouri, 89 per cent of the supervisors and 76 per cent of the educators think that assisting in obtaining spinal fluid should always, or at any rate usually, be the work of a supervisory person or of a R.N.; but this task actually appears on the *Master List of Duties of the Missouri Practical Nurse!* (28, Table 28, p. 30). As a rule, the supervisors do less upgrading than the educators do, for the supervisors are realists. They deal every day with what they have and they learn to "make do!" They all know responsible women in the ranks of the practical nurses and the nurse aides and time and again entrust them with serious business, reserving their smaller complement of professional nurses for work which none of the others can do. The supervisors' intimate knowledge of the hard facts of running the hospital no doubt accounts for a curious circumstance reported in the Missouri study: educators downgrade the task of looking after patients' valuables, as something which has very little to do with nursing; but the supervisors know what trouble can be brewed if this job is mishandled and say that it should be done by nurses in the upper ranks (28, p. 15).

While the educators on the whole stress the "touch" aspects of nursing in considering the proper work of the professional nurse, the professional nurse herself finds this work more and more out of her domain. Yet, she apparently wishes to claim all the traditional things as her own and to think of herself as doing them. Thus, in the Missouri hospitals 38 per cent of the R.N.'s say that hot water bottles are usually filled and applied either by themselves or by the practical nurses; yet 71 per cent of the latter say that they or the ancillaries do it (28, p. 52). The professional nurse may *supervise* the hot water bottles, but there is ample evidence that very heavy inroads are made on her time by matters far removed from hot water bottles, such as paper work and administration. Here is another example. To the question, "Who should chart fluid intake and output?" 75 per cent of the professional nurses in the Missouri sample say that it should always be their duty, and indeed the patient's chart has always been a sacred obligation in their eyes. Yet, while 41 per cent of the practical nurses would agree that it belongs to the R.N.'s, 21 per cent say that it should always be done by a practical nurse (28, p. 80); and we have seen that the same thing goes on in Minnesota hospitals. As Christ surmises, the professional nurse who delegates a task which she considers hers regards the incident as exceptional and by no means a commitment and is sincere in claiming the task as still her own. It is precisely in this way, in incident after incident, in one hospital, then in another, that she has turned into an organizer, teacher, supervisor and administrator, while the practical nurse more and more frequently takes over the bedside tasks which the R.N. no longer has time to do. Thus, the professional nurse insists that the measuring and administering of medicines is her prerogative, yet a fair fraction of even the nurse aides say that they share in it.

However, the professional nurse has not said goodbye to *all* direct patient care. The duties she clings to are in many instances technical tasks which she has inherited from the physician—whose own work changes, too, as he passes down to her procedures which a generation ago she would not have been thought competent to undertake; taking blood pressures is an instance. She cherishes tasks involving the use of instruments on patients; but this frontier, too, the subordinate ranks have breached. One can imagine how the professional nurse easily can forget without being aware of it the occasions when it has been convenient—it may be in the spirit of "just this once"—to permit invasions of prerogative.

Some tasks are important to the R.N. as symbols. These she insists upon as appropriate to her status in the hospital. She may delegate them, but never routinely. The practical nurse as a rule is not included among those present at the beginning of shift to "hear report," nor at the end to "give report." The charts are usually closed to the practical nurses and so are the staff meetings; but we know that even nurse aides have been known to chart and somewhere, at some time, we may be sure, the other sacred rites have been invaded. At least three middle-aged, experienced practical nurses in New Hampshire have done charge duty, charted, heard report and given medications (22, Pt. II.

Being responsible, the professional nurse bears the heaviest burden when the institution is understaffed or the patient load excessive. At "Crestville," a hospital of 100 beds in Alabama where patients are bedded in the corridors and nurses work to the point of exhaustion, the professional nurses not only administer and supervise but also perform almost every task, many of which they say should be the aides' work; but in 30-bed "Noah" and in 285-bed "Alabama City" they undertake a far smaller number of duties. "Crestville's" aides, on the other hand, are given work which most respondents thought calls for more training than the aides' (10, p. 83).

Of course, the professional nurse often leaves her own work— however defined!—to give a hand when needed. A practical nurse in a shorthanded, small-town hospital tells an appreciative tale of generous sharing of burdens:

The head nurse has the responsibility of the floor but I haven't had one that just takes the responsibility. They all work. Like Mrs. M; she works just as hard as we do. Although, when she's busy giving medications or taking care of a patient, then she doesn't answer the bells and things like that. But if we're busy and the bell rings, she'll leave her desk and . . . she really gives us a hand. I never had any that just sat at the desk and just gave out orders. They usually all pitch in and do it (22, 'Ward H').

When the head nurse returned to her desk, she still had all her charts, reports, requisitions and a million-and-one other bits of paper work which she is not supposed to delegate, to attend to.

The overworked professional nurse, hurrying from one pressing duty to another, ends with an amorphous pattern of work that may "never be the same two days running." She would be amazed if she had time to stop and look at the situation, to realize, for example, that a professional nurse was cleaning the refrigerator while a practical nurse was giving a hypo! Or, to take an illustration from the study in the state of Washington, that the graduate professional nurses were attending to 31 per cent of the sterile and 40 per cent of the unsterile treatments, but the nonprofessional ranks were doing 44 per cent of the sterile and 22 per cent of the unsterile treatments (2, p. 55 and Table 13, p. 58). In other words, the more highly qualified of the nurses were doing twice as much of the unsterile treatments and three quarters as much of the sterile as were the less qualified; and they did considerably more unsterile than sterile treatments!

It is sometimes proposed that the easy tasks should be allotted to the auxiliary nurses and the hard to the professional; but if it were ever possible to redivide them along such simple lines, the same forces which brought about overlapping and all the other anomalies would no doubt operate again to restore chaos. There are other objections: the professional nurse has to know the "touch" tasks and the routine jobs that fall to the subordinates because she must teach them; and a further point was raised by the lone practical nurse who said that trays ought to be served by the registered nurse because, as she remarked, "Maybe that would be one way each shift to get the R.N. into the patient's room. God knows, she never goes in otherwise!"

The practical nurse, in effect, is repeating the history of the R.N., building up her career by the piecemeal accretion of activities which someone higher up has no time for; and once she has undertaken a task, she is likely to think that it is hers, and from that, to think that she ought to do it and that it is expected of her, while the R.N. continues to claim it as her own. Thus, it comes about that, as found in the Minnesota hospitals, seven out of 11 tasks which 90 per cent of general duty and head nurses think should be the professional nurse's work are also considered their own by at least 75 per cent of the practical nurses! (8, p. 96.) The practical nurse is certainly right in asserting that the professional nurse no longer monopolizes the highly responsible jobs, though the latter may think she does.

In a 57-bed hospital in the resort country of the North, a licensed practical nurse, now in the 19th year of her employment there, is entrusted with charge duty. She began as a kitchen helper and in time advanced to maid. Then, learning first one task then another from her associates, she was promoted to be an aide. Still with no formal training but learning on the job, she mastered more and more skills and became a practical nurse. Eventually, she gained her license and is now doing, to all intents and purposes, the work of a professional. Every step of her career was only possible because the registered nurses who supervised her work recognized her capacity (22, Ward "X").

However, so young an occupation is naturally an internal battleground, and indeed the practical nurses are rarely of one mind. Those in the Missouri sample—*never* unanimous—were almost equally divided on the question of who should give the immediate care of the body after death. This disparaged task 28 per cent of the practical nurses allocated to themselves. Slightly fewer thought that it should be done always by the professional nurse, and the same proportion thought that it should be done by either, while 19 per cent would assign it to an ancillary person (28, Table 68, p. 68). The work of the practical nurse is undergoing continual change and appears to be the most erratic and unstandardized of any in the hospital.

Consensus is reached among practical nurses, it seems, when they well outnumber the professional nurses with whom they work. Christ found that when the ratio of practical nurses to professional nurses reaches three to one, for instance, there is a marked increase in the tendency to take over functions as their own (28, p. 102). Under such circumstances, they are disposed to broaden their claims to include even very responsible and risk-bearing tasks, while perhaps remarking that they wished there were more R.N.'s to do them; and, of course, it is precisely then, when the professional staff is small, that the harried R.N., charged with the direction of teams of subordinates and burdened with managerial responsibility, has no choice but to entrust the bedside nursing to them. The situation might be covered by a tentative hypothesis: that as the morale of the professional nurse goes down, the esprit de corps of the practical nurse goes up; perhaps not invariably, but at least in these circumstances.

Ironically, the practical nurse in contemplating the next lowest echelon, the nurse aide, talks just like a registered nurse! Thus, a licensed practical nurse complained of the aides, the volunteer high school students (who in her hospital are invited to sample nursing as a possible career) and other ancillaries:

> So far as I am concerned, [they] . . . are not members of the nursing staff, but just learners and part timers and kids who are in and out. The orderly who helps us with the heavy work and with catheterizations, and preps and so on is I think of in the same sort. At least I don't think of him as in the same category with me, but as someone I tell what needs to be done, like a porter or janitor, but just a little bit higher. Now, I think that any of these people, if they apply themselves and study and get more experience can get a license, and become a Licensed Practical Nurse, but, I think until they do prove that they can handle that kind of work they ought to be kept down and doing only the things they are supposed to do, for the sake of the patient, who is entitled to competent care. That's why I wear my pin and my sleeve-band, so the patient knows that when I am working with him he is not getting the care of just anybody but the care of a Licensed Practical Nurse (28, p. 60).

One is reminded of the fagging in an English boys' school!

There is every evidence that the nurse aides' sphere is now being created before our eyes by the practical nurse, just as the latter's domain was carved out for her by the registered nurse. In the same way, the scope of the aides' duties is expanding piecemeal, now here, now there. The practical nurse has fairly complete command of the bedside nursing and of the work disparaged by the professional nurse, but the cleaning and housekeeping jobs she is bequeathing to the lesser orders; and this level of personnel is building up her own status, just as her "betters" build up theirs, by delegation. Her work, presumably delimited, is beginning to overlap theirs until we find, as in Minnesota, that at one time or another a few aides have undertaken gravely responsible and highly technical tasks; and in New Hampshire, "the longer the aides are here, the more they do what the practicals do. . . . 'I like taking temperatures and blood pressures,' said a young aide, 'it feels more like a student.' " (22, Pt. II, also "Ward H").

Few occupations are so much in flux as nursing is today. Not many years ago, virtually unpaid students did the nursing, under supervision. Now, many hospitals have staffs of graduate and practical nurses and some rely, too, on students to some extent, but the new order of things has not quite "set." Leaders of the profession believe that the uncertainty and confusion have been made worse as a consequence of shortages which cause pressure, overwork and daily crises of all sorts. If so, order may come into the profession and chaos cease when the supply of professional nurses grows up to meet the demand.

The practical nurse and the nurse aide, often spoken of as temporary, are certainly permanent members of the hospital team; in the California survey, for example, it was shown that auxiliary nurses furnish 56 per cent of all time given to direct patient care and 31 per cent of all time needed for indirect patient care (4, p. 254). Moreover, the occupational standard of living, if one may call it that, of the professional nurse has risen so much that she is unlikely to wish to have back *all* her old tasks. Hence when, if ever, the division of labor in hospital nursing is stabilized, we can be sure that it will recognize a variety of ranks of nurse.

chapter seven

roles and relationships

If, in this chapter, we appear to overemphasize conflict and discord, it is not because they are predominant, but rather because they indicate the areas in which relationships need to be improved. The purpose of these research projects has not been to eulogize nursing, and most of the "good" has been glossed over rapidly. The ultimate purpose is to arrive at an understanding which will lead to the improvement of nursing care. Improvement implies that all is not perfect, and for this reason we will attempt here to throw the spotlight on the imperfections—to underscore the difficulties, the faults, and the problems confronting the modern nurse in the multitude of personal relations thrust upon her.

A role is a relationship which a person is expected to have with his associates in functions like or unlike his own. It involves far more than the delineation of tasks and activities which were the focus of the preceding chapter; it is a set of expectations on the part of each party to it, and these expectations include, in addition to the performance of tasks, the assumption of certain responsibilities and privileges. The theoretically frictionless situation would be one in which both parties know exactly what is expected of them and what they can expect of the other and behave accordingly. Naturally, this very rarely exists. Our task here is to examine some of the major role relationships in which the nurse is required to participate in an effort to uncover conflict and competition. It will be simpler to examine her role in relation to a number of groups, but it should be recognized that roles are not played in isolation; many other kinds of people occupying many other kinds of roles are constantly entering in.

nurses and patients

At the heart of the nurse-patient relationship lies a dilemma which appears repeatedly in the research. In one study, it became the central concept around which most of the data and observations were organized and interpreted (18). The dilemma has to do with the gradual yet steadily increasing separation of the graduate nurse from the patient's bedside, which was described in Chapter 6. This state of affairs is brought about by forces beyond her control; but, though she did not will it, it apparently evokes in her more than a little feeling of guilt. Yet there is impressive evidence from New Orleans (18), New York (20) and Kansas City[1] that, although with the majority of nurses she states that she wants to know her patients and to work more closely at the bedside so as to be assured that they are receiving good care, when provided with an opportunity, she makes little or no effort to do so.

This dilemma is clearly illustrated in a New York maternity hospital (20), where it was found, in response to the question "What do you think is the most important thing the patient needs from the nurse?" that nurses consistently stressed a comforting presence. A typical response is:

That she have some support and some assurance. The important thing is to be with the patient as much as you possibly can . . . I think more than anything, most women need human contact—not to be left alone. The patient wants comfort from the nurse—the knowledge that you are here and that everything is secure. They like you to hold their hand. . . .

This is the dogma—the things which the nurse intellectually understands and the things of which she feels she should approve; but inter-

---

[1] New, Peter, and Nite, Gladys: Nurse-Patient Relationship Study: An Experiment in Nursing. Kansas City, Missouri: Community Studies, Inc. In preparation.

views with patients in the same maternity hospital indicate an inconsistency:

I was more frightened than in pain. I wasn't so interesting—just one of those normal cases, and they all went out and left me alone. When the pain came, it wasn't that that made me scream; it was that I knew I was by myself, and I didn't know what was going to happen. I could hear the nurses outside, laughing and talking among themselves.

In my other labor, a couple of nurses in my room were complaining about how much fuss another woman was making—just sort of talking to each other. I didn't like it because I figured if they're not sympathetic with her, they won't be with me, either. I don't think they know enough about how people feel.

A nurse sat with me constantly reading a book. She would examine me, then go right back to reading. I felt sorry for her, listening to me groaning, but I guess they see so much of it, it is just part of a day's grind. I don't think it meant anything to her. I don't think I even interrupted her reading.

Of course, these are unfavorable examples, picked intentionally; most nurses do not behave so. These interviews show in extreme form what can and sometimes does happen.

The New Orleans investigators (18) observe that the nurse seems to be caught up in the press between the needs of the mass hospital and the textbook values. The choice most frequently goes to the former which are the more urgent and which provide the easier solution. It then becomes the function of a special auxiliary group in the institution, the visitor-attendants, to give the patient care and comfort; in other hospitals it may be aides, practical nurses, students, or nursing assistants of one type or another.

In the New York maternity hospital, the nurses are reported to recognize the need to educate patients but to insist that it is done more effectively by classes, conferences and printed instructions than by the individual nurse. The authors say that the nurses' great faith in group instruction and in the printed word is not shared by a large segment of the patients with whom they have contact. It appears that to the nurses there, the greatest source of satisfaction lies in carrying out efficiently and swiftly the task of getting through as many patients as possible. In other words, the nurses survive in the busy, overcrowded institution, accepting it as a challenge and rationalizing the pressure as their reason for being unable to provide individual attention to patients. The patients, in turn, cannot help being aware of this air of busyness and hesitate to "impose" on the nurse with requests or questions.

There are things that the nurse is not interested in—things that she does not care to do. By appearing busy or harrassed, she is able to escape them. "Being so constantly under pressure, the nurse may develop a harrassed manner and viewpoint, so that even if pressure decreases, she still feels busy, and communicates this to her patients by facial expression, tone of voice, and general manner and appearance" (20, p. 214). This may be far more effective than words in conveying her real feelings.

It was found in a large psychiatric hospital that the attendants have the highest rate of interaction with patients. They are followed by students, then graduate nurses and, finally, supervisors (6A). Although a psychiatric hospital is different in many respects from other hospitals, in the relative frequency and intensity of the nurses' contacts with patients it seems to be similar to the maternity hospital, and both are not unlike the general hospital (20, 18). Both quality and quantity of interaction are governed in part by the absolute numbers of persons involved in the given situation. This postulate is illustrated by research in the same psychiatric hospital, and the illustration holds implications for those who assume that the solution to all nursing problems lies in obtaining more nurses. The investigators discovered there that the interaction of patients with nursing personnel increased with the number of nurses, up to a total of five. As the number of nurses on the unit increased to more than five, they began interacting more with each other and less with the patients. Apparently, there is an optimum number of nurses for any particular unit, and increases beyond that number bring diminishing returns for patient interaction. Although this observation was made in a psychiatric unit, very similar conclusions are being reached in a study of medical and surgical units in two hospitals in Kansas City.[2]

The definition of the nurse-patient relationship and the responsibilities that it implies is not clear or consistent, and there seems to be little agreement on the part of the two parties involved as to what it should be. The patients in the New York maternity hospital, "show a remarkable and fairly uniform tendency to place the lowest value upon

[2] New, Peter op. cit.

the very functions that nurses often regard as the central core of their job" (20, p. 211). When patients describe the nurse's job, they respond typically with, "All she does is check my weight," "She just gives me pills," She just comes in to ask if I've had a bowel movement." The authors interpret the patients as saying, indirectly, that functions which occupy the nurse's time have little meaning to them personally: "They are not concerned with what the nurse 'does.' What she *is* to them, and what she gives of herself, has the most meaning and value" (20, p. 211).

It is clear from Chapters 4 and 5 that as nurses do different kinds of work they may be expected to enter into correspondingly different relationships with patients. There are some nurses without patients, the educator being the most common. Others are those employed by drug companies, professional journals and magazines, administrators in large institutions, officials in nursing organizations, those engaged in research, and a scattering of others. These have no problems centering on patients, other than their oft-stated feelings of guilt at having none.

If the nurse's dilemma truly is a conflict of the demands of mass treatment with those of the traditional image of the lady with the lamp, then, if there are no mass demands, she may find no dilemma at all. This is borne out in part by a study of small nonmetropolitan hospitals in central Missouri (9) where her relationship with the patient takes on a very different complexion from that found in the studies made in New Orleans or New York. For, like the teacher, the nurse in the small community finds herself an integral and highly visible member. Typical of her comments are: "Patients are always coming back over and over and you get to know them and their entire families. Many is the time that you get so you have taken care of enough members of the same family you get to feel like you are a part of it," or, "That is one of the advantages of a small community hospital. You make a great deal of friends and your acquaintanceship becomes much wider. I know many of our gals [nurses] drop out to see their former patients" (9).

In a real sense, the scrub nurse and some of her companions in the operating room can be thought of, like some of those mentioned above, as nurses without patient relationships. To the extent that the patient is unconscious during most, if not all, of the nurse's contacts with him, the association is purely technical rather than personal. As an object of surgery, the patient ceases to be a person. As one nurse told an interviewer, "I just don't like surgery, *period*. I like to be around patients that are awake. In surgery they are asleep" (9). In addition, the presence of the surgeon clearly defines ultimate responsibility, and the nurse is relegated to the position of a technical assistant.

At the opposite pole from surgery is the kind of relationship which the private duty nurse has with her patients. Just as the general practitioner in medicine comes closest to seeing his patient as a whole, so does the private duty nurse; she is the general practitioner of nursing, as already noted (Chap. 4). In Georgia (7) and in the District of Columbia (30), the studies indicate that the crux of private duty nursing lies in the nurse-patient relationship. She not only nurses in the usual sense of taking care of the patient according to the doctor's orders, but in a way she acts as insurance. She reassures the patient and the family that there is an expert present at all times, thus engaging in a sort of preventive psychological medicine. A Georgia private duty nurse says:

> Actually, I think it's to prevent something which might come up. You have a private duty nurse when a patient is critically ill, and the nurse is there to know exactly what symptons to watch and what to look for, and I think it is to keep the patient relaxed. That really helps more than anything else. When people get critically ill, they get panicky, not only they themselves, but the whole family.

It is significant that, in the District of Columbia (30), the reason most often given for dismissal of a private-duty nurse from a case is "clash of personalities" between nurse and patient. Where the general-duty nurse with her more diffuse responsibilities can leave a patient's room under any number of pretexts for any length of time, the private-duty nurse, for the most part, because of her specific and exclusive responsibility, cannot evade her patient's demands and his endless casual conversation. She escapes from the eight-hour-a-day pressure only momentarily when she goes on an errand or when the patient is sleeping, and even then some member of the family may be present (7). The major complication in the relationship between private duty nurse and patient is, as we shall see, the patient's family. The general duty nurse, because of responsibilities to the hospital organization, cannot be expected to exhibit such consistent orientation toward the patient; the same limitation would apply to the public health nurse and to the industrial nurse.

The Georgia investigators conclude: "It is obvious that the field of private duty attracts nurses who are characterized by a real sense of concern for the patient" (7, p. 269), for when private duty nurses describe "critical incidents" (see Chap. 1), they almost invariably are related to the patient. Their motivation is revealed by such statements as: "Bedside nursing was my reason for going into training and no other phase of the nursing profession offers this opportunity now—general duty now includes mostly office work, and supervision of the aides and students." Another typical response is, "The only true soul-satisfying work to me is bedside nursing. It involves patience, skill, teaching, psychology, and, by giving your best you feel that you are giving some degree of good and happiness to others and they give to you."

To the nurse in private duty, flexibility in role is an important part of the therapeutic process. She must decide whether to indulge her patient or to wean him and to refuse his demands, even at the risk of his disapproval. She must decide on whether to serve solely as the agent of the physician or of the family and also on the extent to which she should exercise independent judgment. "Successful adjustment to this situation is central to her status as a nurse. If she fails here, she loses status with the patient and possibly with future patients" (7, pp. 284-85).

As will be seen, the private duty nurse provides an intriguing case of professionalization in that in some respects she might be considered the most "professional" of all nurses but in others she appears as the least "professional" (Chap. 10).

In the maternity clinic studied, the nurse-patient relationship is sometimes so flavored with the nurse's image of the physician's expectations that it can almost be said that there is *no* nurse-patient relationship:

So thoroughly does the clinic nurse accept the traditional role of being "the doctor's assistant," that she tends to view the patient's needs as something set apart from her "regular job." Her assigned duties in the clinic re-enforce these beliefs, since her functions continue to center primarily upon the needs of the obstetrician. She does not see herself as a professional team member, functioning in her own right, but as an extension of the doctor, whose vital work might be impeded or made more difficult without her help (20, pp. 95-96).

The finding in this study that the patients have an extremely limited view of the nurses' functions is explained by the fact that the patients' view actually conforms with the nurses' own self-conception. When the clinic nurse is asked to describe her job in the clinic, the functions she mentions are all related to the activities of the doctor. She makes no mention of any relationship with the patient as part of her work. These nurses do talk about "care of the patient," but in a very different sense from the private duty nurses. To the clinic nurse, care of the patient means literally assisting the doctor by saving him from having to perform a variety of tasks and technical chores. Thus, in answer to the question, "What is the main job of the nurse in the clinic?" the New York investigators got this kind of answer from the nurses:

The main job is the patient—to see that everything is taken care of. Seeing that she's examined, that the doctor sees her. Carrying out the orders the doctor wants her to have, like a special diet, or if he feels that she should wear elastic stockings. Actual care of the patients means assisting the doctors with any treatments, getting the patients on and off the table and taking dictation. You weigh each patient, see that she has a specimen for the doctor, and prepare her for his exam.

It is not strange then, that a gap in communication should exist between these clinic nurses and their patients. The nurses seem not to realize that patients learn what to expect from them by observing what they appear to be willing to offer. For the patient's role is a new kind of role and one which is structured for her by the nurses' definitions of responsibilities and obligations. It could be structured as easily in one way as in another. Patients may conclude that nurses are not adequately prepared or are too busy to give them the information and the reassurance that they want (20, p. 81). As a result, the patients, whether clinic or rooming-in, begin to turn to auxiliary personnel for personal interest and warmth.

In Pennsylvania, the research team asked a state-wide sample of graduate nurses, "How often have you come across nurses who are not sufficiently concerned with patient care?" (19). About 80 per cent had "sometimes," "often," or "very often" come across nurses who were not sufficiently concerned, and only 20 per cent responded "rarely" or "never." They seem to feel that doctors have more concern for patients than do nurses. When the research team asked them about doctors, it found that only 12 per cent had "often" or "very often" come across physicians who are not sufficiently concerned with patient care, in contrast with the 28 per cent who had "often" or "very often" come across nurses who were not sufficiently concerned. However, one must remember how dangerous it is for a nurse to criticize a physician. At the other extreme, 43 percent of the nurses had "rarely" or "never" come across such doctors, while only 20 per cent had "rarely" or "never" come across such nurses. Of course, there are varying definitions on the part of these nurses as to what constitutes "sufficient concern." Depth interviews with 100 nurses in Kansas City reveal a significant difference between those who were graduated before and those after 1940 (27); the younger nurses tend much more frequently to emphasize technical and administrative knowledge and skills, while for the older ones the main thing is the direct care of the sick at the bedside.

The psychiatric nurse, to an even greater degree than the private duty nurse, is an integral part of the therapeutic process and must engage in measured and purposeful interaction with her patients. Her most important and most difficult task is to establish appropriate personal relations with patients whose sickness is primarily their inability to behave in appropriate ways toward other people.

Interviews with psychiatric nurses in North Carolina reveal a second difficulty—that the expectations of the psychiatrist regarding her proper role are somewhat different from those she had learned to anticipate from most other physicians (29). Thus, the role of the nurse is poorly defined both in relation to the physician and to the patient—a situation which results in much conflict and frustration. Martin and Simpson, noting that the literature and also their respondents in North Carolina made much of the manner in which the nurse relates herself to the mental patient, probed the nurses' understanding of the phrase "relating to the patient." As might be expected, they found that the term meant a variety of things to a variety of nurses. Some simply did not know; others thought it meant anything to do with the patients; some defined it as getting along with patients. Still others thought of it in terms of communicating with patients, and some gave answers which could not be placed in any of the above categories (29, pp. 113-115 *et seq.*).

The importance of being "busy" to the nurse has been discussed already. She thrives on having more work to do than can possibly be done. Her motto might be similar to that of the U. S. Marines: today she does the difficult; tomorrow the impossible. What, then, happens when the nurse is thrust into a work situation where she cannot always appear to be busy? The North Carolina investigators report such comments as, "There is a much slower pace in psychiatric nursing and less hustle and bustle." It must be hard for one whose function it is to help sick people get well to be confronted with patients who may not get well and, when they do, do so only after painfully slow treatment and numerous relapses, calling for the exercise of great patience. It arouses feelings of guilt on the part of the nurse who has always felt that nursing meant a high rate of activity. One nurse reported that she had a bad conscience when she "was just sitting around doing nothing," particularly if her supervisor or doctors were in the offing. (Other important facets of the role of the nurse in a psychiatric setting are discussed below in the section on nurses and doctors.)

If, as is assumed in one study (6B), a good technique with mental patients is the reactivating of the interests and of the leisure pursuits which they had prior to their illness, then the nurse is indeed in a difficult position, because that study indicates clearly that the nurses did not have any clear perception of the patients' previous backgrounds or interests. They tended to judge the patients' interests in terms of their present social situation, i.e., the mental hospital. This being the case, they could hardly be expected to be effective therapeutically. Other divisions of the hospital—the social work and admissions office, for example, which might enlighten them, appear not to "mesh" with the nurses' work.

In any setting, the nurses become familiar with the general range of patients who come to them and develop certain methods of coping with what they conceive to be certain "types." Lesser and Keane believe that this can hinder understanding: "Whenever a nurse has a rigid concept about a patient or a 'type' of patient, she establishes a barrier to discovering the actual needs of the individual, and to meeting them" (20, pp. 214-15). Examples of such stereotypes which were found in the maternity hospital that they studied are: "All multiparae know about babies," "All clinic patients are uninformed," "All private patients are demanding." But there are other ways to classify people than by stereotyping them. For there are types derived from extensive and rich experience with a wide variety of the kinds of persons in question. To assume that the nurse must "individualize" the needs of every patient is to assume that she has never learned anything about people in general and of patients in particular.

As the teacher learns from experience that the relationship required for success with some "types" of students is different from what is needed with other "types," so does the social worker come to recognize distinct types of clients who require certain relationships, and so too does the experienced and competent nurse use her previous knowledge of other patients in determining the kind of relationship which would work best with a new patient. Thus, the private duty nurse feels that she must be sensitive to differences in patients, not only to differences in "personality" but also to differences resulting from "background, religious affiliation, family behavior pattern, attitude toward hospitals, previous hospital experience and prior experience with private duty nursing" (7, p. 211). Indeed, these things all influence patients' behavior, and the experienced and observant nurse learns to predict and to anticipate it.

Of course, personal prejudices and stereotypes can interfere with this process, can erect barriers to a proper therapeutic role relationship. In the Boston Psychopathic Hospital where it was assumed that the nurse operates most effectively with the patient when she understands his background and his interests, it was found that patients who were "liked" were thought to have interests in common with personnel (nurses and others), while those who were disliked were thought to have little in common. As a result, "There is little relationship between the similarity of interest that actually existed between patients and personnel and the similarity which personnel attributed to patients" (6B, p. 7).

Is it stereotyping or is it generalizing from wide experience when nurses say, "I prefer male nursing to any other kind of service,"

"Men are more easy to please," "Men don't have to be babied like women," or "Women are more spiteful than men. They are just harder to take care of than men" (9). It is very possible that there is a general difference in the response a nurse evokes from male and female patients. As long as she is not rigidly convinced that this difference must exist in every last individual patient, her knowledge about probable differences in response to nursing and to the hospital can be a valuable aid in helping her to establish a favorable relationship.

Just as any waiter can describe a "good" or "bad" customer, or any teacher can describe a good or bad student, or lawyers can speak of good and bad clients, so, quite naturally, nurses develop and maintain images of the "good" and "bad" patient. In the central Missouri study, such patients are characterized as follows:

If there is an "ideal" patient, besides being male he should preferably be a post-surgical patient. His age doesn't matter a great deal, but nurses, professionals and auxiliaries, are agreed that they are more satisfied to deal with patients whose recovery or improvement is rapid and dramatic. This is usually the case of the patient returned from surgery. Patients who refuse to accept orders, who are "neurotic," or who are demanding are listed as "problem" patients; treatment for this group generally becomes most perfunctory and most impersonal (9, p. 68).

nurses and doctors

Doctors, like nurses, define their role and that of the nurse differently in different settings. When the expectations which the two groups have of each other are mutually shared, they can then operate effectively and efficiently as a team on behalf of the patient.

This is one of the major underlying themes of Martin and Simpson's interviews with psychiatric nurses, which reveal that the nurse-doctor role in a psychiatric setting is most poorly defined—perhaps more so than in any other field of nursing (29). As one of their respondents put it, "The surgeon tells you what he expects out of the nurse and so does the pediatrician. . . . If we could find out exactly what the psychiatrist expects of psychiatric nurses we could come up to it." When the investigators asked the nurses what they thought the doctors ought to be doing, the most frequent complaint was that they should be spending more time with the patients; when the doctors were asked what they thought the nurses should be doing, the most frequent response was the same! Although each accuses the other of delinquency in this respect, the nurses are more critical of the doctors than vice versa. When nurses were asked what doctors should *not* be doing, most had no complaints, although of those who had, the most frequent was that the doctors do not take enough responsibility toward the patients. Doctors tended to excuse the nurses from not doing more because of the "shortage." Those who did complain, for the most part, mentioned that the nurses spent too much time in the nursing office.

It further appears that, in this psychiatric setting, there is no agreement among nurses, doctors and attendants as to the nurses' most important tasks. For example, when the doctors were asked, "What is the most important function of the nurse?" their responses predominantly were concerned with "interaction with the patient." Few of the nurses responded along those lines; their most frequent response had to do with "administrative responsibilities," the answer of a mere six per cent of the doctors.

An interesting phenomenon appears when we consider what the doctors mean by "interaction with the patient"—providing a humane understanding of illness, establishing an atmosphere which reduces his anxiety, giving him a feeling of being understood and cared for, and noting his moods and behavior in order to be able to make an intelligent report to the physician (29). These appear to be the very highly valued responsibilities which private duty nurses refer to as "human relations functions" (7, 30). However, whereas the psychiatrist complains that his nurses do not perform them adequately, the private duty nurse rates them high in her skills and complains that the physicians do not recognize their importance (30, p. 12).

What do physicians complain about in private duty nurses? "The physicians in this study indicated that they appreciate the work of the private duty nurse but feel that she may not be up-to-date on the latest techniques and drugs, particularly in the medical specialties. They would like the private duty nurse to realize the importance of noting and reporting changes in the patient's condition" (30, p. 12).

The notion of responsibility is a major component in the structuring of any role relationship. Who has how much responsibility and to whom or what? If this question can be answered clearly, there is not likely to be a great deal of conflict or confusion of role. Unfortunately, it is inherent in the organization of modern medical care that conflict in responsibility and loyalties should exist. Is the nurse ultimately responsible to the patient, to the physician, or to the hospital? It is not surprising, under such conditions, that the people who are most likely to agree with private duty nurses as to their functions are those least closely tied in with hospitals—the doctors. After making this observation, one study goes on to note that those most closely bound to the hospital as an institution, the hospital administrator and the director of nursing service, are in least agreement with the private duty nurse as to what her functions are and should be in the future (7, p. 245). It would appear, then, that from an organizational perspective, the private duty nurse should find less conflict of roles with the physician than does the hospital staff nurse.

There is a long-standing tradition to guide the private duty nurse in anticipating what the physician expects of her and what she can expect of him. We may contrast this with the relationship which must often exist between them in the relatively new and ever-changing field of psychiatry, where the nurse must discover which of several orientations the psychiatrist may have toward mental illness and must reconcile his approach with the particular school of thought with which she was indoctrinated. As a doctor reported to the North Carolina investigators, "The only way to get a team approach is when the doctor and nurse operate in the same frame of reference" (29, p. 66). In psychiatry, where many winds of doctrine blow, this may be a difficult goal; therefore, we may expect strained relations between doctors and nurses from time to time. Barschak points out a comparable confusion in industry; the doctor is the boss in large multiple-nurse units with a plant physician, while in the one-nurse unit, the doctor may put in only an occasional on-call visit; meanwhile, the nurse finds herself under the authority of an engineer or a businessman (21).

On his side, the doctor may play any one of a number of roles in relation to the nurse. In industry, he may serve primarily as a buffer, a protector and a spokesman. In the proprietary hospital or in the doctor's office, he is an employer as well as a physician. In public health and school nursing the doctor is often her advisor and consultant, while in research and nursing education he becomes a colleague of equal status. Of course, in general duty the physician serves as a professional superior and often acts in a supervisory capacity.

Nurse-doctor relations vary widely, not only by the specialty or the field of nursing but also according to the size of the community, the size and the type of hospital, and the age of nurses and doctors. Habenstein and Christ, on the basis of their observations in proprietary and osteopathic hospitals, make the following comparisons:

> Distinguishing the proprietary hospital, the relationship of nursing service personnel to medical staff personnel is more frequent, more intimate, and by and large more satisfying. . . . The role of the *osteopathic* physician to his nurse subordinate is probably best described as a "big brother" relationship, but the role of the *medical* physician to his nurse subordinate is at best in most instances, patriarchal, at worst despotic and tyrannical, and very often lacking in a benevolent social grace (9, p. 149).

Great differences are found in 3 Alabama hospitals, which, it will be recalled, range from a small hospital in a small community to a large hospital in a big city:

> There appears to be a much more informal, joking relationship between the nurses and doctors at Noah [the smallest] than at either of the other two. At Crestville the nurse's usual greeting for the doctor is, "Pull up a chair if you want to sit down." In Alabama City [the largest] the nurse still rises, but seldom verbally acknowledges the physician's presence. She continues with her work standing at the desk until he leaves (10, p. 25).

Operating room nurses in different sizes of hospitals have different patterns of communication with the surgeons (16, p. 29); it is more personal and informal in the smaller hospital where activities classified as "conferences and consultation" consume a relatively small part of the nurses' time.

Differences in hospitals are found even to affect the orientation of student nurses toward physicians. A study conducted in Kansas City indicates that students in small religious institutions see themselves as "dependent" upon the physician, in contrast with students in larger and nonsectarian institutions who have more "autonomous" orientation. This was found to be related to the kinds of physicians with whom the students have most frequent contacts. Thus, those in the larger institutions saw much of residents and interns, in contrast with the students in smaller hospital schools whose contacts were with a visiting staff, described by the author as "socially remote and personally powerful" (26, pp. 69-70).

The kinds of images physicians have of nurses are discussed more fully in Chapter 8, but at this point we should remark that doctors over 55 years of age are found to cherish significantly more favorable attitudes toward nurses than do their younger colleagues. On the other hand, the younger physicians apparently resent the nurses' achievement of professional status and independence. There is a difference according to age among nurses, too, but here we find both a mellowing process and a generational difference. The Alabama study concludes that the older the nurse, the more informal, perhaps, will be her relationship with the physician (10, p. 25). This is "mellowing." On the other hand, difference due to one's generation is described by an older nurse in remarking on the behavior of student nurses:

. . . the way they handle doctors—and I do mean handle them. Back when I was a student, I wouldn't have thought of saying some of the things these girls do to the doctors. I was scared to death of them. Why, every time a doctor came to make rounds, I wanted to melt in the wall. Now, they fight among themselves just to walk in a patient's room with some doctor (10, p. 104).

The North Carolina psychiatric nurses appear to be more critical of physicians than vice versa, as was noted earlier. However, the Pennsylvania study indicates that nurses are also highly critical of their own colleagues; but, although nearly half of the Pennsylvania nurses (46 per cent) indicate that they "sometimes," "often" or "very often" come across doctors who are unfair in their treatment of nurses, two thirds of them respond in the same manner when asked how often they come across supervisory nursing personnel who are unfair in their treatment of nurses. Then they were asked how often they had come across supervisory nursing personnel and doctors who were incompetent. The results were similar; they thought that nursing supervisors were more likely to appear incompetent than doctors (19). This study reveals a more critical attitude on the part of younger nurses. The Kansas City study of student nurses also finds that somewhere during the course of their education, students begin to lose some of their awe of the medical man; 63 per cent of the freshmen described their relations with physicians as "good," while only 44 per cent of the seniors did so (26, p. 68).

Doctors also complain. Many of the Kansas City physicians did not approve of the recent trends in nursing, objecting that nurses are becoming too "professional," too distant from the patient, and some-

times even callous (11, pp. 20-21). Complaints vary according to
the field in which physician and nurse are practicing. Plant physicians may complain that industrial nurses go beyond their training in
doing their job, that they "practice medicine" (21, p. 63); private-
duty nurses—to repeat—may be accused of not having adequate
knowledge of the newer and more specialized techniques (30, pp. 7-8);
and the office nurse has been charged with having "no experience in
bookkeeping or meeting the public graciously" (11, p. 21).

Any role involves status, prestige and power relations, symbolized
by deferential behavior on the part of one party. Thus, when asked
what it means to work with doctors:

> . . . the nurses place themselves in relation to the doctors in much the same
> way as they have interpreted the relation of others below them in the
> hierarchy to the nurse. Working with the doctor meant "assisting him,"
> "anticipating his needs," and "providing a learning situation" for the nurse.
> . . . Nurses said that "a doctor expects a nurse to follow or carry out
> orders," or "to assist him" (18, p. 77-8).

In industry, it was found that the doctor-nurse relationship in the
large units is patterned after that in the hospital. The author of the
Ohio Valley study was told by an older industrial nurse that whenever
the young doctor entered the health unit, she always felt that she
should stand: "I was brought up like that," she said. "We were told
to respect the doctor's word, not contradict him, and carry out his
orders" (21, p. 67).

Deference is examined most extensively by the Pennsylvania investigators, who discuss the philosophy of authoritarianism versus democratic organization as it is related to the social organization of a
hospital (19, Chap. 7). It is suggested that an authoritarian structure
is required in a hospital because of the life-and-death matters which
are dealt with by the personnel—that the hospital, like an army,
would be unable to accomplish its purpose otherwise. However, the
notion of the hospital as the setting for an ever-present drama of life
and death—an endless repetition of scenes of dire emergency—may
be one of the myths of the organization. It is certainly true that, for
the most part, an enlightened citizenry no longer views the hospital as
a place to which one comes to die. Death does not hover over those
who are in for "observation," for physical check-ups, for minor surgery, or to deliver babies, nor over most of the others who inhabit the

rooms of the modern hospital. Only a small percentage of patients are found on "critical" lists today, and many of these are "routine," for death itself is part of hospital routine.

There are practices which do not appear to be medically functional and serve primarily to remind persons, variously placed, of their true positions on the social scale of the hospital. Among these is the practice, already referred to (Chap. 4), of requiring the nurse to rise when a doctor enters the room, the maintenance of separate dining facilities for doctors and nurses, and the refusal to permit practical nurses to wear caps similar to those of the graduate nurses. Thus, the Pennsylvania research team remarks:

> The hospital salute is the practice of rising in the presence of doctors. . . . The *willingness* to rise for doctors can best be interpreted as a recognition on the part of those who approve of this practice that the doctors are in fact a superior breed of men whose contributions to medical science are immeasurably more important than the nurse's and that this superiority should be constantly affirmed whenever the elect and the unworthy happen to congregate. On the other hand, those nurses who object to this practice are denying, in effect, that the doctor's function is more vital than theirs, or, accepting the differences in functions, they question the necessity of requiring daily recognition of its existence (19).

It is of interest that over three fourths of their 2,425 Pennsylvania nurses agree that a nurse should rise when a doctor enters a hospital room which, they think, shows that "there is no appreciable articulate discontent with the authoritarian mode of organization" (19).

That nursing personnel will generally defer to the authority of the physician, at least verbally, is clearly demonstrated by the survey in New Orleans. When asked how they would react if the chief of staff asked them to do something which was not really a part of their job, only five per cent of the respondents declared that they would question the orders in any way. Although almost all of the aides would carry out the order, a few nurses indicated that they would do so only if it were "correct" or if they were "capable" of carrying it out. Some of the professional nursing staff, then, appear to reserve their right to professional judgment; but "the implication seemed clear that his [the doctor's] orders were to be followed even though they violated rules of the floor; as if the modification of the rules was a prerogative of higher status" (18, pp. 149-150).

This conclusion is re-enforced by responses of nursing personnel to other hypothetical situations involving physicians. The pattern of deferring to the physician is found by the Pennsylvania investigators to be specifically on the job and, in inappropriate settings, to disappear. To repeat for convenience a point made in Chapter 4, their conclusion is based on three questions asked of the Pennsylvania nurses:

Table 18. Nurses' Responses Concerning Deference to Physicians

Answers	Questions		
	Should nurses rise in hospital situation when a doctor enters the room?	Should nurses and doctors have separate dining facilities?	Should nurses rise in the presence of doctors in a social situation?
	(N = 2425) Percentage	(N = 2425) Percentage	(N = 2425) Percentage
Yes	77	50	16
No.	19	37	80
Undecided.	4	13	4

Source: (19).

On the basis of answers to these questions, the Pennsylvania nurses are divided into groups which show "high," "medium" and "low" deference to the physician. The authors then ask if there is not a relationship between the social class of the nurse and her acceptance of the hospital status system (as reflected by the deference group in which she falls). Estimating social class from husband's occupation, they find that this is the case. For example, only 11 per cent of the upper-class nurses are in the high-deference category, in contrast with 16 per cent of the middle-class and 21 per cent of the lower-class nurses. In other words, the higher the nurse's social class position, the less is she willing to accord deference to the physician. Apparently, the nurse who is used to being deferred to on the outside does not enjoy deferring to the physician in the hospital. In contrast, the nurse with a lower status in the community is less resentful of having to defer to him while at work (19).

While the doctor exerts formal power and authority in the hospital, he is in it but not of it. In fact, the research repeatedly makes it clear that a consistent source of irritation and discord among hospital personnel is reducible to the physician's paradoxical situation in having more authority than the members of the organization themselves and in being under no compulsion to respect either the formal or the informal balance of power as he finds it. (Illustrations of consequent predicaments appeared in Chap. 4).

But if the doctor with his formal authority can get things done in his own way, so too can the nurse by the use of her informal power. For nurses do overrule doctors, usually in diplomatic and subtle—not to say wily—ways. Thus, an operating-room nurse speaking of herself with humility and of the surgeon with all due respect, related:

> She [the patient] just did a little more bleeding than I was accustomed to seeing during a section. So I was worried. But everything came out all right. *I had the feeling that I would like to jump in and help.* But I know I shouldn't.
>
> (Question) What do you think would happen if you did?
>
> I might just do the wrong thing. *I've had the feeling where I'd like to hand him the instruments that I think he should have.* I have it ready in case he should ask for a suggestion.
>
> (Question) You mean a doctor will say, "what shall I use now?"
>
> *No. But he will be working and maybe hesitating occasionally and I'll say, "Would you want this?" and he'll say, "yes."* Of course I was always taught in training that the doctor's word was law. I think the younger group that's graduating from training now will sooner suggest things to a doctor, and *I think I too am getting over this idea of waiting for the doctor to do all the suggesting* (9, pp. 95-6).

While some nurses use such subtle techniques, others apply more direct pressure on the doctor. One gets the impression from the Habenstein-Christ report that, in the small hospital in the small town, the nurse may undertake to act as the community's conscience. Now, the doctor may not be personally subject to the social control of the community; but the nurse, who often has some local standing, is, after all, a major means of communication between the community and the hospital—and, as the authors point out, the hospital is an extremely important institution in the small town. For example, a nurse had discovered that a doctor was doing something which she felt he should not be doing and she was quite certain the community would not approve of it. She was asked, "Will you take any course of action at all?"

> Yes. Or I will reveal it. I would maybe say, "Now, here, nobody knows

about this except myself and somebody else, and you'd better correct it before it becomes known. To save your face correct it." And then just give them so much [time] to correct it, "But if it goes on it will become known and then you will have to do it, so you'd better do it without any pressure." Of course, that's pressure in a way, but it's light (9, p. 98).

The nurse need not always assert herself to make her influence felt. Where she has had long experience in a specialized capacity and especially where the doctor is still in his internship or residency, he may ask her to recommend a course of action; but even then, he never surrenders authority. Of just such a situation the New Orleans study offers an example:

The night nurse obviously was disturbed, and stopped by the conference room on her way off duty to discuss her problem with the supervisor. An infant had shown signs of becoming seriously ill during the night. The nurse had called the regular resident assigned to the Center, but was unable to get him. She was referred to another physician who was relieving the regular resident. The second physician was not experienced in the Premature Infant Center, and the nurse reported that he asked her advice as to the treatment to be given the infant. The nurse told him that she thought the infant needed fluids by mouth and suggested to the physician that he order a glucose solution to be given by mouth, which the resident did. The infant became steadily worse during the night. When the regular resident arrived on morning duty, the order for fluid by mouth was criticized. The nurse was most disturbed because the physician who had substituted, stated that he was angry with her because she had "told him to give the baby the fluid." The nurse said, "Well, I thought if he wrote the order, he is responsible." After the nurse had gone, the observer inquired of the supervisor if the nurse had given the fluid without a written order. The supervisor replied: "No, he wrote the order, but he's an interne and he blames her for telling him to write it. You see, they [the doctors] know the nurses know so much more about the babies than they do. He got mad because she told him to order it, and the order was criticized" (18, p. 194).

Another possibility is outright insurrection or rebellion against medical authority and this too probably happens more than one might suppose. In the New Orleans report, it is stated that nurses may openly reject or deliberately circumvent changes suggested by the medical staff. One such drama, described already in Chapter 5 in the discussion of the "home guard," is worth repeating here:

During one of the weekly staff meetings in the Premature Infant Center that was attended by the medical and nursing staffs, a professor of pediatrics explained in graphic detail why he felt that some of the premature infants should be placed on their abdomens to facilitate liquid drainage from the chest. As he finished, he said, "Now, I remember when I was in the Center we did some study on this and as I remember, it was successful. There was one baby I especially remember. Do any of you remember him?" No one responded to his question and he sat down. After a few minutes a supervisor said, "Well, Dr. Blank, the nurses believe that turning the babies over on their abdomen embarrasses their respiration." The physician laughed and said, "I am sure that there are some instances where it doesn't affect the infant adversely." Another nurse spoke, "Doctor, I remember that baby you referred to. He turned blue when you turned him on his stomach." The discussion ended with the request that the nurses try turning the infants on their abdomens and to call the physician if the infants showed unfavorable symptoms. The following week the medical director stated during the meeting, "You know it has just occurred to me that the new babies in the nursery aren't turned on their abdomens." A nurse responded by telling of an infant who had shown distress at being turned on its abdomen. A resident asked, "Did you suction it out?" The nurse replied, "Of course. We suction them out all the time, but I'll just tell you one thing—the *babies* don't like being on their stomachs! (18, pp. 200-1).

The relationship between physician and nurse shifts from time to time and place to place. It varies also according to the generation each belongs to, to the size of the community and the hospital, to the field of nursing and of medicine and to the part of the hospital. The research has by no means tapped all possibilities but is enough to show the tone of feeling.

As a matter of fact, one might argue that the spirit in which the doctors and the nurses work together may set the spirit of the institution. In any case, in the relations between professional nurses and the categories that work under them, there are many parallels of the situations that we have just been reviewing.

nurses and auxiliary personnel

The conditions that bring conflict and confusion into the professional nurse's relations with the physician often make trouble also between her and the other ranks of nurses. However, where the physician is formally vested with authority over her, she is the immediate superior of the auxiliaries; and just as she may in quiet little ways circumvent the physician's authority now and then—always, we assume, for good reason!—so, too, her subordinates may circumvent her's. For, as pointed out in Chapter 4, the informal pyramid of power imposes a real, if not openly acknowledged, set of roles. Thus, the Projective Role Test mentioned earlier, which was administered to head nurses and supervisors, and staff nurses and attendants, revealed roles and sites of power that did not correspond to the formal hierarchy shown on the organizational charts (18, pp. 262-4).

The private duty nurse, though of course an R.N., is in a weak position. She is not employed by the hospital, and the auxiliaries who are, may not always be willing to take orders from "outsiders," even if their formal standing ought to give them authority and even though they themselves have duties to patients. Now it may be that auxiliaries take their sentiments about private duty nurses from the staff nurses who, as already noted, do not always show a fraternal spirit. Then, too, the private duty nurses undertake little housekeeping chores for their patients which throw them into competition—for linen and cleaning materials, to mention only very minor items—with the lower echelons. When things go wrong, both parties complain of shirking and un-co-operativeness.

It is possible for auxiliary personnel to exert influence on the patients far out of proportion to their knowledge and formal status. One of the present authors, observing nurses on a maternity floor in a large modern hospital, has seen nurse aides exercising such great influence that it not only bypasses the professional nurses but also actually overrides the wishes of the physicians:

It was apparent that the nursery aides did not approve of mother's attempting to nurse their own babies. Their reasons, unimportant at this point, have to do with the few nursing babies' crying in the nursery, disturbing the bottle babies, and otherwise upsetting a smooth routine. In spite of the physician's initial orders, the aides do feed these infants in the nursery and as a result they either refuse the mother's breast or are fast asleep when brought to her for feeding. The nursing mother becomes concerned, and while she is wondering whether or not to ask her doctor about this, the aides regale her with stories about other patients who care so little for their babies that they have their doctors put a stop to the nursery feedings. When the mothers do insist on not having the baby fed in the nursery, the aides report in minute detail how their unfed infants have been screaming with hunger, day and night, in the nursery. Few mothers can survive this, and ultimately the aides are the victors. The mother yields to the bottle, and the doctor rescinds his orders.

The head nurse admitted being aware of this but confessed that she was almost helpless: "Those aides are like mothers to the babies and just can't stand to see them crying." She recognized without saying so that the motherly qualities that made them good aides led them to ignore orders. This is a common dilemma of management; restaurant owners have like problems with good chefs, plant managers with good foremen, and army officers with good sergeants.

It is the auxiliary nursing personnel that presents modern nursing with its most difficult situation. On the one hand, graduate nurses appreciate the fact that auxiliary personnel need their help, but, at the same time, resent them as the inheritors of the bedside tasks (cf. Chap. 6). Uncomfortable ambivalent feelings lead them, human as they are, to accept myths of malingering and unjustifiable absenteeism in the ranks of the nonprofessionals as true, and some even point out in exoneration that, after all, the auxiliaries never have received the nurses' schooling in ethics. Yet, the facts do not bear out the allegations in the first place (18, p. 221). One hears, too, of groundless preconceptions. Thus, in the New Orleans premature center, where no practical nurses are employed, a professional nurse will remark:

> You can put me down as not liking practical nurses. Now I know that is probably not right, but I just don't approve of them. They don't stick to the things they should do—they don't stay in their place—first thing you know they are running the place. They wear a uniform and a cap and get all the glory and accept none of the responsibility—I just don't think they should be encouraged. I think the hospital administration is trying to get cheap labor (18, p. 207).

The registered nurses studied in Pennsylvania revealed fear that if there were great numbers of practical nurses and aides they would depress the rates of pay of the professionals, bring down the quality of care given the patients, invade the latter's prerogatives and generally lower standards of nursing (19).

We have quoted before the remark that between the professional and the practical nurses there is a "caste relationship" (15, p. 11)—which means that the formal status of the newest professional nurse is superior to that of the most competent and experienced practical nurse. The standing of each is signalized, for one thing, by caps, pins and uniforms. Particularly in very large hospitals it would be otherwise virtually impossible for the ranks to recognize each other in the army of employees, and so the symbols become very important. The Pennsylvania R.N.'s said, "No!" in one great shout when asked if practical nurses should be permitted to wear the same uniform that they do (19). This only *sounds* like a trivial matter. Then there is the fact that the graduate nurses teach and supervise the other grades (15, p. 11; 18, p. 77) and look upon them as adjuncts and pupils. Finally, there are objects and occasions from which the practical nurses and the aides are *supposed* to be excluded—although all the time studies show that the realities may be different, and Theriault has reported most convincingly under what circumstances (22, Wards "H," "X," "Y"). To "hear report" and to "give report" at the changes of shift, to read and to make entries on the patients' charts, to be present at staff meetings, committee meetings, or even at the professionals' "coffee breaks" is not permitted to any but the graduate nurses—but, again, when shorthanded they may have to bring a responsible practical nurse into the realm of the "classified" and are thankful to have her!

These distinctions come to be taken for granted. Just as the graduate nurse does not expect to be a party to all the doctors' conclaves, so the auxiliaries accept the lines that mark them off from their superiors (and if there are hard feelings it is partly because this boundary is newer and not yet well established). The story comes from Missouri of a partition that divided the hospital dining room into a section for the professional nurses and one for the auxiliaries. A new administrator, in the interests of "democracy," had it taken down, but it was the auxiliaries who objected (9, p. 66).

In the premature center in New Orleans, where the professional staff disapproved of practical nurses, attendants were thought of as reliable and desirable: "our attendants know their place" (18, pp. 207-8). The attendants are Negroes, and they simply carry into the hospital the position that they hold in the Southern caste system. They are much less likely to "overstep" than white attendants might be. The outside world impinges on the hospital's social system in other ways. For example, in central Missouri, the husbands of the R.N.'s hold a higher percentage of occupations which command high status than do the husbands of auxiliary nurses, and the husbands of the auxiliary workers are farmers or members of the working class more often than is the case among the husbands of the professional nurses (9, p. 124). A marginal fact, cited already in Chapter 4, may be repeated at this point: the registered nurses of Pennsylvania who approve of according the rituals of deference to physicians also approve of receiving themselves the deference of the auxiliary nurses. In other words, they accept symbolic behavior in principle and are ready to "do and be done by." Consistently, those who were unwilling to defer to their superiors did not wish deference from their subordinates (19).

Nurses of all categories disagree almost completely as to who *should* undertake the tasks which make up the labor which they divide among themselves—as has been so amply demonstrated in the findings presented in Chapter 6, and it is only human for this to lead to antagonism, collective in any case and sometimes even personal. If Alabama hospitals are representative, disagreement is most often between the professional and the practical nurse—the latter being the only auxiliary with the education and the professional aspirations to be anything like a serious competitior of the registered nurse. It is less likely between the practical nurse and the nurse aide and least likely between the professional nurse and the aide. The last-named pair probably do not think of each other as competitors at all, but in each hospital and unit, particular features will shape the situation.

Age, for one thing, is hard to ignore. When distinctions of rank run one way and the deference due to years runs the other, when, as is so often the case, a young R.N. supervises a group of old-time regular employees, 10 or 20 years her senior, the roles of all are hard indeed. Particularly is this true in hospitals in the small towns where country-bred auxiliaries cherish the traditional respect for age and think "the pert young thing" simply outrageous—even when she is trying to be the very soul of diplomacy.

Turning to Habenstein and Christ's classification of nurses, we find that it helps to explain the bearing of the professional personnel toward the others. The traditionalizer, always with her eye on the patient, is willing to be a teacher and helper to her subordinates and is not above sharing in the "dirty" work, for she sees it as a necessary means to an end. The professionalizer, with her eye on up-to-the-minute methods of therapy and smooth administration, sees the auxiliary nurse as one to be instructed and directed, with the aim of promoting effective work (9, pp. 152-3).

The private duty nurse is often found to view the growth of the auxiliary categories with alarm. For one thing, practical nurses in private duty, because their fees are lower than hers, may become a real threat in the market for her services. Of course, it is obvious to her that much of the work in the hospital is now done by these ranks perhaps more than her sisters in the profession she fears that in assuming the historic bedside tasks the newcomers are lowering the status of the R.N. (7, p. 222; 30, p. 7).

In psychiatric nursing, the professional nurse must often cope with untrained, underpaid and almost nomadic attendants. It is sometimes hard even to communicate with them; they are described as "verbal unsophisticates" (29, p. 120 *et seq.*). Particularly in psychiatry, renowned as it is for a controversial vocabulary packed with newly invented words, to teach an attendant what to watch for and how to report subtle symptoms intelligibly is a formidable and frustrating responsibility. Thorny relationships, which in the absence of data we must only imagine, may be presumed to explain high turnover to a certain extent.

As a final complication is the pervasive fact that within the walls of every hospital a number of ranks of women—and men—pursue their separate careers. Each one's reasons for being there will differ more or less from those of her colleagues and differ again from the motives that animate the other categories of worker (cf. Chap. 9). The auxiliaries queried in central Missouri, for example, were frank in mentioning income—Theriault of New Hampshire quotes the remark: "The average P.N. is an unlucky R.N." (22, Pt. III). On the other hand, the professional nurses speak of civic, moral or professional duty, of work to keep themselves occupied, of money for a special purpose like buying a house or starting a family (9, p. 124). Surely it is unrealistic to expect perfect peace in the personal relationships of a collection of individuals brought together for so many kinds of reasons and asking of their work satisfactions no less varied!

other roles in nursing

Colleagues. The great division in nursing today is expressed in the outlook of the professionalizer and of the traditionalizer. In reality, the two attitudes are blended in the good nurse, although any individual may lean more to one than to another. Habenstein and Christ found that neither type would say that the other was not a good nurse, but the traditionalizer may suggest that the professionalizer is too impersonal with the patient, although, on the whole, her criticism is likely to be confined to general remarks such as "They just aren't turning out old-fashioned nurses any more" (9, pp. 93-4). The survey in Pennsylvania elicited criticisms of personal behavior. Less than a third of the registered nurses there claim to have "rarely" or "never" come across incompetent nurses, and 17 per cent say that they do so "often" or "very often." About 21 per cent say that they have met with "unfair" colleagues "often" or "very often," and 34 per cent have "rarely" or "never" done so (19).

Any graduate professional nurse today probably will have considerable administrative or supervisory duties, and whether or not she is a head nurse or a charge nurse, she will bear some responsibility for the auxiliaries who work under her. We talk today of the nursing "team." In turn, the general duty nurse has a superior, but in small hospitals employing head nurses only on the morning shift or, as often happens, not at all, what supervision she gets may have to come from the director of nursing service. Now, as will be made clearer in Chapter 9, many nurses dislike supervisory and managerial duties. Be that as it may, the relationship between those who accept them and those who refuse is not always happy. For one thing, the two may not agree on what is a "good" nurse. The administrative nurse may stress intelligence and technical ability, and the staff nurse wants to add "a warm personality," "patience," "kindness" or "understanding," and they judge each other accordingly (18, p. 156). The floor nurses can make an unhelpful supervisor's life so miserable that she may have to be transferred. So, too, the staff nurses have their own ideas about the "front office people": "They may be smart and know a lot of theory, but they really don't know much about caring for the babies," say those in the premature center in New Orleans. In moments of exasperation they go further: "I don't know what the people in the front office do except drink coffee!" (18, pp. 202-203).

There is many a graduate nurse today who is sorely tried by too great responsibility. This is truer in the hospital with too small a professional staff. It is then that she must parcel out jobs to the auxiliaries which are not supposed to be theirs and be answerable for the outcome. Small wonder she is afraid! For she knows that, no matter what happens, the doctor always can say: "You ought to know that that is no work for a practical nurse!" Moreover, in selecting one auxiliary, and not another, to do a professional nurse's task, she risks offending them all and having, from then on, to work with disgruntled assistants, and always, in the front of her mind, is the patient. Suppose he gets the wrong medicine. . . .

With the best will in the world, all can make mistakes. The professional nurse must get the work done, and the practical nurse must help her to the best of her ability, but often she can hardly be blamed if she fails. Theriault tells of a hard-pressed head nurse who was driven to entrusting medications to a practical nurse:

> She was on my floor a few months ago and I was told that she was capable of giving medications. For two days I went with her and I watched her give them out and I watched her give hypodermics and she seemed to be all right. I had a medication of a dram of medicine to give to a child. I happened to turn around to the counter from the desk and I saw the glass was full. I asked her if she didn't know the difference between a dram and an ounce and she said, "I didn't know there was." So after that I didn't allow her to give another. . . . If you're giving medicines, you *must* know what you're giving and you *must* know what the symbols mean (22, "Ward X").

The pressure on this driven woman—to assess her staff and make sound judgments, to do justice to her patients and keep her unit running—is staggering. It would not be so bad if this were only a passing crisis. Theriault, for one, found that it is the natural state of things in the small hospitals that he studied. These things are only the professional nurse's fate! To the practical nurses, who are equally afraid of failure and error, Theriault pays a moving tribute: "They bear the shortcomings and the disadvantages of their chosen careers with dignity, humility and strength that inspire respect in those who have come to know something of their lives and work" (22).

Mere size poses special problems of communication and makes it difficult to put even the best-devised and most popular improvements into effect in large institutions. Now it will be recalled (Chap. 6) that the inquiries into who does and who should undertake tasks revealed that the greatest discrepancy of all is between the opinions of the nurses who teach and those who supervise. The first cherish an idealized picture of nursing; the second deal with the hard facts of things as they are. Both may be bedeviled besides by hindrances in passing down directives to the staff nurses. Thus, we are told that in a big city hospital when an attempt was made to give the staff nurses more choice in timing their days off and their vacations, the announcements were made in interviews and meetings. Nevertheless, the scheme was never sufficiently noised abroad and ended in unpredictable staffing, while the victims of the fiasco lamented that they were "left holding the bag while everyone else is off" (18, p. 202).

So, too, in the Boston Psychopathic Hospital, we hear of failure to "get to" the nurse on the part of the occupational therapist, the social worker (who secures information on admission) and the patient's family (6B, p. 446). This is of particular interest because this report concerns obstacles to the application of new experimental methods in the socializing of mental patients which are shown to bear on the ultimate desideratum, the patient's recovery.

The private duty nurse has difficulty with colleagues in maintaining "case continuity"; to take her patient back from another private duty nurse at the beginning of the shift and then to turn him over at its end to still another nurse without friction calls for tact. Here only does the private duty nurse feel herself inadequate (7, p. 288). She also may have trouble with the nurses who staff the hospital. For, while she believes that her most important function is to give her patient competent care and emotional support, her colleagues in the nursing office conceive of her as one who is there to help the general-duty nurses and to give individual attention to patients who need instruction, such as colostomy cases. The staff nurses say that her work is to lighten the load of general duty nurses. Now it is hardly likely that three groups of women with such divergent ideas always will manage to work in harmony. Moreover, the general duty nurses with their heavy case load occasionally complain that the private duty nurse with her single patient has an easy time. They also are under the impression that private duty nursing brings greater financial rewards, and this, while not supported by the facts, leads now and then to jealousy and bad feeling. (See Chap. 4 for additional discussion of the role of the private duty nurse.)

The operating room nurse lives in an entirely different world from her colleagues on general duty. While the latter must learn to come to terms with responsibility for the critically ill, to which usually will be added supervisory duties, the operating room nurse is in a more enviable position—or, at least, some think that she is. The surgeon is responsible for *her* patient. We have already quoted one nurse on this: "Operating room nursing is nursing technique without nursing responsibilities (16, p. 8). She is likely to be somewhat apart from other nurses and in and around the operating room finds the ideal conditions under which to form those close cliques which have been referred to as "home guards." (Cf. Chap. 4.)

On the relations between sisters and lay nurses in Catholic hospitals we have little data, although the subject is broached in the study of central Missouri nurses. In the church-owned institutions there, most of the positions of power and prestige are likely to be filled by sisters. Thus, there is a limit to promotion of the layman nurse, no matter how competent she may prove to be. In institutions affiliated with Protestant bodies, the denomination's only role may be financial and administrative.

In Missouri, in some Catholic hospitals, sisters supervise lay personnel even when, as occasionally happens, the latter are the better qualified, and the reason given is that secular employees must be kept subordinate for the sake of the order's morale. Yet, in hospitals where assignments are made solely on the basis of professional ability, whether the nurse is a sister or not, relations between the two seem to be healthier (9, p. 22).

In the nature of the case, any discussion of roles should tell the story of two parties, for a role is played opposite someone else and in interaction with him. Our data on Catholic hospitals suffer from lack of the sisters' version; and yet the sisters give the hospital its tone. However, the position and the sentiments of the lay nurses and the aides are convincingly relayed in a study of an institution accommodating a little over 100 patients in a remote part of New Hampshire (referred to in Chap. 4).

This hospital is a culture, as close, consistent and distinctive as, say, the culture of a large, closely knit family or a small isolated tribe. Much at home in it is an older R.N., bred in the old-fashioned tradition of personal ministering to patients. Even happier appears a middle-aged nurse aide, daughter of a working-class family of the parish, used to hard work and not actively dissatisfied with her very slender earnings. They seem to accommodate themselves to being under tutelage and long ago accepted exacting standards and unremitting hard work as though in the nature of things.

The other side is told by younger nurses and those trained in secular institutions elsewhere who have accepted employment in Catholic hospitals. They grow restive under the discipline of the sisters and complain of the low salaries. They do not conceal their scorn of the locally trained graduates' submission to the sisters and their reliance on them:

The nuns like their own ways and means. As a graduate you're still treated more or less on a student basis; like, I mean they still have the whole say, and I don't go for that. I've got a mind of my own. . . .

I think that once a month there ought to be a meeting of the staff. . . . In some matters I think nurses should be consulted. . . . Because—something to do with students or something like that—I think the head nurses should have something to say about it, once in a while, anyway (22, "Ward H").

Visitors and Patients' Relatives. Daily, the hospital nurse must adopt some sort of role opposite friends and relatives of the patients.[3] They are in an unfamiliar milieu and do not know what is expected of them. The nurse, for her part, may not realize that what from time to time appears to her as thoughtless or naive behavior is nothing more than innocence or ignorance. In any case, wherever visitors or kinfolk are considered in our research reports they have elicited from the nurses responses which are, on the whole, unfavorable (7, 9, 18, 20, 27, 30).

To discover nurse sentiments about visitors, a Kansas City research team gave a word-association test to a group of 66 nurses, which included all ranks (27). The word "visitors" appeared in a printed list of words opposite each of which the nurses were instructed to write whatever came into their heads, the examiners meanwhile giving no hints or comments. Although blanks were left by many after a number of the words, the word "visitors" provoked a response

---

[3] Cf., Abdellah, Faye G., and Levine, Eugene: (Division of Nursing Resources, U.S. Public Health Service), "What Patients Say About Their Nursing Care," Hospitals, Vol. 31 (Nov. 1, 1957), pp. 44-8; and "What Factors Affect Patients' Opinions of Their Nursing Care," *ibid.*, (Nov. 16, 1957), pp. 61-4. Also New, Peter Kong-Ming: *op. cit.*

in every case, and 70 per cent made uncomplimentary remarks after it; for instance: "visitors are a nuisance in a hospital." Only 18 per cent saw visitors in a favorable light: "visitors can do much for the patient's morale." The remaining statements were neutral.

It is true that these were all nurses in a city. However, the nurses in rural Missouri made it clear that patients' relatives are "the bane of the nurse's existence." "I can take *anything* from *any* patient," exclaimed a nurse, "but brother!—spare me from those crazy, mixed-up relatives!" (9, pp. 70, 151-152). There may be more in this than meets the eye. When husbands were permitted to stay in the labor rooms in a hospital maternity service unit, the nurses felt displaced and uncertain of what part to play. As one explained:

Some men are much too apprehensive and an awful lot of them—they start to demand things. Some of them think they know everything just because they majored in physiology at college. They think they know it all. They can get to be a nuisance in a situation like that (20, p. 140).

The "relatives problem" presses most on the private-duty nurse. Not only is the patient's family her source of income but also a source from which she should draw strength and moral support for him, and seeing that her role is in a sense interpretive, she must, above all, get on peaceably with them at a time when they are not perhaps at their most reasonable. Indeed, an anxious and helpless family may make her a scapegoat on which to pour out their laments, fears and sorrows. Some do not hesitate to set private problems, in no way connected with the patient, before her for her advice—which may be more flattering than welcome.

In the gigantic Charity Hospital in New Orleans, which has been so well depicted for us, it is thought good and proper for a ward to be literally swarming with relatives by day and night. Here, in place of the supine, growned sick, patients wander about with their train of visitors. These are put to work, dignified with the title "visitor-attendants" and given, as it were, a patient-load. Through this maneuver, the visitor learns quickly how to act in the hospital— more accurately, in *that* hospital! It may be that occasionally a visitor-attendant tries to go beyond the simple assigned chores; even so, that may be a small price to pay for what seems to be a realistic device for controlling an occupational hazard (18, pp. 28-29 *et seq.*).

Hospital Authorities. The general duty nurses, as a rule, deal with the administrator, if necessary, through the director of nursing service. The administrator's job is to operate the institution so as to keep the deficit as low as possible. The director of nursing service, on the other hand, has the single goal of providing the best care that she can for the patients. When these aims are incompatible, friction is bound to be created. The Board, being usually made up of businessmen, sympathizes with the administrator's point of view. If the administrator is a layman or an employee who rose from the ranks, he will be disposed, in all likelihood, to side with the Board. However, a professional administrator may have achieved a better understanding of nursing problems and may deal with each problem on its merits (9, p. 151).

The situation is rather like one that arises in the life of the industrial nurse. (Cf. Chap. 5.) If she is answerable to the safety director, she probably must deal with a man who, like the hospital's lay administrator, is a nonprofessional person who came into his position through experience in the plant. She is more gratified if her superior is in the personnel department, but if he is a professional engineer, again his orientation may be foreign to hers, for, as Barschak describes it, he will seek the cause of accidents in mechanical failure and not always be patient with her version of them as human shortcomings and weaknesses. When this is the case, each may become a stumbling block to the other. Finally, like the nurse confronted with a lay administrator, the industrial nurse resents the fact that policies which closely concern her may be decided without inviting her opinion or presence (21, pp. 37-39).

On the relations between the director of nursing service, the administrator and the medical director, three whose power and influence pervades the whole structure, we have no data. However, one can imagine that if there were ever serious quarrels between them, the repercussions would blast the hospital from subbasement to sunroof! More probable are rivalries and ranklings in the relationships between professional and nonprofessional hospital personnel, broadly conceived. In a hospital in rural Missouri, for example, the housekeeping and the maintenance departments which, as in some hospitals, were independent of the director of nursing service, were at odds with her, and the cleavage took on larger dimensions when she sought the support of the administrator (9, pp. 150-151).

The Nurse and Her Family. To many a nurse her most important role is that of wife and mother and sometimes as daughter. Like so many professional women today, she must divide allegiance between her home and her work. This is no problem to the type of nurse to whom Habenstein and Christ gave the name "utilizer," for she does not feel dedicated to her work and can pick it up or lay it down without a pang, but to the extent that the professional nurse is truly professional, she feels the need to make a just peace between conflicting obligations. As was shown in Chapter 2, the nurse with young children is in the worst impasse. Theriault collected what are obviously equally sincere statements from nurses in New Hampshire: "My home comes first," "I would never sacrifice my family for my work," "but—I would not want to retire after marriage, it would be a great waste of experience," "I wouldn't say I could give up nursing completely, I don't think I could do it." These confessions are probably a fair sample. However, there must be many women whose earnings are absolutely indispensable and they do not even have a choice. When Theriault asked a second question; "What effect has being married had upon your career?" he learned that it had reduced the amount of nursing they had undertaken, caused them to leave positions and seek new ones, and had made it hard for them to rise in the profession (22).

Marriage is a leading cause of dropping out. Of the nurses queried in Kansas City, already half of those who had left the profession did so when domestic duties intervened; but those in central Missouri for the most part said that they planned to come back to it when their youngest child was in school (9, pp. 68-70).

On this subject, more will be said in connection with professionalization and careers (Chaps. 10 and 11).

as others see her

Unlike most of the other data included in this book, the materials discussed in this chapter are derived not from nurses but from other people who tell us something of what they think about nurses. The source of all statements made in this chapter, unless otherwise indicated, is two reports in the Kansas City series: *The Evaluation of Nurses by Male Physicians* (11) and *Public Images of the Nurse* (12). The former is based on a questionnaire mailed to a representative sample consisting of 379 male physicians stratified according to age and specialty. The public image material is based on the same questionnaire, administered personally to a random sample of 974 persons in the Kansas City metropolitan area.

Some kind of picture or image flashes through our minds when an occupation is mentioned. It may have a sound basis in careful judgment of past experiences, or it may be a strangely warped and perverted stereotype, based on limited experience or none at all or corrupted by unfortunate contacts or personal prejudices:

Literature and common sense, and in these latter days, the press, have given us stereotyped pictures of persons engaged in various occupations: the old maid school teacher, the parson, the village blacksmith, the farmer, the professor, the politician, the financier. All of these and many other types so created are expected to react to the situations of life in character-istic manner. To many the cartoonist adds a face and a costume.[1]

Real or unreal, true or false, accurate or perverted, these public images are of the utmost importance to the members of the occupation depicted; for the image is real to the person who holds it, and he acts as though it were real. It determines in large part his initial relation-ship to the individual in the occupation. His acts—real in any sense of the word—have very real consequences.[2]

In the complex urban community, there are many "publics" and hence many potential images. Thus, men may entertain a different image from that held by women, old people may differ in it from the young, the social elite from the down-and-outers who live on the wrong side of the railroad tracks. Moreover, those in closely related work come to form a very different image from those in no way connected with it, and those, again, who have been clients or patients or cus-tomers form a different image from those who never have had any business or professional contacts with it.

A score, called an Occupational Evaluation Index (OEI), was devised to represent the respondents' notion of how nursing compares with other women's occupations, of the nurse's social standing, and whether or not he or she would approve of a daughter's becoming a nurse. Although admittedly crude, the score based on these compo-nents enabled the investigators to compare different publics as to their evaluation of nurses and nursing.

the man in the street

People's attitudes toward anything, whether it is an occupational group, a political candidate, or a breakfast cereal, are molded and determined by many factors—perhaps an infinite number. Students of public opinion have learned that many kinds of opinions vary accord-ing to three basic elements which have strong cultural connotations in our society: age, sex and social class (or socioeconomic status). There is a standardized method of measuring the first; and the second, at least in our society, can be determined visually with a high degree

---

[1] Hughes, Everett C.: Personality types and the division of labor, Am. J. Sociology, 32:762, 1928.

[2] On the consequences of imagery, see Merton, Robert K.: "The Self-Fulfilling Prophecy" recently reprinted in Merton, Robert K.: Social Theory and Social Struc-ture (Revised and enlarged edition), pp. 421-436, Glencoe, Ill., The Free Press, 1957.

of reliability. However, social class is not so easy to ascertain. It was measured in the Kansas City study by a method[3] by which each respondent was given a weighted score based on his occupation, source of income, the type of house he lived in, and the area of the city in which his house was located. With the help of those scores, the sample of the population was divided into four socioeconomic groups, referred to as I, II, III and IV.

Analysis of the OEI scores reveals that sex and socioeconomic status are significant differentiators of attitudes toward nurses, while, strangely enough, age appears to have no important influence. The average scores show that women have a more favorable image of the nurse than do men and that, regardless of sex or age, the image becomes more favorable as one moves *down* the socioeconomic ladder. Although age differences are not significant, it is worth noting that there is a steady, if slight, increase in favorable disposition toward nurses as the respondents get older: each older group has a little more favorable image of the nurse than the next youngest.

Because these are average scores, and in spite of the fact that on the average some groups differ from others, we should not forget that individual scores range widely. There are certainly some with high status who rate nurses favorably and some with low status who rate them unfavorably. In like manner, there are men who rate nurses favorably, and women who rate them unfavorably. However, it is important to know that one public *generally* tends to think more favorably of nurses than another does. The relative evaluation of nurses by different groups of Kansas City people can be seen in Table 19. Although the scores tell us this much, we should look beyond them and observe the content or the quality of the images.

In observing class differences, let us first see what the typical person in each of the four social classes looks like. Group I (about 10 per cent of the sample) is roughly equivalent to what might be called the upper middle class. These are mostly professional and executive people who live in large houses in the more prosperous areas of the city. Thirty-six per cent of the sample falls in Group II, which consists mostly of lower middle class or white-collar people. Most of

---

[3] Warner, W. Lloyd, Meeker, Marcia, and Eels, Kenneth: Social Class in America: A Manual of Procedure for the Measurement of Social Status. Chicago, Science Research Associates, 1949.

Table 19. How Different Groups of People Evaluate Nurses

Kind of People	Number	Mean Evaluation Score*
General population	937	7.96
Men	401	8.17
Women	536	7.80
People who are friends of R.N.'s	91	7.91
People who have been under the care of an R.N.	66	7.98
People who have no R.N. friends and have never had any R.N. care	116	8.53
Doctors	198	8.80
Upper socioeconomic class (I)	88	8.62
Upper-middle socioeconomic class (II)	338	8.08
Lower-middle socioeconomic class (III)	375	7.83
Lower socioeconomic class (IV)	136	7.57

Source: (12).

* The lower the evaluation score, the more favorable the evaluation of nurses.

these own at least an equity in a small house in a "respectable" neighborhood. Many work in clerical or sales positions, while others have small businesses of their own. The largest single group, with 40 per cent of the sample, is Group III, which consists mostly of what might be called blue-collar or working-class people. These are factory or industrial production-line workers and skilled tradesmen. Most of them live at a distance convenient to their work where rents are relatively low. Their income is derived largely from hourly wages, and they may find themselves hard pressed financially when business is not good. At the bottom of the heap is 15 per cent of the sample— Group IV, composed of those who live at a bare subsistence level in the worst slums or "shanty-towns" of the city. Most of them work at whatever is available, usually unskilled labor or service of one sort or another. In this class there is a disproportionate dependence on city or county welfare to supplement irregular and insufficient incomes.

Because the scores for these socioeconomic groups consistently run in the direction of being more favorable in the lowest group to less favorable in the highest group, we will examine only the extremes. It may be assumed that the images run continuously in the one direction between the two extremes. Any public image contains a number of elements which may be interpreted as either "good" or "bad." Class images at the extreme top and extreme bottom of the socioeconomic ladder tend to concentrate on different elements, and even though not all persons in Group I agree in their evaluation of nurses, most base them on the same features. This is also true of Group IV, except that the elements of the images are not the same as those found in Group I.

A woman in Group I speaks for 69 per cent of her "classmates" when she says, in response to the question, "How do nurses differ from most other women?":

Nurses are not different. However, I would not want my own daughters to be exposed to so many types of illnesses and especially not the nursing of male patients. It's hard to explain but probably they would become calloused. A nurse's duties are too intimate.

According to Group I's standards, professional nursing is not lady-like. Although it is permissible according to those standards to serve as Gray Ladies or other volunteers, young women should not be placed in a position where they are exposed to intimate contacts with strange males. A girl should be sweet, gentle, and not too sophisticated in the hard ways of the outside world. Thus, we find these people describing nurses as opinionated, hardened, cynical, brusk, indifferent to human suffering, not as refined as the average woman, detached, scientific-minded and hard-as-nails, unsympathetic, nervous and high strung. This element in the image of the nurse is almost completely lacking in Group IV; only one lower-class respondent made such a reference in describing the nurse.

However, Group I's image is also of nurses as emotionally stable, not apt to go to pieces in an emergency, with stout nerves, composed, competent and physically stronger; one respondent says, "It takes a lot of fortitude to go through training that is hard and tedious and long."

A different note is voiced by another Group I respondent: "Nursing has acquired a bad reputation because girls from small towns, without financial means use it as an 'out,' to get away from home." Such statements were rarely found and could be a result of the brevity and the lack of intimacy in the interview. At any rate, there appears to be sufficient evidence that in some cases Group I's image of the nurse centers around the departure of the young woman from a sentimentalized version of her traditional feminine role.

In contrast, one in the lowest socioeconomic level said:

Nurses are kind—they are sympathetic and they are very understanding. I just think they are tops. I always wanted to be a nurse and hope my daughter is one when she grows up.

This statement represents the point of view of 80 per cent of the Group IV respondents. Lower-class respondents consistently evaluate nurses as more sympathetic, having a better feeling for people, very understanding, more patient, kinder than most people and very nice. Only four individuals in Group I took this tone. More often found in the lower-class image than in the upper is the conception of nurses as clean, hygienic, sanitary and neat. The only respondent in Group I who mentioned this complained that nurses are "overhygienic." Neatness and cleanliness are more visible and more striking to those at the bottom of the socioeconomic ladder whose customary environment is one of dirt and squalor. In Group I, one is much more likely to allow the nurses' neatness or cleanliness to pass unnoticed as naturally expected.

Class differences in the image of the nurse can be summed up thus: to Group I, the nurse stands in a subordinate or even a servantlike relationship, whereas those in Group IV see her as a protective, superordinate figure—somewhat like a mother. More lower-class respondents say favorable things about nurses than do those in the top class, and many more in Group I say unfavorable things about nurses than do those in Group IV.

The one element in the male image of the nurse which appears most consistently is a differentiation of the nurse from other women on the basis of her training, education, or knowledge. As one man puts it, "The nurse is trained in medicine, which most other women are not, and this is important." Although a majority of the men select this element, there is a wide variety in the feeling tone, ranging from the approving, "Nurses are better trained in medicine; they are trained to care for human life more than others and are cleaner, kinder, and have a broader knowledge of the physical characteristics of people," to the neutral, "The only difference is in their training," to the suspicious:

I'd rather not say. Oh, some nurses are O.K., but you know yourself what they are like. (Interviewer: No, what?) Well, a young nurse has spent a lot of time on her education and she feels like she is somebody and you can't tell me they don't get out and find out what things are all about.

There is more than a little hostility in the accusation that "She feels like she is somebody." Another man is more blunt: "Nurses are ego-centric, self-centered."

We might hazard the guess that many of these references to the nurses' education, training and knowledge carry with them the resentment of males who feel that such women are encroaching on their traditional male superiority and are threatening the male role. In other words, the unfavorable aspects of the image appear to rest upon the assumption that women have no right to assume superiority in any area over men. This is certainly the feeling one gets from the man who informs the interviewer that "their training affects their family life. Why, my cousin is a nurse and she won't even let her child have its tonsils out." He seems to be saying, "Who is this woman who thinks she knows so much? If she were not a nurse, she would be a better mother." In the upper class, there was not the resentment and feeling of competition which appears among men in general; moreover, their unfavorable comments contained more of condescension, pity, and a feeling that somehow it was indiscreet for a lady to be a nurse.

Far fewer females mention training, education, or knowledge in their image of the nurse (only 32 per cent as compared with 53 per cent of the men). When they do refer to the nurses' schooling, unlike the men they show a certain consistency: "Nurses have training which *helps* in the home." "They have more training so they know more about what to do for the sick." "They are taught about medicine and the sympathetic way of getting along with people." "They perform a great public service; their training has taught them to be more competent and businesslike." These remarks all reveal a favorable impression. The competitiveness, the resentment and the hostility conveyed by many of the males who employ the same criterion are missing.

There is no single outstanding element in the women's image of the nurse. One woman points out that the nurse has a "stronger constitution"; another elaborates this theme with the opinion that nurses are more "willing to give shots and things like that and can stand the sight of blood and not get nervous and sick." Perhaps the best summarizing statement is that women see nurses as less self-oriented than most women are usually thought to be and, conversely, more interested in the problems and the well-being of others. As one woman puts it, after referring to the nurses' sympathy for others, "A lot of women aren't that way." Another woman, sharing this notion, seems to reflect the general feeling of females when she says: "Nurses have an outstanding will to help others without thinking of themselves. They do a job that has a lot of work and bother that most women just wouldn't bother with."

Of course, it is true that not all women think favorably of nurses; one, for example, says that they are "opinionated, hardened, not very sympathetic, cynical, and brusk in their manner," while another believes that "some nurses are hard-as-nails." Nevertheless, women make a considerably higher proportion of favorable comments about nurses—42 per cent of the women in contrast with 20 per cent of the men. It is also true that a much smaller proportion of women make unfavorable comments about nurses; only four per cent as contrasted with 10 per cent of the men.

The Kansas City study reports that whether a person grew up in the country or in the city does not appear to be relevant in so far as his image of the nurse is concerned. However, it does appear to be relevant whether or not the respondent has any daughters and, if so, how many. This is a matter of vantage points. The questions about nurses take on a different complexion when one has his own daughter in mind instead of looking at the matter from a purely hypothetical viewpoint. Thus, those with one daughter generally evaluate nurses less favorably than do those with no daughters or those with more than one. This is true of both women and men and of every socioeconomic group except the highest. In Group I, the evaluation of nurses steadily diminishes as the number of daughters increases.

Speculating as to some possible reasons for this low evaluation by persons with only one daughter, one may reasonably assume that there is an indirect relationship between the extent to which parents are involved with their children and the number of children that they have. That is to say, the average adult has a limited amount of time and energy to devote to his children, so that the fewer children there are the more intimate the relationship between any one child and the parents is likely to be—other things being equal. When there are several girls in a family, a profession such as nursing offers a relatively easy means for the parents to fulfill their responsibility and launch a child into the working world. Nursing offers a degree of security for all, an increase in status for many and an education which is not excessively long or expensive. When there is only one daughter in the family, the parents may be unduly concerned about sending her out into the world and may want to hold her at home, until a supposed "best chance" comes along.

Then, too, the father-daughter relationship is likely to be closer than the mother-daughter relationship. This would explain, in part, the lower evaluation of nurses by fathers than by mothers. Possibly, many fathers face with distaste the thought of their only daughter's entering an occupation which deals with the human body, with sickness and with death.

doctors

Of those who know the nurse and her work as a result of different kinds of contacts and associations, her personal friends have the most favorable image of her, and only slightly less favorable is that of persons who themselves have had the experience of care from an R.N. Both groups have a far more favorable image of the nurse than do physicians or other people, who neither know any nurses nor have ever been attended by one. The doctors rate nurses even lower than do men in general, but not as low as do people in the highest socioeconomic group. However, if doctors are compared only with men in the top two socioeconomic groups (from which it may be assumed most physicians derive), they are shown to rate nurses more poorly than does the comparable group.

Although nurses' friends are the most favorably disposed of the groups mentioned above, they are exceeded in this respect by persons in the lowest socioeconomic group and by elderly physicians. Although age played no important part in determining the image in the general population, it does among doctors; those over 60 years of age have a significantly more favorable opinion than do their younger colleagues. Medical specialty was found to be unrelated to the doctors' evaluation of nurses. Why?

In that complex world which is the modern hospital, certain lines of authority, of subordination and superordination must be maintained, it is supposed, for efficient operation, and the status system helps explain some of the differences noted in the evaluation of nurses. That the physician is in a superordinate position is most apparent when life is in danger, for then the nurse must move rapidly and obediently: there is neither room nor time for debate. She follows the doctor's orders. Although such emergencies may be the exception, it is to them that all medical behavior has traditionally been keyed. One must be prepared to cope with them when they arise, and this means that certain habits of behavior must be established. This interpretation is supported by the finding in Arkansas that one of the major suggestions for improvement of nursing service made by doctors has to do with the nurses' obedience to their orders. These doctors criticized nurses for giving treatments and medications which had *not* been prescribed (not for failing to give those which had been prescribed). Several physicians attributed this behavior to an attitude of independence which they thought that nurses had developed in recent years (17, p. 12).

The young doctor, especially, may need to keep reminding himself and others that he is the doctor and that she is the nurse and that he must be the boss and that she must obey. Therefore, the emphasizing of his own professional superiority is most important to the young doctor working with older nurses. However, the older physician has his age to support his professional authority. In addition to being the doctor, he may be a "grand old man" or a frightening martinet. In either case, his age backs him up, and he can better afford to be generous in his image of the nurse. This, of course, is only one of several possible explanations.

Another line of explanation begins with such questions as these: Do doctors tend to become more "mellow" with age? Or is the difference one of generations? That is, does it result from the fact that the older group of physicians lived most of their professional lives during a period when nurse-doctor relations were of a different nature from what they are today?

Several bits of evidence bear on these questions. The fact that the only real (significant) difference in scores appears between the older group as compared with all others suggests that they may be retaining an image of the nurse as being a faithful, obedient, and generally subservient subordinate. Perhaps they are not, as are their younger colleagues, fully aware of the trends toward professionalization which have occurred in nursing in recent years (see Chap. 10). Some of the comments made by doctors on their questionnaires give hints that this may be true. For example, a 39-year-old physician who rates nurses most unfavorably writes, "The present trend, as I see it, is to be as demanding as other groups and to forget the idea of 'profession' as taught 20 years ago." Of course, the nurses' notion of their professional role has altered radically in the last 20 years, which this younger doctor appears to resent. On the other hand, a 74-year-old physician rates nurses very high and states that they are "more likely to be obedient, sympathetic and loyal." Two of his contemporaries (who also rate nurses favorably) concur: "They are trained to take orders and follow through"; "They have had the right kind of training and discipline."

The Kansas City study shows the older medical men as retaining an image of the nurse which their younger colleagues would describe as being 20 years out of date. Such statements appear to indicate a generational shift in physicians' images of nurses, rather than a shift resulting from aging as such. However, there is some apparently contradictory evidence in other studies. For example, in Arkansas, it was found that a disproportionately larger percentage of older physicians indicated that only "some" or "a few" general duty nurses qualified on three questions of adequacy (17, p. 12). In Alabama, it was concluded that "older doctors are more inclined to believe that nursing is not what it should be at present" (10, p. 139). The Kansas City doctors were asked to check their preference on a list describing how nurses *should* be and then to repeat the procedure on a list describing how nurses *are*. Among older physicians, there was a nine per cent discrepancy between the items checked on the "should be" and the "are" lists, while among the youngest group of physicians, the discrepancy was 17 per cent. Unlike the Alabama study, the Kansas City data indicate that older doctors are more likely to believe that nursing *is* what it should be.

As was pointed out above, the older doctors in Kansas City seem not to have an accurate conception of the recent changes in nursing and thus may have an unrealistically rosy image of what nursing *is*—an image which tends to conform to their image of what it should be.

Unlike the Alabama doctors, all of whom were practicing on the staff of a hospital, the Kansas City doctors were a random sample of members of four county medical societies, and it is possible that many of the oldest were not practicing at all and had not for many years. Then, too, the Kansas City physicians were all in a metropolitan area while two of the three hospitals from which the Alabama sample was selected were in small towns. Other differences between the two studies include the fact that, as the Kansas City sample represents the whole of the medical profession, the results depend on a wider variety in both frequency and kind of contacts with nurses than would exist among the Alabama hospital staff men. Moreover, "age" in the Alabama study was measured by years in medical practice, while in Kansas City it is actual years of age. This means that similar age groups may not be exactly comparable. Finally, it should be pointed out that in neither of these studies was over 60 per cent of the questionnaires returned from physicians—and the Alabama investigators have evidence that those who did not return their questionnaires may hold more favorable views toward nurses (10, p. 123).

In spite of the fact that the Kansas City studies indicate that physicians have a less favorable image of the nurse than do many other publics, it is only comparatively so. Most of the doctors are not unduly critical of nurses. In one Arkansas hospital, on the whole physicians' opinions were quite favorable; of the 96 doctors queried, 76 thought that most of the general duty nurses there provide sufficient care and attention to their patients; 56 of them report that the nurses carry out their orders completely and accurately, and 70 responded "Yes" to the question, "Do you think that the general duty nurses in this hospital give their nursing care without causing any undue pain and discomfort?" Of these Arkansas doctors, 76 gave an unqualified "Yes" when asked if they would recommend nursing as a career to a younger sister, a daughter or some young person who seemed to be interested and qualified (17, pp. 11, 13).

The Alabama study indicates a significant amount of criticism of nurses by 105 physicians on three points and a significant amount of approval on three others. They agreed that nurses spend too much time in administrative and clerical tasks and not enough time doing bedside nursing; that nurses want the prestige of professionals but the hours of organized labor; that nurses frequently waste time performing tasks which could be done by well-trained auxiliary nursing personnel. (Is it possible to satisfy critics on both points one and three?).

On the other hand, a majority of the doctors *disagreed* with the following statements: nurses today seem to be more concerned with wages and hours than with patient care; nurses have become too impersonal in their care of patients, treating them more as objects than as individuals; recent graduates of nursing schools are not sufficiently well trained in the routine techniques of nursing care. Finally, there were 47 per cent more agreements than disagreements with the statement that quality of nursing service has improved within the last 10 years (10, p. 141). This discussion of the physicians' images of the nurse can end on an optimistic note by citing the Georgia private duty study which found doctors making practically no negative comments about the private duty nurses. The only exception seems to be the one physician who complains about the lack of availability of a private duty nurse when he needs one (7, p. 202). (Are some of the doctors who criticize nurses really mourning the decrease in private duty nursing?)

patients

An important fact is that people think more highly of nurses after having had the experience of being attended by an R.N. Interviews with 127 patients in Arkansas corroborate this Kansas City finding. In fact, the Arkansas investigators had difficulty in obtaining any criticism of nursing service from patients. More than 90 per cent of the patients offered unqualified approval of nursing service. Occasionally, there would be criticism of the quantity or the quality of food, of hospital practices, such as those regarding visiting hours, or of the cost of being in the hospital; but nothing about the way nurses did their work. Offered 10 statements about nurses and nursing, the patients disagreed with all the unfavorable statements and agreed with all the favorable; for example, 99 per cent agreed that most nurses are respected (17, Table 1, p. 10).

The study of nurse-patient relations in a New York maternity hospital indicates that under some circumstances, patients do not have as favorable an image of the nurse as has been described above. Typical of responses from antepartal patients when asked about the functions of the office nurse is:

Well, she's quite important there. She answers the telephone. I suppose she does the office work and helps the doctor in every way and makes appointments. She keeps an eye on the doctor; he shouldn't have a patient in there too long. . . . The first thing when I come into the office, she helps me on the table and gets me ready for him. It must be a very boring job, I guess. (20, p. 52.)

The authors state that women cared for in private practice seem even more doubtful of the professional abilities of nurses than do those under clinic care:

Using what they see the nurse doing at antepartal visits as a measuring rod, most women conclude: (a) that nurses are not adequately prepared to give them the information and reassurance they want. (b) Even if they "know enough," nurses are "too busy with their jobs" to have time for conversation and answering questions. (c) Nurses usually do not seem interested in assuming any role other than the one of chaperone, recorder, receptionist, and advisor on weight, during antepartal visits. (20, p. 81.)

The New Orleans investigators believe that the changing definition of the nurses' role requires a redefinition by the community. They suspect that the image of the nurse held by most of the public is essentially based upon her traditional role rather than upon her present function:

The legends of Florence Nightingale seem to have remained relatively undisturbed in the image of the nurse portrayed by our mass media. In these, she remains predominantly the "lady with the lamp," with compassion, understanding, and attention for each of her patients individually. The reality must come as a shock to those of the general public who encounter the nurse when they are patients in the hospital. (18, p. 15.)

Evidence from Kansas City shows that this bit of speculation is half correct and half incorrect; by and large, people do retain the traditional image of the nurse. However, on entering a hospital, they are not shocked by the reality. Former patients, we may recall, are among the most favorably disposed toward nurses.

personal friends

The group which evaluates nurses most favorably is, of course, their friends. However, one is surprised that the friends do not rate nurses even more favorably than the inquiry shows; but it should be remembered that people confide in friends, and confidences include the bad as well as the good. Nurses, like others, are not always their own best advocates in public relations. One respondent reports:

I think some nurses are ornery, rough and tough, loose women. I don't care much for nurses because of the things my cousin tells me about them. She's a nurse.

A note written by a nurse on the back of a questionnaire used in connection with another study reads:

I would *not* advise a girl to enter nurses' training at the present time, for several reasons. Nursing standards have been disgracefully lowered since nurse aides and practical nurses have become so prevalent. Why should anyone spend a large sum of money and several years preparing to become an R.N. only to . . . be giving baths and doing general aides' work? It just aggravates me to think about girls spending the time and money to prepare for a so-called profession that is rapidly becoming just a job that any woman can have by a few weeks' experience or . . . six month's course. This all boils down to one thing: if you have the nursing desire, be an aide or a practical. Don't waste time and money trying to be a professional nurse.

Although not very many R.N.'s are likely to agree with her statement, it may be that her friends take over her attitude. On the other hand, many a nurse exhibits a pride in her profession and a proselytizing zeal which she communicates to her friends. The matters of status and self-conception probably enter in, for a friend is most often on one's own social level, and one may hesitate to belittle friends because to do so is to belittle one's self.

Theriault, on the basis of his New Hampshire study, reaches conclusions identical with those of the Kansas City study:

There is no denying the fact, however, that nurses themselves are the most influential factors in recruitment into the profession. Quite unconsciously, merely in the practice of their profession and in the relationship they bear younger girls in their families and their friends and acquaintances, they serve as models to be emulated. We wonder if nurses are as fully aware of their roles as models to children and young people as they might be, and whether the indirect importance, for recruitment, of satisfaction in nursing and the pride and sense of dignity in the profession that go along with it, is recognized by those responsible for the status of the profession. The negative influences, of course, are also clear and may be deeply destructive. The discontented, disaffected nurse may also serve as a model in the sense of, often without intending to do so, dissuading youngsters from considering nursing as a career. (22).

This favorable evaluation by friends is much more important for nurses than for some others, because a larger proportion of the general population claims nurses for friends than they do persons in any other occupation inquired about (Table 20). This becomes especially true

Table 20. Answers* to the Question "Do You Have Any Friends Who Are (Teachers, Waitresses, Nurses, Secretaries, Social Workers)?"

Occupation	Number: "yes"	Percentage: "yes"
Nurses	531	55
Secretaries	512	53
Teachers	468	48
Social Workers	249	26
Waitresses	214	22

Source: 12, p. 18; N = 966.
* There are more answers than respondents since, naturally, many people have friends in more than one occupation.

when we consider that the 55 per cent who know nurses, in turn know a large number of other people who are not nurses and are, at least in part, responsible for the image held by them all.

how people compare nurses, teachers and social workers

Although we now have some idea of how favorably or unfavorably various publics look upon nurses, we have nothing to compare it with. Are they images people have of all working women or only of nurses? To answer this question, the Kansas City research team (11, 12) obtained from doctors and from the general public sufficient information to complete Occupational Evaluation Indexes also for teachers and social workers who are, on the whole, in women's occupations with roughly similar educational requirements.

Greater than any difference between publics is the difference between ratings of these three occupations by the same people. The extremely low evaluation of social workers accounts for most of it. The 937 Kansas City respondents who rated all three occupations rate the social worker, on the average, significantly less favorably than they do teachers and nurses. Although teachers are rated slightly more favorably than nurses, the difference is not statistically significant. Doctors do the same, and the difference between younger and older doctors holds for each of the three occupations. The young doctors set a low value on all three occupations and on social workers the lowest of all!

We have already observed that women have a more favorable image of the nurse than do men; this is also true of their images of teachers and social workers. Women, not necessarily only those involved in the particular occupations, tend to identify themselves with professional women more than do males. As mentioned earlier some men may see the professional woman as a threat to their self-defined superior male status. By both sexes, teachers are rated most favorably, while social workers receive the poorest average evaluation.

The evaluation of social workers, like that of nurses, becomes more favorable as one passes down the socioeconomic ladder. But this is *not* true of teachers: the highest and the lowest socioeconomic publics rate teachers about the same, and their evaluation is less favorable than that of the two middle groups. The most favorable evaluation of the teacher comes from Group II—the lower middle or white-collar class. Of all three occupations, teachers receive the most favorable evaluation from all but the lower class: Group IV rates nurses slightly higher than teachers.

Several questions are raised by these data. Why is it that the teachers differ from nurses and social workers who receive consistently more favorable ratings as the socioeconomic status of the respondents becomes lower? Again, this is explained by relative status. In brief, people at the bottom of the ladder, looking up, acknowledge that nurses and social workers have higher status than they themselves by evaluating them more favorably than do people at the top of the ladder, who, looking down on nurses and social workers, make no such concessions and therefore rate them less favorably.

Why does the theory not hold for teachers also? It is commonly accepted among Americans that education is "good." If one is to succeed in life, to better his position, to get ahead in the world, then one must attain some amount of formal education.[4] The teacher is

---

[4] On the relationship between American educational values and the American social class system, see Warner, W. Lloyd, Havighurst, Robert J., and Loeb, Martin B.: Who Shall Be Educated? New York: Harper, 1941.

the one to whom responsibility for this widely accepted value is entrusted, and so it is not strange that teachers receive a more favorable evaluation than do women in nursing and social work. If this attitude to education is weak anywhere in our society, it is in the lowest socioeconomic strata, to whom schooling does not appear to be rewarding. The conviction that education is "good" is most deeply rooted in the numerical majority, the lower middle classes, and is one of a set of values which emanates from the middle ranks of society and seeps with dwindling strength both upward and downward.[5]

What of the top socioeconomic class? For one thing, this group need not lean heavily on education as a route upward; they are already "up" and they derive recognition of status from other sources. Secondly, they take education as a matter of course. It is not something for which one sacrifices, sweats and strives; it is something which one naturally and automatically attains. The position of the teacher in their minds is exemplified by the story of the young society matron who was called in to see the headmaster of her son's exclusive prep school. After being informed that the major source of her son's difficulties lay in the fact that he could not get along with the faculty, she replied unbelievingly, "But I don't understand; he never has any trouble with the servants at home!" Such people might well define their relationship to a nurse in a similar manner.

Over half of the general population claims to have friends who are nurses or teachers, while only 26 per cent can say this of social workers. Does lack of acquaintance with social workers enter into the generally low opinion of them? It is hard to say. Although, in general, the sample ranked teachers a little more favorably than nurses, those with friends who are nurses are slightly more numerous than are those with teacher friends. This is not what would be expected, since it has been shown that nurses' friends do rate them more favorably than do other selected publics.

It is true that practically all Americans have had at some time in their life a professional relationship with a teacher. Contrast this with the fact that only 20 per cent of the Kansas City respondents answered "Yes," when asked if they ever had been treated by a nurse, and only 18 per cent answered "Yes" when asked if they ever had had profes-

---

[5]Loeb, Martin B.: Implications of status differentiation for personal and social development, Harvard Educational Review, 23:168-174, 1953.

sional dealings with a social worker. This means that there is not only a difference in the degree of personal familiarity with these three occupational groups but also a difference in the amount of professional familiarity with, and therefore knowledge of their professional functions.

how people distinguish between the r. n. and the practical nurse

One of the most important elements in the hostility and the resentment directed toward auxiliary personnel by some graduate nurses is the feeling that the auxiliaries are being accorded status to which they are not entitled by some who do not understand that there are differences among those who go by the name "nurse." The graduate nurse is accordingly suffering an assault on her status. Nurses have indicated over and over again in the studies which form the basis for this book that, as 1 of them put it:

> The disgusting thing about it is that the lay people don't know the difference between a practical nurse and a R.N. Some R.N.'s have told me that they have been asked if they were practical nurses. Why can't something be done about practical nurses wearing caps? (12, p. 44.)

The Kansas City study of public images obtained from 960 residents an answer to the question, "Do you think there is any difference between a practical nurse and a registered nurse?" For those who answered "Yes," a follow-up question was, "What is the difference?"

Eighty-five per cent of the respondents indicated that they think that there is a difference between the R.N. and the practical nurse. The remaining 15 per cent said either that there is no difference or that they do not know if there is a difference (from the point of view of the R.N., "Don't know" is no different from "No"). Every age group and both sexes responded in approximately the same proportions. However, when the sample is broken down into the four socioeconomic groups, a somewhat different picture takes shape. As noted earlier, as we move down the socioeconomic ladder the evaluation of nurses becomes more favorable, but as we move up the ladder a consistently larger proportion of people makes a distinction between practicals and R.N.'s. Of the sample of the lowest socioeconomic group, almost a third say that there is no difference. Yet this is the group which rates nurses most favorably. Conversely, in the highest socioeconomic group, which rates nurses least favorably, 93 per cent recognize a distinction between the R.N. and the practical nurse. Thus, there is no relationship—and possibly even an inverse relationship—between attitudes toward nurses and the ability to distinguish graduate nurses from auxiliary personnel.

The next question then is, if people do see a difference, what is it? Although one might expect an "ignorant" lay public to make almost infinite distinctions between these two occupational groups, the responses (Table 21) of the 816 who said there is a difference, fall into

Table 21. Distinctions Between the Practical Nurse and the Registered Nurse Made by Laymen

Basis for Distinguishing Between Practical and R.N.	Number of Comments	Per Cent of Comments
Total	955	100.0
Training, education, knowledge	566	59.3
Functions, duties	101	10.6
Patient relationships	81	8.5
Work setting	37	3.9
Rank, status, authority	35	3.6
Evaluation of competence	34	3.5
Professionalization	21	2.2
Cannot explain difference	20	2.1
Age	18	1.9
Experience	14	1.5
Practical is student R.N.	14	1.5
Pay	9	0.9
Miscellaneous	5	0.9

Source: 12, p. 46.

a limited number of categories. Because many of the 816 provided more than one answer to the question "What is the difference?" the analysts had to classify 955 different responses.

By far the most frequent comments were those concerning training, education, or knowledge. The general picture presented is that the registered nurse has received more formal education than the practical nurse and therefore has more knowledge and is more qualified to perform nursing duties. Of the 566 persons who indicated a difference along these lines, only five had the clearly erroneous impression that the practical nurse had more education than the R.N. did. Many of the respondents said that because the R.N. has had more rigid training and is "more like a doctor," they would prefer an R.N. to a practical nurse when ill. The public does not seem to see medical and associated personnel as performing different functions. One gets the impression that people see a continuing procession, with the doctor on top, the R.N. next, followed by the practical nurse, and finally aides and orderlies, all doing the same thing, but some doing it better than others and being better qualified to do it. Thus, there are such remarks as "The R.N. is almost like a doctor" or "R.N.'s know more about the practice of medicine than practical nurses."

Some people say that the R.N. must have a college degree or that she must go to school for five, six or even seven years; others inform the interviewer that the R.N. can practice medicine or administer treatments without a doctor's orders. Nevertheless, it is clear that people know that a professional nurse is distinguishable from a practical nurse on the basis of education and technical knowledge; but is this enough to enable them to make a distinction in individual cases? Can a patient *see* education or knowledge from the sickbed? The answer is probably, "No." For that reason, the second most common category of distinctions is important.

People can see what the nurse does, and if they are aware of the differences in functions between the practical nurse and the R.N., they should be able to make the distinction. Of the 101 comments to the effect that registered nurses are different from practical nurses because of what they do, almost half differentiated the duties of the R.N. on the basis of her administering of drugs and medicines and "giving shots," e.g., "The practical nurse cannot give shots and medicine like the registered nurse does"; "The registered nurse takes temperatures and prescribes medicine; the practical nurse does cleaning." The task specifically mentioned more than any other was the giving of shots, although some respondents claim that a practical nurse "cannot give shots without special permission, like a registered nurse can." Another recurrent remark was that "The practical nurse does not have as many duties; the R.N. has more work to do." Other examples were: "The R.N. is qualified to do more things while the practical nurse just does the dirty work," and "the registered nurses do some of the duties of the doctor and are trained for this. Practical nurses are much more limited in what they can do." The relationship of the nurse to the doctor is involved in the notion of different functions just as it is in the notion of different education and knowledge: "The R.N. is an assistant to the doctor and not just an aide to the patient."

Also a number of respondents emphasized the housekeeping functions of the P.N. They are aware that the "practical nurse fulfills household duties as well as nursing," or that "the R.N. does only nurses' duties in the sick home while a practical nurse has to do all kinds of work in the home." Some of them refer to the practical nurse as doing "menial work" or "maid's work," while others say something to the effect that "The R.N. is more interested in the care of the patient and the practical nurse is more ready to please and wait on you personally." One respondent says that "the R.N. does more things than a practical nurse but you can't tell the difference when they are waiting on you." Another says that "the R.N. is supposed to do more for you than the practical nurse, but you get the same treatment from both of them." Both recognized functional differentiation in the abstract, coupled with an admission that actually "you can't tell the difference." A good number of people feel that only an R.N. can "give a shot," but what criteria do they have in hospitals where practical nurses do sometimes administer injections of one sort or another? It is possible that even differences which can be observed do not enable people to identify the R.N., in contrast with the practical nurse, in actual practice; intellectual understanding cannot necessarily be translated into comprehension of specific behavior.

The third most frequently mentioned category of reply is that the difference between the R.N. and the practical nurse is basically a "difference in attitude toward the patient." There is some disagreement as to its specific nature. One group says that the R.N. "takes more interest in the patient," "has a better personality," "knows how to handle people better," "is more reliable," "more patient," while the practical nurse is "too rough with handling patients." In contrast is the group which says that "the practical nurse is more sweet and considerate while the R.N.'s just perform their duties and are more stern." The practical nurse is "more sympathetic," "kind," "friendly," "takes more pains" and "has more heart."

A variety of status distinctions is made between the practical nurse and the registered nurse, and in every case, the respondent feels that the registered nurse is higher in some hierarchy than the practical nurse. There is only one exception—the respondent who states that "The practical nurse has more authority; she is next to the doctor and tells the registered nurse what to do!" The word "authority" is used frequently in distinguishing between the R.N. and the practical nurse. Some people seem to visualize a power hierarchy in which the practical nurse finds herself in a subordinate position: "I don't know why, but the R.N. does have more authority." There were respondents who expressed this notion by telling the interviewer that the practical nurse is a "helper," that she "takes her orders from the R.N.," "is just an assistant," or, "just waits on patients for the R.N." One respondent who is partial to the practical nurse concedes the hierarchical superiority of the R.N. by saying, "the practical nurse does all the work; the R.N. just supervises the practical."

Another conception which was expressed places both kinds of nurses in a medical hierarchy. One person states this idea succinctly: "The R.N. tells the practical what to do and doctor tells both what to do." A few people speak in much more general terms—in terms of something loosely referred to as "class": "I look upon the R.N. as a higher-class person." "The practical nurse can be just as good, but the R.N. has a higher-class distinction." Finally, there are those who differentiate on the basis of the status symbols, the cap and the pin and the degree. These are unlike the distinction on the basis of education because the emphasis is not on knowledge, skill, or training; it is clearly on the symbol itself. "There is no difference except that one has an R.N. by her name." "The R.N. has her pin while the practical nurse does not have a pin." "It's just that you can tell the difference because they wear different color uniforms so you can tell the R.N. is higher." Actually, the laymen made much less of the status symbols than did some of the nurses themselves. This is certainly not an important means by which people tell the practical nurse from the R.N.

The category, "Evaluation of Competence" (Table 21) contains the answers of the 34 respondents whose only comment was a value judgment. In every case it favored the R.N. These people say that the R.N. "is best," "is better qualified," "is more capable," "is more competent." The best summary—the one which seems to represent what most of these people are trying to say—comes from the respondent who states: "Oh, an R.N. is always more sure of what she's doing and she goes about it different. She is more apt to be able to take care of any situation—not that I don't have respect for practical nurses."

Many respondents made an explicit point of differentiating the R.N. from the practical nurse on the basis of professionalization. The frequent comparisons between the R.N. and the doctor have already been mentioned, e.g., "Registered Nurses are professional like doctors." In addition to those who simply state, "The R.N. is a professional and the practical nurse is not a professional," others virtually spell out valid criteria of professional status (cf. Chap. 10). These include a professional ethic backed by a professional society—"R.N.'s follow the code of ethics of the A.N.A."; a sense of occupational involvement—"R.N. is more of a lifetime profession"; a high degree of specialization—"Specialization is the difference in favor of the registered nurse"; formal recognition—"R.N.'s have professional licenses from the state, they have to pass a tough examination"; a colleagues' organization—"She must work usually in hospitals with other professional people"; and authority and the initiative to act according to the needs of the individual patient—"The R.N. should be more efficient to care for the patient and does not have to wait for orders from anyone as a practical nurse does." It is not difficult to infer from their remarks that many respondents are according professional status to the R.N. and denying it to the practical nurse.

Twenty-seven people distinguished the R.N. from the practical nurse according to the features of age or pay. All who mentioned income agreed that the R.N. is better paid. Of the 18 who differentiated on the basis of age, 15 said that the R.N. is younger or that the practical nurse is older: "The practical nurse is an older woman who is too old to go into nurses' training;" 1 believed that the practical nurse is younger, and two, although they were sure an age difference exists, did not know what it is. These impressions may arise from direct experience, contacts, or hearsay, but it would seem that recruitment advertising has a strong influence; one of those who did not know who is older says: "I've seen signs advertising nursing and they say if you are between some ages you should be an R.N. and if you are between other ages you should be a practical nurse." Such advertisements are common on radio, television, and posters in public conveyances, and it is not surprising that people who know nothing about nursing should mention age because age is usually the only difference specified in the brief text of the advertisements.

The three categories, "work setting," "experience" and "practical is a student R.N." (Table 21), all involve major misconceptions of the difference between professional and practical nurses: one has to do with the place in which each works; 37 people claim that the difference is that one works primarily in hospitals, the other primarily in private homes. The confusion here may be between the practical and the private duty nurse. All but four place the practical nurse in the home and the R.N. in the hospital; three of the exceptions, although somewhat confused, retain a more favorable image of the R.N. As one puts it, "The practical nurse takes care of patients on the wards only, but the R.N. is a specialist who can go out into homes." The other exception sees the practical nurse as an itinerant: "The practical nurse goes into different hospitals and the R.N. stays at one hospital. A practical nurse can go anywhere."

The other two misconceptions are closely related; 14 people say that the difference is that the R.N. has had more experience than the practical nurse or has worked longer. Although this may be true in many or even in most cases, it is a misconception because it implies that a practical nurse with a great deal of experience automatically becomes an R.N. The last group is different only in that it makes the implication explicit. They are people who state that the "practical nurse is in the process of becoming a registered nurse"; "practical nursing is the training period to become a registered nurse"; "the practical nurse is practicing while the R.N. has finished her training"; "the practical nurse is just an apprentice."

To conclude: most people are aware that there is a difference between the graduate nurse and auxiliary personnel and, in addition, most are aware of the fact that the R.N. has more knowledge, training and education, performs more technical functions and has higher professional status than the practical nurse. Although some laymen may labor under some misunderstandings, and although others may not be precisely accurate, they do appear to have the general idea. However, what is lacking, is a test of the hospital patient's actual ability to distinguish on the spot between graduate nurses and other nursing personnel.

her rewards

Chaotic though they say nursing is, a great many nurses are very happy in it. They may be torn in mind on the subject of their proper duties but they are certainly articulate about the rewards and the punishments in their profession. The facts are brought to light by inquiring into what the students and the young nurses hope to find in their careers and what experienced women tell about it after they have tasted reality.

nursing per se

Interviewing 60 students in the Boston Psychopathic Hospital, Kandler (6F) discovered that while many girls become nurses because of special attributes of the profession itself, many others enter it for irrelevant reasons. Of reasons directly related to nursing, the commonest, given by 37 of the 60, is that they want to help others. Of nine, nursing had been the ambition since childhood; and of 18, since high school days. Other reasons were given by small numbers of them: to understand others, to feel useful and to enjoy people.

A surprisingly large group among the 60 students entered their profession for reasons which could have been satisfied just as well by some other means of livelihood. For instance, 44 took up nursing because they could not or did not achieve their first choice of career

Of these, 23 said that they did so because they could not go to college. A few chose it as a steppingstone to "some allied field with more prestige," and a few others thought that nursing offered a way of meeting eligible men. It attracted 25 as a road to social and financial security. There were a few who mentioned glamor and prestige; some who wanted to get away from home; and two who wanted to spite their families! (One wonders if it worked!) Four did not know why they went into nursing but, curiously, were able to tell why their friends did.

The situation appears to be the same elsewhere; in hospitals from Maine to California, some nurses reported that they became nurses because they wanted to nurse, and others—invariably a smaller number—because they did not go into something else. In a survey of five North Carolina hospitals it is shown that of 107 nurses in psychiatric wards, one quarter had wanted to be nurses since the age of 13 or earlier and 85 per cent since the age of 18. As in the Boston sample, humanitarianism enters in but so does lack of money or lack of qualifications for other work. So, too, when the research team went on to ask why they went into *psychiatric* nursing, it turned out that a little less than one third of the reasons were intrinsic, that is, they bore directly on psychiatric nursing; and the rest were incidental, or extrinsic—as, for example, that it paid better or that an opening was close at hand or that it was the only available job at the time. However, these conditions sufficed to keep them in psychiatric nursing: 42 per cent said that they hoped to be in it five years hence, and another 10 per cent expected to be combining it with domestic duties. Of a total of 105 reasons given for continuing, only eight were "attachment to the patient" (29, pp. 33, 42-43, 48, 56).

Attendants in the same North Carolina institutions demonstrate by their mode of response that life is different for males—who numbered 81 out of 144—and for the 51 Negroes who were included in the sample. The wages were the attraction for 35 per cent, while only seven per cent claimed that it was the desire to help people. Another seven per cent said that they had grown tired of their previous jobs. However, it must be remembered, that the Negroes have a limited market for their services, which gives undue weight to the extrinsic reasons: for them, just to be hired at all is a problem. The women among the attendants who said that they wished to help others were for the most part those who had wished to be nurses but could not afford the schooling; but 66 per cent of the sample said that they were not planning to leave psychiatric work for other jobs, and they gave intrinsic reasons slightly more often than extrinsic, mentioning more often than any other attraction their attachment to the patients (29, pp. 26-27).

Almost one fourth of the attendants who said that they like psychiatric nursing spoke of the advantage of having relatives and friends as co-workers. It may be that in what is looked upon as difficult and even dangerous work, the presence of familiar faces is a moral support. Nor does this hold only for the attendants: nearly one third of the husbands of nurses in these hospitals were psychiatric attendants, usually in the same institutions. It is pointed out that ties such as these, while they are extrinsic to the work, are personal and may be a force toward long-continued employment (29, p. 22).

The characteristics of those who give idealistic reasons for enjoying nursing are further explored in some of the research monographs. One is the study of the registered nurses of Pennsylvania. The authors designed an ingenious procedure. Selecting the nurses who had been graduated in 1940, they divided them into three classes. The first they called the low-morale group, namely, 93 who said no, or were undecided when asked if they would go into nursing if they had it to do again. Next is the middle-morale group: 302 who would prefer to see their daughters in some other occupation. Finally, the high-morale group consisted of 374 nurses who wanted their daughters to follow in their profession. Now they note that the class with low morale is too small to permit of much generalization and that, moreover, the nurses with the lowest morale of all probably have left nursing and so do not figure in the sample. Thus, they hesitate to come to conclusions, but as far as they go their findings are that two thirds of the nurses, taken together, gave altruistic reasons for being attracted to nursing; 67 per cent of those with high morale held this opinion, as compared with only 53 per cent of those with low morale (19, Chap. 3). There is some suggestion that the nurses with high morale are inclined to be complacent and uncritical and that the two other groups are more disposed to find fault and make changes and, in short, are urged on by discontent, divine or otherwise.

Nurses everywhere seem on the whole to find the gratification in their profession that they asked of it on first entering. We have ample evidence of satisfied women. The facts are dug out in diverse ways, but the research teams confirm each others' work again and again. For example, Theriault, when interviewing 132 registered nurses in 11 New Hampshire hospitals, came to the conclusion that, trite though it may sound, nurses like people and often from childhood have yearned to help the sick. Like other people, they find it difficult to confess to altruistic love and they gave such answers as: "I know it sounds silly. It is silly; but I like people." "I went in for the idea of the cause, you know, gonna touch somebody's fevered brow and gonna make him well" (22). The last reason might be classified in the pigeonhole which the author labeled "glamor," where the greatest number of answers belong but also in the second most common class of answer, "liking to help sick people." (Theriault admits his classifications overlap.) In any case, love of people and particularly the urge to aid the helpless is firmly established as a pervasive motive for nursing and as the greatest satisfaction found there, once one has embraced the profession. Other reasons that do not bear on nursing per se are less common: the low cost of nursing education, for example, and the economic security enjoyed by the profession. There are no facts to show whether or not the nurses who enter nursing for these reasons are disappointed. Certainly, the New Hampshire sample are a happy lot: 88 per cent say that they like their hospital; 82 per cent like their community; and 80 per cent like the state and of the 132 R.N.'s all but eight said that they would "do it again," if they had to choose a career a second time! (22).

Sledge and Rohrer, surveying nurses in Charity Hospital in New Orleans, show that altruism motivated two thirds of them at the outset and that their commonest source of current satisfaction lies there (18, p. 74). Confirmation comes also from the big study of registered nurses in Pennsylvania, where two thirds of the 2,425 who were asked, "What is the single best thing about being a nurse?" gave altruistic reasons: "opportunities to help others," "seeing patients recover," and so on. Among nurses in their thirties and forties, the second most frequent answer was "application to life," but the younger nurses, those in their twenties, said that the attraction lay in conditions of employment and not intrinsically in nursing. The investigators went on to ask: "Knowing what you do, if you had it to do all over again, would you still enter the nursing profession?" To this, over 90 per cent said yes (19). The majority also would like to see their daughters following in their footsteps. This attitude is even commoner among the younger nurses than among the older. The difference may prove to be permanent, or it may be that time will moderate the enthusiasm of the younger cohort and bring them more nearly to the opinion of their elders.

Although the three hospitals studied in Alabama differed extraordinarily from each other, from a swarming little 30-bed hive in the country to a big metropolitan university hospital, the nurses, throughout, liked *all* their work. Of 4,036 ratings of duties, nine tenths were favorable; half of the functions were "enjoyed" and it was hard to find a task which was unanimously unpopular. The head nurses revealed a trifle less zest than the others and, indeed, as one passes down the hierarchy more and more of the duties are discovered to be liked. The eager, hopeful student nurses favored all but six of 24 tasks "above average!" The leading popular functions were the bedside or "touch" tasks (10, pp. 94-104). They included giving oral medicines, which was the favorite chore, answering the bell to see what the patient wanted, bathing the patient, changing the bed, feeding helpless patients, changing dressings, tidying the patient's room—each of which was an opportunity to "minister" and bring comfort. This is just what the New Orleans nurses said that they liked, too: bed-making, helping the patient to walk and giving preoperative and postoperative care—all of them rewarding personal routines which, at the same time, were among their most frequent activities (18, pp. 82-6).

A 45-year-old practical nurse who had been employed for seven years in a remote small hospital in northern New Hampshire poured out to the research worker her almost infectious enthusiasm for tending the sick:

Question: What is it about nursing that appeals to you the most?

Answer: To tell the truth, I really don't know what interests me. The minute there's a new case on the floor, I like to know all about it. I'm interested to know how he's going to come along and how he's going to pull through. You know.

Question: You enjoy taking care of patients?

Answer: I do. I do; especially when they're real, real sick. You go in and give them their baths and fix them all up, and . . . oh, you know how they're rested after that and how they feel. . . . I really like to do it" (22, "Ward H").

Of 107 general duty nurses surveyed in Arkansas, all but two said that they would recommend nursing as a career to a sister or a daughter or other young girl who seemed to be qualified. Over half of them would do so because, as they put it, "I like nursing" and because of the satisfaction of helping those who need it. Extrinsic or irrelevant answers were less common: one fourth appreciated the good foundation nursing gave for family life, and only 18 noted that it offers good income, prestige, or security (17, pp. 24-28). To validate the nurses' statements, Stewart and Needham probed further. They asked them what they would like to be doing 5 years hence and learned that 48 of the 107 would like to continue in nursing and that 50 would like to be housewives at home. However, when the nurses were asked what they thought they would actually be doing then, 63 thought that they would still be nursing, and only 38 thought that they would be keeping house—which means that some of them were already anticipating disappointment.

The wish to protect and help appears to be strong in the obstetric nurse and is given by many in obstetric units as grounds for the greater popularity of work in the delivery room, as compared with postpartum care (20, p. 133).

The private duty nurse, as observed in several places in preceding chapters, thinks of her work pre-eminently in personal terms and is strongly "patient-oriented." Those nurses studied in Washington, D. C., reported that their greatest reward came from the appreciation of the patient and his physician (30, p. 15). In this the 315 private duty nurses surveyed in Georgia concurred (7, Table 16, p. 139). (This of course distinguishes them from the general duty nurses, whose contacts with the doctors are neither as close nor as protracted and are apt to be categorical rather than individual.)

In hospital after hospital the nurses over and over again told those who studied them that they love to "make the patient comfortable"; "see him get better"; "relieve his pain"; "watch him respond to treatment." Of course, this explains the notion of the ideal patient as one who recovers quickly and completely; he—it is a male—is usually a surgical case who passes dramatically from a very critical state (9,

p. 66-8). For, as she sees it, she can bring this patient by devoted attention to that quick recuperation which is exactly the reward that she wants most of all. It is a reward of which the private duty nurse can be fairly certain. She—lucky nurse—not only prefers but usually gets the quickly responding postoperative patient. Her cases, ranked in the order of their frequency and then in the order which she prefers, show that she nearly always gains her wish (Table 22).

Table 22. Private Duty Nurses' Desire for
Versus Achievement of Kinds of Patients

Kind of Patient*	Rank Order of Responses Indicating "Usually Get"	Rank Order of Responses Indicating Preference
General surgery	1	1
Medical	2	2
Cardiac	3	3
Accident	4	5
Orthopedics	5	6
Obstetrics	6	8
Pediatrics	7	7
Chest surgery	8	4
Brain surgery	9	9
Alcoholics	10	13
Psychiatric	11	11
Heart surgery	12	10
Narcotic	13	15
Contagious	14	14
Polio	15	12

Rank Correlation +.91

* Data drawn from tables from 7, pp. 152-3. The categories are those named by the nurses. Tubercular cases are not included, perhaps because they are thought of as belonging in special institutions, while polio cases, for example, are nursed in general hospitals. Geriatric cases are not named as such; they may come under medical cases, for example, or cardiac or accident (7, pp. 154-155).

The industrial nurse has other rewards. She, too, takes pleasure in people but, to quote a common remark of industrial nurses in Pennsylvania, "in meeting normal, healthy people." For one thing, in industry, people are a more constant presence; after all, the sick pass in and out of the hospital and do not often become enduring friends of the nurse. Moreover, in industry, her relationships with plant employees appear to be more personal and easy than is always the case with the hospital nurse and her associates (31, p. 56).

levels of satisfaction

As several of the investigators remark, the satisfactions which nurses claim to find in their profession are general and diffuse, but when they talk of their grievances and frustrations they can render a bill of particulars that shows plenty of thought. The exception is the nurses in New Orleans, who stuck to "safe" criticism of their work and confined their complaints to "overcrowding," "shortages," "pressure of work" and the like (18, pp. 153-154).

The 599 general duty nurses queried in 37 hospitals in Minnesota were presented a list of conditions of employment and asked to state if they were "satisfied" or "very satisfied," "dissatisfied," or "very dissatisfied" with them (8, pp. 122-123). Among the general duty and the head nurses, 25 per cent were dissatisfied with salary (after those "dissatisfied" and those "very dissatisfied" had been added together). Next, came opportunity for advancement, which failed to satisfy 22 per cent. The distribution of duties among the R.N.'s, the practical nurses and the nurse aides was unsatisfactory to 17 per cent. The remaining conditions on the list all polled smaller proportions.

Salary, again, was the greatest cause of complaint among Minnesota's practical nurses; 28 per cent of a total of 238 checked this item, and the same fraction was dissatisfied with the opportunities for advancement. The schedule of hours displeased 26 per cent; 15 per cent did not like the distribution of duties.

The 319 nurse aides recorded more widespread discontent. Salary was a cause of dissatisfaction to 33 per cent, opportunity for advancement to 34 per cent, and distribution of duties to 15 per cent.

Seeing that jurisdictional disputes over tasks are universal (Chap. 6), it is surprising to learn that the distribution of duties displeased less than one fifth of the highest category of nurse of the three, and just over a seventh of the two lower ranks; but a nurse, like any human being, might challenge every item on a long list of functions and still register a fair degree of satisfaction when asked her sentiments on the work as a whole.

Matters like the length of the working week, the security of tenure and relations with other groups of nurses were satisfactory to high percentages of the two upper ranks of the Minnesota nurses. However, more than three times the proportion of nurse aides was distressed in mind over job security as was found among their superiors. The situation of nurse aides is shared by nurses in other places who complain of irregularity of employment. For example, private duty nursing is avoided by many because of the gaps between cases. Of the minority of eight general duty nurses in Arkansas who said that they would not recommend their profession to young women, all but one mentioned irregular hours as a real deterrent (17, Chap. 2).

So, too, in Pennsylvania, the attitudes expressed by the registered nurses brought Bressler and Kephart, who studied them, to the conclusion that if the morale of the local nurses is to be maintained, something must be done about the hours of working. In fact, their sample of 2,425 R.N.'s, when asked "What is the single worst thing about being a nurse?" (19, Chap. 2) concentrated on hours, pay and job grievances, which made up 70 per cent of the complaints. Only 28 per cent of the older nurses, who had been graduated in 1930, complained of salary, as compared with 36 per cent of the class of 1940 and 40 per cent of the class of 1950, but the sum needed to bring the older nurses' income up to what they thought it should be was substantially larger (19). The New Hampshire nurses, on the whole, are ill-paid, and the majority recognize it. The satisfied minority is chiefly of the older and the married (22).

In general, private duty nurses are not disposed to complain of salary—after all, they can accept more work or less, as they please. Since in the Georgia sample, for instance, one third say that they went into this branch of the profession because of the higher income and the flexibility of days and hours of employment, they can be expected to be satisfied (7, pp. 138-150). The more the private duty nurse is dependent on her income, the less is she satisfied, for then, presumably, she must work more than she finds convenient (30, Tech. Supp. 3, p. 12). The Georgia nurses are reported as unhappy over their relations with the auxiliaries and the students. On the other hand, in Washington, D.C., the complaints are over relations with the administration (30, p. 15).

Professional nurses everywhere complain that they are obliged to devote a very large portion of their day to keeping records. The secrecy and the ritual surrounding the patient's chart is time-consuming; yet the professional nurse is made to feel guilty if she permits a subordinate to share in it. But the worst thing of all about the paper work is the sneaking conviction that the endless forms and records which she fills out are really a waste of time. The doctors, it is sometimes said, merely glance at reports—if they do even *that*. They *ask* the nurses what has been done for the patient.

Almost half the general duty nurses surveyed in Arkansas lament that a quarter of their time is too much to spend on desk-work. In fact, in one of the 10 hospitals, it amounted to 30 per cent (17, p. 47-8); and they, too, believe that the papers are seldom consulted. The only suggestion anyone has to offer is a radical re-examination of procedure—and a fresh start.

Like the hospital nurses, industrial nurses complain that too much emphasis is placed on paper work (21, pp. 94-95); but they have a distinctive grievance: professional isolation—one quarter of a sample of 212 in Pennsylvania named that as their chief complaint. An equal fraction found their work monotonous (31, p. 57).

Three of the reports under discussion provide unusual insight into the lives of nurses. This they do, each in its own way, by classifying nurses into types on the basis of attitudes, which of course is not the same thing at all as the conventional classification based on rank or function in the hospital hierarchy. Bressler and Kephart produced one of the schemes, described more fully in Chapter 7. They divided nurses into three groups on the basis of morale and went on to discover other qualities of each class. A second classification is the work of Habenstein and Christ whose promising division of nurses into traditionalizers, professionalizers and utilizers has been referred to here repeatedly. The third case is the work of Reissman in Charity Hospital, New Orleans.

After asking why nurses enter their profession in the first place and if they intend to stay in it, Reissman combined the replies to the two questions and arrived at four types of nurse (18, Table 12, pp. 170-174):

1. Nurses who enter the profession for positive reasons and say that they expect to stay in it, he calls the *dedicated*.

2. Nurses who took up nursing on negative grounds but aspire to continue as nurses, he calls the *converted*.

3. Nurses who came into nursing for positive reasons but do not wish to remain in it are the *disenchanted*.

4. Nurses who came into nursing for negative reasons and plan to leave the profession are the *migrants*.

Now all four types listed "patient care" as the outstandingly satisfying work. For the dedicated it was *the* great reward; so too for the convert, who had not anticipated the joy of bedside nursing but learned it after she had entered the profession. To the other two types, patient care was less rewarding; most particularly for the migrant, to whom hospital work is just a job like any other and one task, on the whole, as good as the next.

To the dedicated person, nothing in nursing is unsatisfying. However, the converted nurse takes a different attitude. When things go wrong, she blames herself rather than the institution or her colleagues; not so does the disenchanted, who finds fault with other people who, she declares, impose upon her, shirk their duties and bungle. The unhappy migrant, who seems to be hopelessly miscast in hospital work, not only blames the institution and everyone in it but sometimes even herself.

Detail by detail, Reissman builds up the picture of the four types. For example, the dedicated individual obeys the rules and seems to believe that they are shaped by people who know what they are doing. The converted takes a middle course, believing less in the rules than does the dedicated, but more so than the disenchanted. The migrant makes her way among the rules in her own fashion, is given to arguing and sometimes finds "good" reasons for violating them. Since a hospital, like any institution, is run by rule and policy more or less continuously, her sentiments about them will go far to determine whether or not a nurse finds her work sweet or sour.

A related question is on the attitudes to making decisions and to accepting responsibility for them. The first two types are willing to accept the burden of making judgments, but the disenchanted would undertake no more than is necessary for the arranging of her own schedule of work. The migrant wishes to decline completely; she avoids being embroiled.

Entirely the happiest appears to be the converted. She came to love nursing as she found it. The dedicated nurse, who is the next happiest, may have entered nursing with more pronounced expectations and be destined to occasional disappointment.

In passing, it is intriguing to try to translate the four types that

Reissman analyzed in New Orleans into the three types described by Habenstein and Christ in Missouri; for all these conceptions of nurses are presumably applicable everywhere. Of course, the traditionalizers are the dedicated and may also include some of the converted. The professionalizers may come from among both the converted and the disenchanted. There are probably none of the dedicated among them, for the dedicated, to repeat, develop personal relationships with the patient, but the professionalizer focuses her attention on giving the case efficient care with the best techniques. One thing is certain: the utilizer and the migrant are a close fit.

To complete the comparisons: The high morale group which was set up in the Pennsylvania study would correspond to the traditional-izers and to the dedicated and the converted. The group with low morale could wear the shoes—worn smooth, we suppose—of the migrants and perhaps of the utilizers; and those in the middle might have to be distributed, in the main, among the disenchanted but perhaps also in small lots among the other classes. The creators of the systems of analysis may differ, of course, on the details. However, each has committed himself on one point; the nurses with administra-tive responsibilities are to be found in disproportionate numbers among the professionalizers, the disenchanted and the migrants, and among the nurses with limited morale. To say so is to describe them in three ways with only slight shifts in emphasis.

The professionalizers in the small hospitals studied in Missouri are most frequently head nurses or nurse supervisors (9, p. 87). They enter the profession at higher levels of authority, as a rule, and from the outset of their careers carry administrative burdens. If their joy is in "mission accomplished," in the patient's recovery as proof of work well done (while the traditionalizer enjoys "tender, loving care" for its own sake), and if the professionalizer is the more often dis-appointed, it is because it is often harder to keep an organization running smoothly than it is to cool the fevered brow. This is not to belittle bedside care but only to acknowledge the plight of the woman who is bedeviled by the million-and-one pits and roadblocks that beset the path of the organizer and the manager—other people's shortcom-ings, mechanical failures, Acts of God. The Pennsylvania nurse with "middle morale," whose attributes include, ". . . intelligence, ambition, a tendency to be concerned about the hospital situation and perhaps to see the need for improvement . . . is more likely to hold a rank above the level of staff nurse than is a nurse who has the attributes of the high morale group" (19); and in New Orleans, the head nurses are concentrated in the two types who say that they want to leave nursing: the disenchanted and the migrant (18, Table 12, p. 170).

Why? We can only conjecture. Some may be older women who entered the profession years ago with the traditional love of the "touch" tasks, and, upon rising to positions of authority find their days to be desk-bound and conference-ridden. Others, again, may be young graduates of highly regarded nursing schools who, as very often happens, almost from the beginning are thrust into the management of nursing units and are promoted rapidly. For, beyond doubt, the head nurse's situation is peculiarly hard. As Hans Mauksch so aptly points out, two independent streams of power converge upon her; not only the physicians' but also the administrators'. For she is answerable to the hospital authorities for the running of her part of it and for the eternal flow of work, the use and the care of equipment and supplies, the bedding and boarding of the patients and so on. The administrator's concern with the balance sheet, as one investigator put it, will clash at times with her concern for the patient (9, p. 151). Her uneasy position leads Mauksch to remark: "In the entire range of occupational pursuits, there is hardly a work situation to be found which compares in complexity and built-in frustration with that of the head nurse. Few persons have so many responsibilities with so little power."[1]

Responsible women that they are, the head nurses and the supervisors seem to be cursed with too little help in what is already a difficult task. Equally nerve-wracking is the work of the nurse in these echelons who has too many subordinates for one individual to direct. Thus, she confesses in moments of discouragement: "I hate to go home when the time comes because I feel so uneasy about all these patients. I can't check them as I feel I should when we are so short of well-trained personnel." "It is so depressing when you go of duty knowing your patients aren't cared for. You feel tense and worried" (18, pp. 41-42). The nurse who enjoys most of all the swift and

---

[1] Mauksch, Hans O.: Nursing dilemmas in the organization of patient care, Nursing Outlook 1:32, 1957.

efficient fulfillment of tasks, to whom the best news is "mission accomplished!"—in short, the professionalizer—finds herself living with a sense of chronic defeat.

This makes clear what at first appears to be a paradox in Reissman's findings. When he asked, "Would you rather work on a job where everyone was friendly or where everyone was doing her job?"; the first alternative was chosen by only eight per cent of the nurse aides but by 25 per cent of the head nurses. Reissman interprets this as each seeking the place where her own work is easiest; the lower ranks want everyone to do her part, since work undone will often be left to them, but the nurse whose job is managerial appreciates a work climate which promotes smooth running. In fact, six head nurses said that teaching and administration give them the greatest satisfaction in their day (18, pp. 134-135, 153). They already had stated that they thought patient care a more important duty; but that is the right answer and not merely a pious one, for one can imagine a hospital, if it is small, being without supervisors and teachers, but nurses must tend the sick if it is to be a hospital at all.

Although the nurses are able to give detailed accounts of what they dislike in their profession, the impression grows that salary, hours, hospital conditions and other physical features of their work are not the things that matter most (18, pp. 75-76). At present, theirs is a seller's market. In many places, a nurse can get the shift she likes and work in the type of hospital that appeals to her. The private duty nurse can take the kind of case which she most enjoys (as was shown earlier in this chapter). Indeed, nurses are in an advantageous position to secure improvements in working conditions, if they want them, but one suspects that they are like soldiers and schoolboys who universally complain about the food and all the while they really mean that they don't like "the brass" and the teachers. It may be that status, recognition, and assignments fitting, in their estimation, to their station, are the hidden and unnamed reality. In short, their roles are the raw points (see Chap. 8). The nurse who says that "handling bedpans is not nursing," is restless if she has to do much of it. The deepest anxieties come when she is overworked, when she is short of helpers or when others are un-co-operative; but these are just the very occasions when she has to pitch in and do the practical nurse's work, the aide's work, even the doctor's work, while her own "proper" work lies undone.

The wound to status is most grievous to the most status-conscious: the professional nurse. She smarts under the fact that the patients may not differentiate her from the practical nurse who also wears a pin and a uniform. These things are matters of recognition and one's conception of one's self. Her resentment, of course, is sensed by the practical nurse and the nurse aide whose lives are already heavily fraught with problems of status.

Conscious of their professional claims, the R.N.'s suffer if they think that they are professionally cramped. In rural institutions, they lament that they are missing the advanced techniques and the innovations that always are initiated in the metropolis; while the auxiliaries in the same institutions say that they would prefer the big city because of the higher salaries. The point is made from another angle; when a charge nurse works overtime in the Alabama hospitals and undoubtedly elsewhere, she does it, we are told, to finish work of high status, like bringing the charts up to date; and the medications nurse stays late to finish giving the medicines. So, too, work left undone is work that is little esteemed, like cleaning the pantry (10, p. 65).

Nurses squirm under assaults on their calling because, happily, they entertain a high opinion of it themselves. Among the Pennsylvania R.N.'s, 56 per cent think that the nurse has the same social standing as the teacher, 15 per cent rank the nurse higher—which means that just 29 per cent think that the teacher enjoys the higher position (19, p. 193); and the industrial nurse is hurt and indignant if she is classed with the safety director and not with the plant physician and if she cannot use her professional skills to the full (21, pp. 43-44, 73; also 31, pp. 38-41).

More evidence appears in the Missouri study in which an analysis is presented of the tasks which the professional nurse disparages and the practical nurse complains are "thrown" at her. The practical nurse dislikes some of them because she thinks that they are undignified and of low status, better suited to employees of inferior ranks. The "worst" are jobs such as cleaning the patient unit after use, caring for the incontinent patient, carrying trays and preparing the operating room. Others she dreads. They call for skill and judgment befitting the professional nurse—an example is starting subcutaneous infiltrations—and if she performs them and fails, she fears that her right to professional aspirations will be called into question (28, p. 39).

In like manner, the industrial nurse is most distressed, in the first place, by being treated as a "hired" hand and paid by the hour, rather than as a professional worker and a colleague in mangement; and, in the second place, by being compelled—in establishments with no plant doctor—to take responsibilities which she knows are his prerogative (21, pp. 66-68). Then too, her complaints of violated safety measures and neglected health rules are, in the end, evidences of the belittling of her functions. She says, "We nurses are not being fully recognized in the personnel organization," "Our opinions are not asked," "We are not asked to sit in on conferences when nursing procedures are discussed." Most galling of all, some are relegated to being inspectors of rest rooms (31, p. 53).

Very vulnerable to abuse is the frontier of duty between the professional nurse and the doctor. When the doctor fails to give orders in writing, when he leaves it to the nurse to order sedation or to declare the patient dead (29, p. 138), he forces her to exceed her authority and subjects her to grave risk of undermining her position, if she fails. For to be upgraded momentarily because it is convenient, that is, to be made to do things beyond one's status, can be even more painful than to be downgraded; and how can she be sure that the doctor will not turn on her and accuse her of "trying to practice medicine"?

The patient wants his doctor to act as if he were the only sick man in the world. The doctor, for his part, would like the patient to think that he thought so, too; but all his other patients compete for his time and attention. However, those accommodating women, the nurses, will observe the patient, take his blood pressure, count his pulse and see that the tests of his hemoglobin and his basal metabolism and his sedimentation rate are all run, and can be relied on to put it all down on paper for the doctor to see at a glance. To the doctor, the ubiquitous and trustworthy nurse is in reality a substitute for his own personal attention to the patient. When he reads the sick man's blood pressure on a chart, he is saved the more time-consuming work of reading it on the apparatus itself. In this way, he has more time for this patient and for all his other patients. Some people say that he fills this saved time by taking on still more patients.

We have seen what this does to the professional nurse. She is under orders from all the doctors whose patients have been assigned to her. The worst beset is the head nurse, answerable as she is to all the doctors of all the patients in her unit, all putting in individual appearances and issuing orders independently. As if that were not enough, some patients have more than one doctor and someone—as a rule the head nurse—must co-ordinate, reconcile and sometimes perhaps even discreetly qualify their orders. The doctor, quite properly, is concerned only with the welfare of his patient as he sees it and is not likely to, and probably should not, be deterred by the thought that there are other patients and other doctors whose claims and demands, when all is said and done, must compete with his for the use of equipment and the attention of the nurses. So the nurse spends a quarter of her time writing figures on the chart, or filling in forms that admit that patient to the x-ray room or to diathermy or to any one of a dozen treatments, and spends some more of her time teaching the team that works under her and in supervising them. In short, she is living with the patient just as the doctor does, on paper and not in the flesh. If she has left the bedside of her patient it is because the doctor has filled her time for her in other ways.

levels of achievement

Something fundamental to the association between doctors and nurses is the effect that they have on each other's careers; but, to go back behind that, their careers are vastly dissimilar in one very important respect which aggravates the nurses' quandary.

The physician lives and gets ahead in the medical world. His is one of those professions so structured that he can rise to very satisfying heights in it and yet continue to be what he is. We hear of the great neurologist, the internationally known rheumatologist, the surgeon after whom an operation is named, and we know the names of Pasteur, Hunter, Freud, Osler, Cushing. They all had patients and grew famous for their successes in caring for them in new and superior ways. Occasionally, a doctor becomes widely known as a hospital administrator, but it is no longer common. By the same token, the legal profession has its great pleaders, like Clarence Darrow, who continue to have clients when they become famous. Now it is true that great lawyers may become judges and never have another client or plead another case, but the point is that a lawyer does not have to leave off having clients to become great. So, too, scholars who gain reputations still meet their classes in the universities.

But in professions of another sort, the successful are among those who have ceased to practice them. The teacher who succeeds in becoming a school principal may, if it is a large school, never teach another class and may go higher to fill the office of superintendent of schools. In these professions, one does not become great and famous by sticking to the work for which the professions were named; and so we hear of superb and beloved bedside nurses, just as we hear of fine high school teachers, but neither is great, *as such*. The big reputations in the nursing as in the teaching world are enjoyed by people who administer, organize and manage and see little or nothing of patients or of pupils.

The aspiring doctor is helped on his road by competent nurses to whom he can entrust the care of his patients. His trust lays upon nurses—at least on some of them—the burden of seeing that the care is provided; and this becomes a full-time job in itself. So, while the doctor makes a name for himself, the nurse may make one, too; but his will be a reputation as a medical practitioner; hers will *not* be as a bedside nurse.

Perhaps it is no accident that certain of the professions—nursing, schoolteaching, social work and library work are among them—in which success requires abdication from the original commitment, are women's worlds; the point calls for further study. Be that as it may, the nurse administrator walks a tightrope in a man's world. The woman doctor walks the tightrope, too. So do her sisters in engineering and the law. Soon we will see women balancing themselves warily in the latest professional arena to which men have admitted them, the Protestant ministry. True, in nursing, schoolteaching, social work and library work, the professional woman walks with more confidence, surrounded by women colleagues; yet, even here the ringmaster is male, and she jumps to his whistle and his whip. The most important nurse is still the newest doctor's underling.

Leaving her securer place in the women's world of tending the sick, the nurse who becomes an administrator crosses the frontier into the male world. For it is the simple truth that the big executives, the top hospital administrators, are men. As things are now, the nurses who find themselves in it and like it have to face the fact that in all probability they will never reach the summit, though as directors of nursing service many of them have become powerful figures.

To a certain sort of ambitious person, to have to be content with the lower ceiling on achievement is crippling. In our day, the world is full of women whose morale is more or less shattered by this bitter compromise. However, there are signs of change; some exceptional women actually are in charge of important hospitals. We can count on the stress of the times to make it too expensive to stifle talent indefinitely, and already we have seen how war opens avenues of employment and promotion to classes which never set foot in them before. However, at present, there seems to be no choice available to the supervising nurse, the head nurse, the directors or others by whatever name called. They cannot leave their paper and desk work for the bedside. In the middle-sized hospital surveyed in Alabama, it is reported that when the shortage of personnel is extreme, head nurses are compelled to attend to patients, leaving their administrative problems unsolved—at which point the whole organization becomes demoralized (10, p. 108). On the other hand, few are prepared for high administrative responsibilities. Their careers might be more rewarding were they frankly trained and equipped to advance into the upper levels of management. Indeed, here and there postgraduate courses are offered in hospital administration, but one does not hear yet of young women who study business organization in general with the avowed hope of entering hospital work through the front office.

Of course, there are very many nurses who do not wish to "advance" to managerial positions, if that word may be used to cover administrative and supervisory work. It calls for a particular temperament or type of personality. No doubt, there are many so endowed among nurses, but among both professional and practical nurses, there are also many—those thought of as the motherly type are an instance—strongly attracted to nursing but appalled by the idea of organizational responsibility. There can be no doubt on this point. The professionalizers, if Missouri nurses are representative, say that the doubtful worry of supervision is its own reward. Nursing supervisors and head nurses, who know whereof they speak, agree (9, p. 85; also 22). Only 24 per cent of the sample of R.N.'s in Pennsylvania, who were defined as of "high" morale because they said that they hoped their daughters would be nurses, declared that they would welcome higher rank and increased responsibility. Of those with "low" morale, who said that they would not go into nursing, knowing what they do now, 46 per cent repudiated the idea of promotion (19). The rewards for nurses who are happy in bedside nursing lie purely in the exercise of their own good offices to the sick, and if this is unjust, if there ought to be some way of recognizing outstanding performance, no one has thought of it yet. This is much the sort of problem which the medical men, who sing the praises of the "family doctor" while busily gaining fame and fortune as specialists, have hoped to solve by setting up the annual award for the Doctor of the Year. (This is referred to only as a similar situation, not to suggest that the reward is appropriate or adequate.)

To revert to the subject of what doctors and nurses do to each other's careers, the nurses help the doctors to win reputations, and the doctors help the nurses to get out of bedside nursing into a career which has no room for them at the top. Now there seems to be no real reason why, for example, a good general duty nurse, busy with her charts, records and requisitions and with running her team of subordinates, should be made to feel that she ought and is expected— as the research monographs prove—to give medicines, particularly since there is at hand a second category of women, the practical nurses, who are educated to do it and anxious to have the task for their own. Nor is there any sound reason why she should be made to suffer pangs of conscience because her day is spent in doing other things. Yet, whole sections of the nursing profession have somehow been made to squirm under the pricking of a bad individual and collective conscience.

One of the difficulties may be that women, cast in a variety of roles in hospitals, have titles, each containing the word "nurse," and all begin with an education in the "touch" tasks, as if they were all going to have identical work. For the name "nursing," as we have seen, has become a catchall for an array of occupations including among them administration, supervision and teaching, in which the road to advancement leads of necessity away from the tending of the sick, and for women, for the most part at present, down a blind alley. The chaos and the personal frustration that the nursing educators speak of as chronic—all amply demonstrated by the research—may be restated as the struggle of some new occupations to take form and split off from what has always been regarded as a single career.

chapter ten

profession is as profession does

The purpose of the authors in this chapter is not to judge whether or not nursing *should* be considered a professional undertaking. However, because the question is of some concern to nurses, we first will attempt to clarify what is meant by a professional as distinguished from other orientations to work and the kinds of responsibilities that such an orientation entails, and, second, the extent to which the available research indicates that nursing is becoming a profession.

what is a profession?

Perhaps the simplest way to describe a profession is to distinguish it from other kinds of work. Kinds of work differ not only in a functional sense but also, more importantly, in a qualitative sense: in respect to how and why people are drawn into them, the extent to which people become involved in them, the extent to which they impinge on all aspects of the worker's social life, the demands they make on him, the gratifications he receives from them, the public's and the worker's image of them, and the relationship of the worker to those social and cultural objects which make up his world.

People are related to others in their work roles in a variety of ways, the differences being vaguely reflected in the words used to denote the "consumer," e.g., customer, client, patient. The distinction is more than verbal; the words tell something about the worker's orientation toward his work.

In the light of the manner in which people enter an occupation, six types of work may be distinguished: missions, professions, enterprises, arts, trades and jobs.[1] With this typology as a starting point, let us try to describe what is a profession and what is not.

In the first place, unlike "missions" to which a person is called or converted,

The professions are entered by long training, ordinarily in a manner prescribed by the profession itself and sanctioned by the state. The training is assumed to be necessary to learning the science and the technique essential to practice of the function of the profession. The training, however, carried with it as a by-product assimilation of the candidate to a set of professional attitudes and controls, a professional conscience and solidarity. The profession claims and aims to become a moral unit. It is a phenomenon of the modern city that an increasing number of occupations are attempting to gain for themselves the characteristics and status of professions.[2]

In distinction from other kinds of work, the entrepreneur deals with a commodity. The implication is that, by and large, those in other kinds of work, including the professions, deal with something other than commodities: the professional person deals basically with other people rather than with material objects. More specifically, his saleable product is *services* rather than goods. Although the shoeshine boy, for example, might meet this one of the criteria, he does not meet the others cited above. Therefore, the professional is one who deals with people rather than objects, sells services rather than goods, and sells only certain types of services in a manner to be distinguished from those who sell other types.

The professional is not one who is called or converted, as to a mission; nor is he one who learns his work as a result of practicing, as in the trades; nor is his entry into the work basically the result of some inherent talent or gift, as in the arts. The professions are entered through a relatively lengthy, formal, academically standardized education, prescribed by the profession and sanctioned by the state.

---

[1] Hughes, Everett C.: Personality types and the division of labor, Am. J. of Sociology, 32:762-763, 1928.

[2] *Ibid.*, p. 762.

The professional organization has unique functions:

In the first place the [professional] association guarantees the technical efficiency of its members, not by supervising their work, but by testing their ability before they are admitted to practice. This involves an indirect control of their training. Secondly, it imposes a code of ethics which includes the duty to offer service whenever and wherever it is required, to give only the best, to abstain from competition, advertisement, and all commercial haggling, and to respect the confidence of a client. Thirdly, it does what it can to protect its field from invasion and to keep up the standard of remuneration of its members, and in general to safeguard the conditions of their work.[3]

Perhaps the very essence of the profession lies in the nature of the relationship between the professional person and his client. There must be trust. Between buyer and seller this is not necessary—sometimes it is not even expected—hence the ancient warning, *caveat emptor* (Let the buyer beware!). For one who buys groceries can inspect and judge, but if he "buys" an appendectomy, he cannot judge but must accept and pay for what he was given. The product of the surgeon, as of all professional workers, is unstandardized, and no contract can be drawn stipulating explicitly what is to be given and received. When the professional gives his services, authority rests with him; this is not true of those who sell commodities. The professional must provide the client with what he judges is needed, and this is not always what the client may think that he wants. The customer may be always right; the client is neither invited nor expected to judge.

The professional man or woman enters into a personal relationship with his client or his patient, as the case may be, and he renders his best service when he knows the latter's temperament and mentality, his family and his circumstances. Only to a very limited extent can he "deliver" his services through assistants and subordinates but must undertake the ministrations himself. Whereas the surgeon consents to delegate some tasks like the administering of the anesthetic and the preparing and the passing of instruments, he gives them to persons whose ability and integrity he trusts; yet he reserves for himself the essential task, and this will be the most professional of the services the patient receives while on the table. It can never be mass-produced at reduced rates. It can never be standardized.

---

[3] Marshall, T. H.: The recent history of professionalism in relation to social structure and social policy, Canadian J. of Economics and Political Science, 5:325-340, 1939.

Finally, an occupational group, before it can truly be thought of as a profession, must command public prestige. Although other kinds of occupations such as the sciences or the arts may have high prestige too,[4] the worker in a profession enjoys the trust and the confidence not only of the client but also of the whole community. Certainly, if the client is to put himself in the hands of the professional, to trust him implicitly, to accept his authority, then the profession must be one which stands high; and if an occupation is striving for professionalization, it must achieve this high prestige. Some occupational groups, putting the chicken before the egg, assume that by calling themselves professions, they automatically will be accorded high prestige. For example, the chiropractor may have the same kind of relationship with his patient as the medical man has with his, but until he is allowed to share in staff privileges in hospitals, to write prescriptions, to participate in the organized world of medicine and to enjoy all of the other privileges and prerogatives of the healing arts, including official recognition by the state—until such time, he can hardly be classified as a professional. Unlike chiropractic, osteopathy is approaching, in a few states, the power and the prestige necessary to a profession.

A multitude of activities or jobs and kinds of people are sometimes grouped under a single title. For example, the title of social worker may be applied to the untrained county welfare worker, engaged in largely clerical chores, along with the wealthy widow who undertakes a multitude of charitable and philanthropic activities and the degree-holding group-worker, community organizer, or caseworker. All of these, in one sense or another, are "social workers," but certainly they vary in activity, education and prestige. Then, again, although both men are called farmers, there are vast differences in status and prestige between the Mississippi sharecropper plodding in his cotton patch behind his one mangy mule and the Kansas wheat "farmer" who is so busy flying his private plane between New York and Miami that he hardly notices the fleet of combines which rolls over his acres.

The differences among the individuals in it are obvious, but from the vantage point of the outsider, the occupation often appears to be

---

[4] For some distinctions between a science and a profession, see Hughes, E. C.: Psychology: science and/or profession, The American Psychologist, 7:441-443, 1952.

far more homogenous than it is—both in function and reputation. Is the director of nursing services, an administrator responsible for hundreds of nursing and auxiliary personnel, the same as the young girl who doubles as secretary and receptionist in a doctor's office? Compare the widow who, after years of housekeeping, returns to the bedside as a private duty nurse, with the university-trained public health nurse making her rounds of the tenements of New York or the backwoods of Tennessee. These are all nurses, all officially recognized by their states and their professions as registered nurses, all legally qualified, all entitled to the symbols of their occupation—the pin and the cap; but there is easily as much variation among them as there is among farmers or social workers.

The important features of a profession are in the subtle realm of the social-psychological: a profession is a social role defined by the nature of the relationship between the professional and his client. The role may be played, and played well, in any profession by people who vary greatly in training and in kind and degree of skill.

professional commitment and involvement

Women who are wives and mothers are, in the nature of the case, unable to pursue professional careers as continuously and consistently as do husbands and fathers, and in judging their commitment, this should never be forgotten. The price to a woman of utter devotion to a career may be spinsterhood or a childless marriage—a sacrifice no one has a right to expect of any young woman who is otherwise minded. Nor should anyone insist that the married professional woman neglect her family—she will not do it in any case, as the research proves. Thus, as we examine the evidence on the nurse's devotion to her career, we should ask ourselves whether there should not be a double standard—at least this once!

Now to begin with, a strong sense of responsibility may help separate the professional from the nonprofessional worker.

However, not all nurses can be assumed to have the sense of professional responsibility. Habenstein and Christ have described the "utilizers" in nursing (9), while Reissman speaks of the "migrants" (18), and Bressler and Kephart observe a "low morale group" (19). (These have been discussed in part in Chap. 4 and are compared with

each other in Chap. 9.) The research monograph from Washington,
D. C., reports that those who work with private duty nurses complain
that:

> . . . a significant number of private duty nurses do not adequately accept
> professional responsibility. . . . It appears that while in January only 15
> per cent of the available cases are unfilled, in November and December,
> 29 and 37 per cent respectively are unfilled. It is interesting to speculate
> on the reasons why more private duty nurses are more available in January
> (a month notorious for post-holiday penury) than they are during the holi-
> day seasons (30, p. 6).

This study reports some of the private-duty nurses as accepting only
the cases they like. Many refuse to work in the evening or at night,
and they are said to be extremely difficult to get on week ends and
holidays. "There are even reports of nurses who habitually leave their
cases on weekends or holidays, pleading 'sickness' " (30, p. 7). The
problem of staffing certain shifts with general duty nurses and obtaining sufficient staff on week ends and holidays is also familiar to
directors of nursing service.

The survey of all graduate nurses in the Kansas City metropolitan
area shows that only 52 per cent of them are working full time, and
31 per cent of them are not working at all. The remainder are divided
evenly between occasional and regular part-time work (25, Fig. 28,
p. 34). This distribution is not related to age; there are proportion-
ately as many nurses 60 years of age and over working full time as
there are in the ages of 20 to 29. Actually, the age group in which the
greatest proportion is working full time is between 50 and 59, and the
age group in which the greatest proportion is not working at all is
between 30 and 39 (25, Fig. 29, p. 34). The Kansas City data
appear to substantiate the Washington findings regarding private duty
nurses. As can be seen in Figure 2, the field of private duty contains
a far greater proportion of part-time occasional workers as well as
fewer full-time workers than any other field of nursing.

Less than 10 per cent of the private duty nurses interviewed in
Georgia considered themselves part-time workers; yet, in 1953 the
median number of days worked by these nurses was 167 (7, p. 141
and Fig. 13, p. 105). Accounting for vacations, holidays, week ends
and sick leave, staff nurses can be estimated to work at the very least

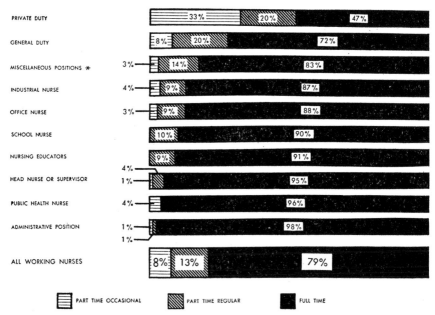

| | PART TIME OCCASIONAL | | PART TIME REGULAR | | FULL TIME |

FIG. 2. Labor force status of working nurses in Kansas City according to their field of nursing (1954). Source (25), Fig. 64, p. 64.

* One-half of this group consists of nurse anesthetists, surgical assistants, and clinic nurses. One-sixth of them, although they remain in the health field and are registered nurses, are not actually nursing. These include such persons as medical librarians, physical therapists, laboratory technicians, x-ray technicians, etc. The remaining one-third of this group is composed of nurses who are employed by nursing organizations, registered nurses who are in school, and those who are in the armed forces.

210 days a year. Only 37 per cent of the Georgia private duty nurses worked that much during 1953.

This raises a question: how much can the nurse control her own work? How much work can the private duty nurse take? For one thing, she can work only when she is offered cases. Moreover, many nurses have home duties. The employed nurse in the hospital, too, has no control whatever over her own case load. Thus the conditions of her employment and the contingencies of her life as wife and mother may give her only limited choice.

A professional person commits himself to his work for his lifetime. To speak of an ex-professional or a former professional is a contradiction of terms. The exceptions only prove the rule. There are few personal tragedies greater than for a man to be drummed out of his chosen profession—whether it is medicine, law, architecture, or whatever—under sanctions from his colleagues and the state.

However, these are men, and our conventional notions of the professions grew up in the world of men. It was found in Arkansas that about 60 per cent of the general duty nurses studied believed that they would be active in nursing five years later. The same was true of 75 per cent of the operating room nurses (16, p. 3). In Charity Hospital "more than half of all personnel wished to leave hospital work within the next five years. . . . For most, the goal was to stay at home" (18, p. 157). When 107 general duty nurses in Arkansas were asked what they would like to be doing five years from now, only 48—less than half—said that they would like to keep on nursing; 50 replied that they would prefer to be at home, keeping house; but not one of these nurses said that she would like to change from nursing to some other occupation (17, p. 27). Indeed, although nurses might prefer to be wives and mothers, they do stick with nursing if they work at all. Of the 2,441 nurses surveyed in the Kansas City area, only two per cent were working at something other than nursing, and most of these were still in the health field, as, for example, medical librarians or physiotherapists (25, Fig. 56, p. 56). This is professional dedication, after the manner of women, and it is evidence of extraordinary devotion.

The manner in which nurses resolve the relationship between career and family responsibilities was touched on in our earlier discussion of role relationships in nursing (Chap. 7) and again in the following chapter on careers. Although it need not be, this problem is posed, time and time again, as one of choice—of being either a nurse *or* a wife and mother; and, of course, such a choice is not difficult to make for a young woman in a society such as ours. Even as senior students, nurses do not identify themselves entirely with their profession or the aspirations which lie within it (Chap. 3). Among senior nursing students in Kansas City, 20 per cent said that their ultimate aspirations lay outside of nursing (26, p. 64). Typical of many nurses is the response given by one in central Missouri when asked if being a staff nurse for the rest of her life could be considered a successful career:

I don't believe so because I don't want a career really. This was more or less a means to an end. I mean, there has to be an interval of something in there before you get married and after high school. I was too young to be married. It was something useful and satisfying to fill in that span. But I believe a housewife is about the only career that I've ever really thought about (9, p. 89).

The implications of women's ambitions are clearly spelled out by the New Orleans investigators:

This orientation away from nursing has consequences not only for the hospital but for the profession as well. The nursing profession, which in a real sense has made an investment of time, facilities, and expectations in the training of these younger women can anticipate only a limited return on that investment. The number of years they intend to give to nursing is about equal to the time they have spent in training. The hospital, too, is likely to bear the consequences because it faces the loss of trained personnel in an occupation where severe shortages already exist. Not only is there difficulty in recruiting new nursing personnel, but there also is the prospect of losing significant proportions of those already in the profession (18, pp. 157-158).

As a matter of fact, an appeal used by those who recruit students for the schools of nursing is that nurse's training will prepare them better for motherhood. However, Theriault found that, if one digs deep enough, many are only taking time out, temporarily or intermittently:

For example, one young, single nurse said, "I like it too much to stop nursing. I'd really miss it." Saying she would be out of nursing when children arrived, she added, "I don't think I'd want to be out of it for too long, because you lose track of too many things." A student nurse said, "I think I definitely would want to go on with my career [after marriage], and I think I would plan accordingly, because after I go through training I wouldn't want that to disappear, because I really do have my heart set on it, and I always have and I don't think that should interfere." (22).

The difficulties of reconciling career and marriage are not insurmountable; many nurses do it successfully; but the problem requires an understanding husband, ready and willing to concede that his wife also is a human being with potentials for accomplishments beyond the domestic. In a society which can make good use of all of the talent that it can find, it cannot be wise or democratic to exclude over half the population from making a contribution because of sex.

The Arkansas study attributes the advancement of supervisors in part to the fact that they are unmarried: 32 per cent married as compared with 58 per cent of the general duty nurses (17, p. 21). In Kansas City, only 33 per cent of nursing administrators are married as compared with 63 per cent of general duty nurses and 70 per cent of industrial nurses (25, Fig. 58, p. 57). It is hard to deny that a nurse is more likely to advance administratively without a husband.

Another clue to the degree to which nurses have assimilated a professional attitude toward their work lies in the extent to which they continue to improve themselves professionally after they have completed the formal requirements for the R.N. Self-improvement may be achieved by reading professional literature or by taking advanced courses of one kind or another. What evidence there is indicates that nurses by and large are not avid readers of their nursing journals. Only 40 per cent of the operating room and 47 per cent of the floor nurses in the Arkansas study subscribed to the *American Journal of Nursing* (16, p. 3); 87 per cent of the general duty nurses in central Missouri admitted that they do not regularly read a professional maga-

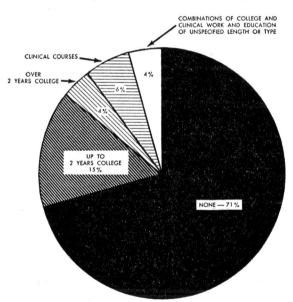

FIG. 3. How much academic and clinical education do Kansas City nurses receive after nursing school? (1954). Source (25), Fig. 117, p. 104.

zine (9, p. 145). The Georgia investigators describe private duty nurses as being "slow to adopt self-education methods" (7, p. 230).

They are not heavy subscribers to the literature of their field. They do not invest in regional or national programs of education offered by their confreres, nor do they take extension courses or correspondence courses from colleges and universities or from other sources.

As can be seen in Figure 3, the great majority of nurses who compose the Kansas City nurse complement seek no further education after graduating from nursing school. Of the 692 local graduate nurses who had obtained education in addition to nursing school, the greatest single group, 102, had sought additional training in public health. This was followed by 90 in nursing education. The remaining 500 are scattered thinly over 19 additional areas of education (25, p. 105). As might be expected, there is a great deal of variation among different fields of nursing in this respect. Figure 4, which shows how

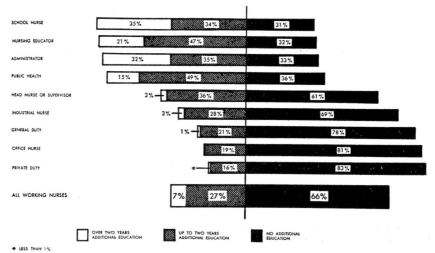

FIG. 4. Nursing positions of Kansas City nurses and amount of education after graduation from nursing school (1954). Source (25), Fig. 125, p. 111.

much further education is sought by the Kansas City nurses, reveals general duty, private duty and office nurses as seeking the least. In four fields, about two thirds of the nurses have education in addition to nursing school; in order, they are school nurses, nursing educators, nurse administrators and public health nurses.

professional organizations

The mere existence of a professional organization as definer and maintainer of a true profession is not sufficient proof of a profession. That organization must have the strength of the persons in the occupation behind it just as those persons must have the strength of the organization behind them. Nor is size alone a sufficient criterion; it is the proportion of potential members who actually belong that counts.

Speaking of Kansas City only, where 61 per cent of all nurses working in 1954 were found to belong to the American Nurses' Association, a wide variation is reported in membership according to fields of nursing (Fig. 5). Membership ranges from 92 per cent for public

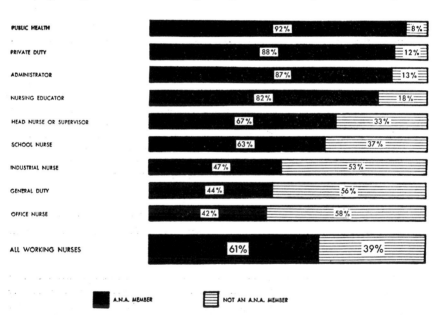

FIG. 5. A. N. A. membership in Kansas City according to nurse positions (1954). Source (25), Fig. 94, p. 86.

health nurses down to 42 per cent for office nurses. It is interesting to compare membership in the A.N.A. with the nurses' opinions about professional organizations. Although the correlation is not perfect, Figure 6 shows that the four fields with the highest membership rates are also the four with the highest percentage of favorable opinions.

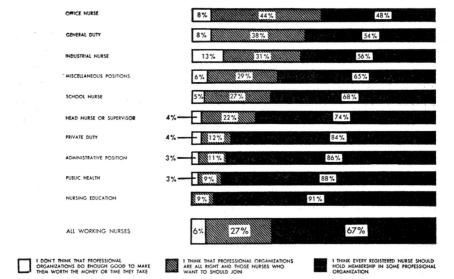

OFFICE NURSE   8%   44%   48%
GENERAL DUTY   8%   38%   54%
INDUSTRIAL NURSE   13% 31%   56%
MISCELLANEOUS POSITIONS 6% 29%   65%
SCHOOL NURSE   5%   27%   68%
HEAD NURSE OR SUPERVISOR 4% 22% 74%
PRIVATE DUTY   4%   12%   84%
ADMINISTRATIVE POSITION 3% 11%   86%
PUBLIC HEALTH   3%   9%   88%
NURSING EDUCATION   9%   91%

ALL WORKING NURSES   6%   27%   67%

☐ I DON'T THINK THAT PROFESSIONAL ORGANIZATIONS DO ENOUGH GOOD TO MAKE THEM WORTH THE MONEY OR TIME THEY TAKE

▨ I THINK THAT PROFESSIONAL ORGANIZATIONS ARE ALL RIGHT AND THOSE NURSES WHO WANT TO SHOULD JOIN

■ I THINK EVERY REGISTERED NURSE SHOULD HOLD MEMBERSHIP IN SOME PROFESSIONAL ORGANIZATION

FIG. 6. Opinions of working nurses in Kansas City concerning professional organizations according to nursing positions (1954). Source (25), Fig. 75, p. 74.

* One-half of this group consists of nurse anesthetists, surgical assistants, and clinic nurses. One-sixth of them, although they remain in the health field and are registered nurses, are not actually nursing. These include such persons as medical librarians, physical therapists, laboratory technicians, x-ray technicians, etc. The remaining one-third of this group is composed of nurses who are employed by nursing organizations, registered nurses who are in school, and those who are in the armed forces.

An interesting observation suggested by Figure 6 is related to private duty nurses and more especially to a conclusion reached in the Georgia study:

If the American Nurses' Association closed out the registry system, and districts no longer required automatic payment of dues and evidence of membership, it is very likely that many nurses presently enrolled in the private duty sections would drop out for lack of motivation toward their profession beyond personal convenience. These nurses are only nominally active at the present time, in that they pay dues and are officially affiliated but do not attend meetings and workshops sponsored by the professional organization (7, p. 143).

The same observation has been heard concerning membership of private duty nurses in other parts of the country—including Kansas City. Yet, Figure 6 shows that private duty nurses are far more favorably disposed toward their professional organizations than are nurses in many other fields. Only administrators, public health nurses and nursing educators have a higher percentage who say that every R.N. should join.

Among institutional nurses, the Arkansas investigators find that the mean age of A.N.A. members is about 38 years as compared with 29 for nonmembers. They point out that an untilled field for professional activity and for recruiting members for the professional organizations is the younger women and those in smaller hospitals (17, p. 22 and p. 89). This is supported by the Kansas City finding that in the youngest group, 20 to 29 years of age, the greatest proportion of nurses do not join any professional organization (25, p. 75).

The proportion of Kansas City nurses who are A.N.A. members decreased in the following order according to the type of control and support of the hospital: the largest percentage of members was found in governmental (city, state and federal) hospitals, then in voluntary, followed by religious and finally private proprietary hospitals. The size of these hospitals generally follows (growing smaller) the same order as their source of support or control (25, p. 88). The findings of the central Missouri study are corroborative! A.N.A. affiliation is highest in tax-supported institutions, followed by Catholic hospitals, with the lowest rates of membership being in the private proprietary hospitals (9, p. 103).

One is inclined to wonder whether or not vigorous and persistent efforts are made to incorporate nurses into their professional organizations, and in particular, to impress their importance on the student nurse. This question is raised by the fact that young people do not show very high membership rates and that, of the Kansas City nurses who were *not* A.N.A. members, 38 per cent indicated a belief that every R.N. should hold membership, and only 11 per cent were opposed to professional organizations (25, Fig. 87, p. 82). When Habenstein and Christ inquired of nonmembers why they did not belong to professional organizations, the response they received and the recommendations they make are in accord with findings in other studies:

One general theme suggested procrastination. A secondary theme was that cost of membership was prohibitive in terms of "return" to the nurse. It was quite obvious that many nurses who were not members of the

ANA-State-District "Package" of associations were completely unaware of the potential "return" which membership offered. In general, it may be positively asserted that from a publicity standpoint the professional association does not reach its *potential* members, the emissaries provided by the state association to disseminate "services," information, and to solicit "services" support, reached almost exclusively only those who were already members. Likewise, there is a certain lack of missionary spirit on the part of those who are already members—a spirit which may require sparking by some kind of incentive. It was quite evident in some communities supporting two or more hospitals having similar forms of control, that the associational membership of one might be maximal while that of the other minimal. This suggests that professional associational membership is probably functionally related to mechanisms which may be set in motion quite easily through promotional activity, and promulgated through unused channels of communication (9, p. 106).

self-esteem

It has been said earlier that a profession is held in high regard by lay persons. Some indication of the manner in which various "publics" evaluate nurses and nursing was provided in Chapter 8. However, before any group can hope to be accorded high prestige by others, it must have confidence in itself and in its worth. Is this true of nurses?

Bullock asked his sample of Ohio nurses in a variety of ways what they thought the public thinks of them. He summarizes their impressions as follows:

There is general agreement among institutional nurses that nursing is looked upon by the public as a profession. Approximately 77 per cent of the institutional nurses feel that nurses are recognized as being very hard-working people. Seventy-two per cent feel that nurses are generally recognized as having a great deal of technical knowledge, and about 70 per cent believe that the public thinks of nurses as very alert and efficient persons. Sixty-six per cent believe that nurses are known to the public for their devotion to duty, and about 65 per cent believe the public generally thinks of nurses as being independent and self-directing in their work. Slightly over 80 per cent disagree with the suggestion that the public looks upon nurses as being inferior intellectually. . . . 61.2 per cent agree that the public does not properly appreciate the work nurses do. In fact in nearly all items very impressive proportions indicate the pessimistic view. Sixty-two per cent agree that nursing is generally looked upon as an unpleasant occupation. About 54 per cent agree that most lay people think nurses are "faster" or "freer" in sex matters than most other women. Nearly 60 per cent agree that the public looks upon nurses as somewhat special servants (33, p. 27).

The Georgia private duty nurses appear to have a clear and realistic notion of what others think of them. It coincides closely with what was found in Kansas City of the public's impressions (12). Nurses there are aware of the fact that not all patients are alike and that it is necessary for them to adjust to different expectations:

Personalities enter into it and also economic status, I think; you can nurse a country farmer, and he's the most humble person in the world, and puts the nurse on a pedestal and thinks you are the best person in the world, and then if you have Miss Gotrocks come in, she treats you being beneath her dignity and puts you on the level of a servant. But usually patients are very nice and don't expect too much from you—they just want to know that they are in good hands, and that you are doing all you can for their welfare, and they usually trust you to that extent (7, p. 212).

One of the most telling reflections of how the nurse thinks others see her is her estimate of how nursing rates as compared with other occupations in which large numbers of women are found. A scientific sample of the general population in the Kansas City area, it will be remembered (Chap. 8), was found to rate nurses and schoolteachers as about the same and both as higher than social workers. When the sample of Ohio nurses was asked which of the three occupations "is more respected by the public?," 19 per cent replied, "nurses," 44 per cent, "schoolteachers," and seven per cent, "social workers" (33, p. 62). In Charity Hospital, New Orleans, the head nurses placed only one occupation above their own—the woman doctor's. Dietitians and private duty nurses, they considered, are their equals. Other hospital occupations—attendant, laboratory technician, nurse aide and clerk—were placed lower. They believed that none of the occupations outside the hospital have more prestige than that of nurses, and they put the social worker on the same level as themselves, the schoolteacher and the librarian being put only slightly lower. Beauty shop operator, stenographer, waitress and sales clerk were all rated as lower in prestige. The staff nurses also rated the woman doctor as higher than themselves and gave only the private duty nurse equal ranking. Outside the hospital, they judged the schoolteacher to command more respect than themselves. All remaining occupations they considered as enjoying less prestige (18, p. 165).

The Pennsylvania investigators asked nurses whether they thought the nurse or the teacher had the higher status; 56 per cent of their state-wide sample of professional nurses thought them equal, 28 per cent thought that the teacher was higher, while 15 per cent said that the nurse was higher (19). In central Missouri, many of the nurses have been in other occupations, including that of teacher in rural schools, and many say that nursing was "the happier choice, if not an escape."

Several admitted that "breaking away" from teaching to enter nursing met with resistance by parents who were not easy to convince that moving from teaching to nursing was not a downward movement. The nurses themselves, however, asked if they could note a change of any kind in the community's reflection of their status, were unanimously agreed that they had not lost prestige by the change; but although they were agreed that rural schoolteaching was less appreciated and more menial, by and large, than was nursing—by the community's standards—they could not agree that their prestige was much increased (9, pp. 123-124).

An incontestable reflection of self-esteem among nurses is the extent to which they influence young women in their choice of career. Nearly half of over 200 student nurses interviewed in Kansas City mentioned as one reason for choosing nursing the encouragement of relatives or of friends who were nurses (26, p. 37, *et seq.*); 90 per cent of the operating room nurses and 93 per cent of the floor nurses studied in Arkansas think enough of their occupation to recommend it (16, p. 3).

We have seen that there are wide differences in opinion, some conflicting research findings, and a great deal of ambivalence among nurses regarding many aspects of professionalization. Some fields of nursing appear to be more advanced in the process of professionalization than do others, and it hardly seems likely or desirable that some fields should ever meet all of the criteria of a profession. The doctor's office nurse can hardly be said to be playing a professional role in making independent decisions, exercising independent judgment, and assuming responsibility. She acts largely in an assisting capacity as, to a somewhat lesser extent, does the private duty nurse. On the other hand, nursing administrators, educators, school nurses, public health nurses, and possibly—under some conditions—industrial nurses are rapidly meeting the criteria and achieving recognition as professional persons.

A term used by Marshall which may be applied appropriately to much of contemporary nursing is "semiprofession":

. . . the remarkable thing is the rapid spread of the forms of professional organization among occupational groups which are not professions in the full meaning of the term. The forms which such groups can adopt are: recognized courses of training in a specialized technique, a means of testing efficiency in that technique the admission of those duly qualified into an association, the building up of the prestige of the association as against non-members, the imposition of certain standards of honourable dealing and the rudiments of a code of ethics. The foundation of the whole structure is the specialized technique, and it is the multiplication of these techniques that has made possible the spread of these organizations. To put it briefly, scientific methods have been introduced into non-manual routine work, like that of the secretary, the accountant, the trade statistician, the advertiser, the office manager. These techniques are not, by older standards, professional. They do not call for creative originality . . . nor must they be linked with sound human judgment and the power to inspire trust in one's character and personality. . . . They demand accuracy and efficiency along established lines. . . .

In the church or in the army, in law or medicine, a man at the head of his profession is on top of the world. He admits no superiors; but many of these new semiprofessions are really subordinate grades placed in the middle of the hierarchy. . . . The educational ladder leads into them but there is no ladder leading out. The grade above is entered by a different road starting at a different level of the educational system.[5]

Much of nursing today fits well this description of the semiprofession, for some nursing, largely because of the limitations of authority and independent action, cannot meet the criteria of a full profession. In most situations, the nurse must act under doctor's orders. It is true that in their movement toward professionalization, graduate nurses have established professional organizations which have done much to standardize and control nursing education, although there remain two-, three-, four- and five-year schools of nursing; also that examination and registration by the state are required before one is entitled to the title R.N.; and that the American Nurses' Association has done much to protect the nurse and her functions from certain untrained or lesser trained auxiliary nursing personnel. Nevertheless, the nurse in the operating room, on the floor, in the doctor's office, on

---

[5] Marshall; *op. cit.*

private duty—all of these, regardless of education or organization or other manifestations of professionalization, are not autonomous but remain under the authority of the physician.

As pointed out, this is not true of all nurses. In varying degrees, nurses in some fields of nursing are approaching the model of professionals. To the extent that they succeed in achieving professionalization, they probably will become further divorced from others who, because of the very nature of their work, cannot hope and may not wish to become professionalized.

The ladders and the roads mentioned at the end of the quotation describing the semiprofessions are a part of the concept of career which is discussed in the following chapter. The career must lead somewhere, and only those careers which lead ultimately to autonomous work involving relationships with clients we have discussed here, can be designated properly as professions.

chapter eleven

careers

When we talk about careers in nursing, or in any other occupational field, two things must be taken into account: the division of labor within it and the way persons move about among the positions it offers them. In other words, we have to take account of the alternative careers and of the choices different people make.

The situation in nursing is more complex than it is in some other fields of work, where an array of positions remains unchanged for relatively long periods and people move through stable sequences of positions as their experience, ability and opportunities develop. Not only do registered nurses move from one position to another within the various specialties and administrative levels of nursing, but also the assortment of work into professional roles is changing. Consequently, the nursing career consists of both movement among positions and changes in the positions themselves.

The first part of this chapter deals with the field of work open to registered nurses and the way that it has changed in the recent past. The second deals with the personal characteristics which influence the speed of movement and direction of choice during the work life of the individual registered nurse.

the choices increase

In the past generation or so, there has been a well-marked shift in the organization of medical service in the United States. Advances in medical technology, specialization of practice among physicians, the development and the spread of prepayment plans for hospital care, changed attitudes toward illness and its care among laymen—all these changes have made important differences in the organization of medical service (cf. Chap. 7). One would expect parallel changes in the work which the registered nurse performs in it.

A generation ago, nursing was one of the relatively few career opportunities open to young women who sought professional education. Hospital schools of nursing were organized around in-service training and provided their hospitals with inexpensive nursing personnel. At the completion of nursing education, the graduate nurse ordinarily found work as a private duty nurse, in either a hospital or a private home. In the early 1930's, a newly opened hospital which wished to establish the idea that its services were luxurious and technically excellent advertised in the newspapers that all its nursing was provided by graduate nurses and that it did not maintain a school of nursing.

The contemporary scene is greatly changed. Rising standards of professional education have shifted emphasis from in-service experience as the backbone of a nurse's education to carefully supervised and selected clinical experience with gains in knowledge and skill above the student's services to the hospital.[1] Expanded utilization of hospital facilities and rising levels of medical technology would lead one to expect a growing demand for the services or fully prepared registered nurses on hospital staffs. Moreover, the use of auxiliary personnel to meet the demands for nursing service in the hospitals, as we have seen, has added administrative and instructional duties to the routine work of the staff nurse in many modern hospitals. One result of these changes has been a general upgrading of standards of nursing education and of the work of the hospital staff nurse.

At the same time that the demand for registered nurses on hospital staffs has increased, the opportunities for them outside the hospital have broadened. Intensified use of the physician's office as a place

---

[1] Esther Lucie Brown emphasizes the importance of this, and other changes in nursing education in Nursing For the Future, New York, Russell Sage Foundation 1947.

for providing patient care, instead of the patient's home, has created openings for graduate nurses there. Other changes in patterns of medical service have created opportunities for them in industrial nursing, school nursing, public health nursing, and so on. The use of more numerous and elaborate procedures in diagnosis and treatment have increased the need for nurses competent in medical technology; for example, the proliferation of specific medications calls for a specialist, the medications nurse. Again, the exigencies of postoperative care call for specialized recovery-room nurses, and the increasing specialization of nursing service presumably brings with it the elaboration of administrative jobs in it. The activities of nurses in these various specialties and comparisons between them are described in Chapters 4 and 5.

These changes in patterns of medical service since the Thirties are reflected in the experiences of 100 registered nurses in Kansas City (27).

Let us consider first whether or not changes in the organization of medical service and nursing education over the past generation have in fact resulted in wider fields of opportunity for the young, newly graduated registered nurse. Table 23 shows the first positions held by younger nurses (those who graduated since 1940) and by older nurses (those graduated before 1940).

We note in the first place a marked shift away from private duty nursing toward staff positions among younger nurses. Private duty nursing was the first job of more than 50 per cent of older nurses; it is rare for a nurse in the younger group to begin her career in it.

Table 23. Comparison of First Jobs Held by Older and Younger Nurses

Kind of Job	Older Nurses (Graduated Before 1940) Per Cent	Younger Nurses (Graduated After 1940) Per Cent
	N = 45	N = 53
Total	100.0	100.0
Private duty	55.6	7.5
Hospital staff	15.6	43.4
Administration (includes teaching)	13.3	20.8
Technical specialties	2.2	9.4
Nonhospital nursing	—	9.4
No longer in nursing	13.3	9.4

Indeed, 25 years ago 55 per cent of graduate nurses engaged primarily in private duty nursing, while in 1951 it was only 21 per cent (7). Thus, we can regard the decline of private duty as a certainty (30, p. 7 and Technical Supplement, p. 26; 7, p. 300).

The second striking contrast between the first jobs of younger and those of older nurses is the increased variety in the former. Nonhospital jobs in nursing and technically specialized jobs, which absorbed only one nurse in the older group, are the first jobs of 10 younger nurses. Since the older and younger nurses are about equally represented in the sample, the evidence suggests something like a tenfold increase in nursing in institutions and agencies other than the hospital.[2]

It was suggested earlier that specialization of nursing service and larger nursing staffs might be expected to enlarge the need for administrative personnel in the hospitals. As a matter of fact, this is the case; Table 23 shows that many more younger nurses than older ones accepted administrative positions in hospitals for their first jobs: 20 per cent of the one, 13 per cent of the other.

trends in job shifts

We can gain further information about changes in the array of positions open to registered nurses by considering the second and later jobs which younger and older nurses held, as found in the Kansas City study. In order to simplify the sometimes bewildering complexity of the job histories of 100 nurses, the jobs were combined as: staff jobs in hospitals and clinics; administrative positions in hospitals and clinics; jobs, both inside and outside hospitals, which call for technical skills and knowledge rather than for the bedside arts; private duty nursing and activities outside nursing. The careers of the nurses were then followed, with positions classified in this way (Fig. 7).

The idea of net movement from one kind of position to another requires explanation. For example, among younger nurses, 12 at some point in their careers shifted from jobs on hospital staffs, where the core of their work was the direct care of patients, to technical

---

[2] The relatively small numbers of nurses in both older and younger groups make statistical tests of significance highly doubtful or impossible. However, when evidence is so clear-cut, even for small numbers, and when evidence indicates the same general conclusions that other more reliable evidence supports, one may begin to draw tentative conclusions.

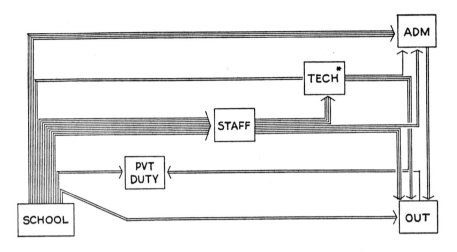

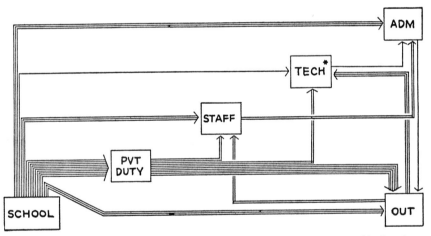

Fig. 7. The net movement of nursing careers into various kinds of positions. Younger nurses are represented in the chart on top, and older nurses below. The thickness of the arrows is proportional to the number of nurses making the indicated moves.

* This category includes positions with technical emphasis, such as surgical nursing and anesthetist, and positions outside hospitals in clinics, offices, industry and schools, where the technical knowledge of the nurse qualifies her, and where the tasks are not directed to bedside care but to other kinds of medical service.

positions in a hospital, such as in the operating room or to a technical service outside the hospital, such as public health or school nursing. During the same period, there were eight younger nurses who moved from technical jobs to become general duty nurses on hospital staffs. With 12 changes in one direction and eight changes in the other, the net movement was a loss of four persons from hospital staffs to jobs requiring technical skills rather than bedside nursing, and, of course, a net gain of four nurses in technical work at the expense of general duty nursing. Again, six younger nurses moved from technical to administrative positions, and four younger nurses moved from administrative to technical posts, a net gain of two administrative nurses. Since the net movement from staff to technical jobs was twice as great as that from technical to administrative, the arrow connecting staff to technical position on the chart is twice as thick as the one indicating net movement from technical to administrative. This is what is meant by saying that the thickness of the arrows connecting points on the chart is proportional to the net number of nurses making the indicated moves.

Thus, Figure 7 is a representation of the flow of nurses from one position to another during their careers. We see that younger nurses and older nurses take very different routes when they leave school. There is a heavy flow into private duty positions among older nurses and a minor flow into private duty positions among younger nurses. Younger nurses go from school into administrative positions and into technical positions in larger numbers than older nurses did. Another striking difference between younger and older nursing careers is that many more older nurses leave nursing early, although they tend to move back into it in later years.

To recapitulate: the younger career leads from school to a position as staff nurse and then into administrative or technical positions, with relatively little leakage into non-nursing activities and bypassing private duty nursing. The older nurse is likely to have worked first as a private duty nurse and then to have left nursing at marriage, to return later in life to a staff job or a technically specialized position. Exceptions to this rule are usually single nurses and married nurses without children who follow administrative careers. A few nurses in each group use private duty or staff nursing as a part-time job during periods when they have other responsibilities.

activity versus inactivity

The mere existence of wider opportunities in nursing today does not explain why younger nurses appear to devote a greater percentage of time after graduation to work in nursing. Nor does it explain why younger nurses are less likely to interrupt their nursing careers at marriage than older nurses. When older and younger nurses are compared by the percentage of total time since graduation which they actually spent in work as a nurse, we find that younger nurses are most heavily represented in the group which has spent 100 per cent of time since graduation in active nursing. Older nurses, on the other hand, are most heavily represented in the group which has spent less than one half of the time since graduation in active professional work. This evidence supports the impression, based on first jobs and on net movement among kinds of positions, that younger nurses are more likely than their predecessors to make extensive use of their professional education and to make a proportionally larger contribution to medical service.

Although this evidence is clear-cut, it is not decisive. It is possible that a comparison of the percentages of time since graduation actually spent in nursing leads one to overestimate the dedication of younger nurses to their work and to underestimate that of the older. Since older nurses may be presumed to have run greater risk of interruption to their careers by marriage, by childbearing, and by other contingencies independent of nursing, it is important to find out whether the difference is due to differential risks in the two groups as time passes, or to marriage and childbearing having been unequal in the older and the younger nurses.

This may be done in two steps. First, we can compare older and younger nurses for a fixed time-span after graduation. Then we can check the effects of marriage and childbearing on nursing careers by comparing the moves made immediately after marriage by older and younger nurses, and again by comparing the moves they made immediately after the birth of children.

Let us compare, then, the percentages of the first 10 years after graduation which younger and older nurses spent in active professional work. No nurse who has been a graduate for less than 10 years enters into the comparison. When the effects of time are held con-

Table 24. Trends in Activity During First 10 Years

Age Group	Total Per Cent	Percentage of First 10 Years Spent in Active Work		
		100 %	99-50 %	49 % or Less
Total	56	19	21	16
Younger (graduated since 1940)	21	5	10	6
Older (graduated before 1940)	35	14	11	10

$X^2 = 1.89$ P is greater than .25

stant, it is shown that in the first 10 years after graduation, older nurses are likely to spend full time in nursing or else less than half the time; younger nurses fall in a middle range (Table 24).

What we find is this; younger and older nurses do not differ significantly in the fraction of time spent in professional employment during the first 10 years of their careers. The differences depend simply on differences in the period during which they run the risk of interruption of their careers by outside pressures; with the period of risk equalized, the two fail to differ significantly.

On the average, nurses in the Kansas City study spent about 75 per cent of time after graduation in active work. This agrees with data from Arkansas (17), which show nurses spending, on the average, eight years in active work out of an average of 13 years after graduation.

Effect of Marriage. Table 25 shows the immediate sequel to marriage for each married nurse in the Kansas City sample. If a nurse continued to work six months or more after her marriage she was counted as having continued in nursing. If a nurse left nursing shortly after her marriage and later returned to it, she appears in the column

Table 25. Sequel to Marriage

Age Group	Total	Continued in Nursing	Left and Returned	Not Returned
Total	75	35	28	12
Younger	38	26	9	3
Older	37	9	19	9

$X^2 = 13.29$ P is less than .01

"left and returned." If a nurse left nursing shortly after marriage, or at the time of her marriage, and had not returned to nursing at the time of the study, she was counted in the "not returned" column.

Table 25 shows two things of importance; in the first place, it shows that younger nurses are, on the average, almost as likely to have married during their relatively shorter careers as are older nurses, who graduated up to 40 years ago. This fact conforms to a general trend in contemporary American life, namely, that women are marrying at younger ages. It also indicates that external pressures toward interrupted careers are not noticeably greater for older than for younger nurses, at least as far as marriage is concerned. But Table 25 reveals that younger nurses were significantly less likely to interrupt their careers as a consequence of marriage. While roughly equal proportions of older and younger nurses are married, three times as many younger nurses continue their careers uninterruptedly. The New Hampshire study has this to say, in the same connection:

. . . at least insofar as the present nursing staffs of New Hampshire hospitals are concerned, the interruption of a nursing career neither occurs as frequently as is often believed, nor is it for as long a period of time as is commonly supposed. Our findings prompt certain reflections. It is true that our sample, since it is limited to those now working, is weighted and should be expected to reflect career continuity perhaps somewhat disproportionately. On the other hand, the fact that nearly half of our interviewees are married and many have families should lead us to expect to find careers interrupted as a result of family responsibilities. That is indeed the case, but it is interesting to find it a less prominent factor in the career histories of this group than might be expected (22).

Effect of Childbearing. It is interesting to note that the difference in the effects of marriage on the nursing career which appears between the group of younger and older nurses, does not carry over in the case of childbirth. Table 26, which treats the effects of children

Table 26. Sequel to Childbearing

Age Group	Total	Continued in Nursing	Left Nursing
Total	45	10	34
Younger	28	8	20
Older	16	2	14

(Frequencies too small to permit X^2)

on the nursing career in the same way as the effects of marriage were differentiated (Table 25), shows no significant difference in younger and older nurses. In both groups, the birth of children is likely to remove the mother from active professional work for a considerable period of time; but here, where the main trend is toward no difference, younger nurses give some slight evidence that they are less likely to interrupt their careers, or to interrupt them for shorter periods, than are older nurses. While 14 out of 16 older nurses (87.5 per cent) left nursing at childbirth, 20 out of 28 younger nurses (71.5 per cent) did so. In other words, about twice the proportion of younger nurses continued their careers shortly after childbearing (28.5 per cent) as in the group of older nurses (12.5 per cent). If these proportions held true for larger groups there would be a clear gain for health service among the newer graduates of nursing schools.

suitability of job versus concept of nursing

In inquiring into what induces young women to become nurses, one may well ask how they envision nursing. For nurses differ in the way they see nursing. We also will ask what effects differing conceptions of tasks of the nurse have on the choices of career. We will consider, too, the importance of economic, familial, and other considerations in the development of their careers.

It should be kept in mind that nurses need not reject an interest in one aspect of nursing when they give greater importance to another feature. Nevertheless, there is clear evidence that registered nurses do differ in their conceptions of their essential tasks.

An assistant supervisor of surgery in a hospital expresses one view (27):

I didn't like the patients. I mean, I think I was born to love surgery and that's all. The rest of the care of the patients I leave to the rest of the nurses who like it.

Interviewer: Why do you think you like surgery so much better?

I think it is just the waiting on people is why I don't. I know you are taking good care of them and you are doing as much as we ever do upstairs for them, but still it's just the idea of waiting on them. Of course, there are some people that are wonderful to do other things. In surgery there is no monotony at all. I think in bedside nursing there is.

Interviewer: What about bedside nursing would be monotonous?

Oh, the routine bath, the routine bed changes, and things like that.

But an alternative conception is expressed by a nurse working as a staff nurse in a veterans hospital. Her career led from school into psychiatric nursing, then to an outpatient clinic; yet, with this history of technically flavored work, she maintains that the core of nursing is at the bedside. When asked how she likes psychiatric nursing, she replied (27):

I liked it very much—it doesn't afford very much nursing in itself due to the fact that your patients aren't physically ill. . . . I find that when you work in psychiatry for very long you get rusty in nursing itself.

Interviewer: Not giving bedside care?

No, you are not giving any bedside care, and you give very few medications, other than vitamins and every now and then you get a patient that you give medications to but just as far as mass medications and mass nursing, no, you don't get any of that.

The nurses just quoted graduated during or after World War II. An older nurse who graduated just at the onset of the depression in 1932, presents views on the central tasks of the nurse which contrast in a still more striking way with the views quoted above of the surgical nurse. This nurse, who has held positions in surgery, in obstetrics, as a general-duty nurse and is now working as a group nurse, says of her work (27):

In surgery you really have to be on your toes to catch everything. Although surgery is still very fascinating to me, in group nursing I can get away from it, and I can take life a little easier.

Interviewer: Do you think surgery would be the most exciting part of it?

It is, yet you never know your patient. He's taken up there draped, his face and head are covered; you never know your patient.

When asked about industrial nursing, she said:

Well, I know there just isn't any comparison to this (group nursing), and it is five days a week, and I would sometimes just like to get away from bedside nursing. But it would be just like not being in nursing anymore. . . . A lot of running around to do and office work—but there isn't any bedside nursing.

About the use of auxiliary personnel in nursing service she said:

That is the coming thing, nurses more just doing the desk work and supervision and the aides do the work, that is, actual nursing. The patients don't get the care they should, although I think some practicals are as good as some registered, they can't have a thorough training in so short a time. And then a nurse's touch means an awful lot—and her personality, but I don't think the practicals have that touch. And that is half of nursing, personality and the nursing touch.

A small number of the nurses take an intermediate position: they regard both direct bedside care and technical and administrative tasks as integral in the work of the registered nurse. In the Kansas City study, replies were categorized by emphasis on one or other of the two conceptions (Table 27). It becomes clear that younger nurses,

Table 27. How Nurses Conceive of the Core of Their Work

Age Group	Total	Type of Emphasis in Conception of Nursing	
		Administrative and Technical	Bedside Care of Patients
Total	97	43	54
Older nurses (graduated before 1940)	44	11	33
Younger nurses (graduated after 1940)	53	32	21

$x^2 = 10.9$ P is less than .01

in the majority of cases, vote for technical and administrative skills, while among older nurses, the emphasis is reversed. If the two did not differ in some fundamental way on this point, such proportions would occur less than once in 100 similar analyses of comparable groups of nurses.

The evidence implies that the professional education or experience of younger nurses leads them to conceive of the essential nature of the registered nurse's work in a way which is rejected by the majority of older nurses. To pursue this line of inquiry a step farther: when the nurses of the Kansas City study were asked about changes in nursing education over the past generation, they agreed in the conviction that contemporary nursing schools emphasize classroom study and closely supervised clinical experience. A generation ago, nursing education in the view of both older and younger nurses included less formal instruction and more direct work experience. Agreement about the change in nursing education, and disagreement about its desirability, are illustrated in the two quotations which follow. An older nurse who worked in private duty for the greater part of her career says (27):

> There is a lot more time [today] given to the study part of it—our classes were just rushed in; you had three hours off during the day; you went to class all the time. You worked so many more hours than they do now, and we had more practical experience. I think for real bedside nursing, we turned out better nurses than they do now, but for the book "larnin," as they say [laugh], they get a lot better today than we had then.

> I think for the contact with the patient that the bedside nursing and all— I think maybe we had better nurses back then. We had to do those things —you did anything there was to do. If you are going to care for the patient, I think you need that bedside training.

A younger nurse, assistant supervisor in an operating room, expresses the consensus of her age-mate about changes in nursing when she says:

> I think students today get more background knowledge—I mean about medications and why you give them—and they are more able to handle paper work and teach—you have to teach a lot to aides if things are going to get done. And I don't think it takes three or four years to learn how to give care and make beds. Graduates hardly get a chance to do that anyway. So R.N.'s need more background and education. I think the day is coming when R.N.'s will all have degrees, at least they should have.

A small number of nurses in each age-group judged that educational changes and degree programs were desirable because they helped the individual nurse in competition for promotion. The nurses who evaluated the effects of present-day nursing education on the quality of nursing service can be divided into those who said that the changes led to improvement in the quality of care received by patients, and those who thought that they lowered the standards (Table 28).

About 60 per cent of the older nurses viewed changes over the last two generations as detrimental to the nursing provided the patients. However, about 70 per cent of the younger nurses regarded the changes as improving patient care. Table 28 corresponds to the evidence of Table 27. (Statistical tests indicate that the evaluation of changes in education is reliably different as between younger and older nurses in the sample.)

Table 28. How Changes in Nursing Education Are Pictured

| Age Group | Total | Evaluation of Current Nursing Education | |
		Beneficial to Patient Care	Detrimental to Patient Care
Total	82[a]	47	35
Older nurses (graduated before 1940)	37	15	22
Younger nurses (graduated after 1940)	45	32	13

$X^2 = 7.09$ P is less than .01

[a] This comparison covers only those nurses who made evaluations in terms of the effect of nursing service; 10 nurses evaluated current education in terms of advantage in getting promotions, 6 made no statement.

Almost two thirds of nurses, regardless of age, holding positions which drew chiefly on technical knowledge and skills, whether in the hospital or outside, thought of technical and administrative tasks as the core of nursing. That is, 18 out of the 28 (64 per cent), regarded the direct bedside care of patients as of only secondary importance in the work of the registered nurse. Of 22 nurses of all ages who held administrative and supervisory positions in hospitals, 12 (54 per cent) also relegated beside nursing to secondary importance; but of 21 registered nurses working in private duty, as general duty nurses on hospital staffs or as visiting nurses, nine (43 per cent) shared this view, while 57 per cent thought of direct bedside care—they were, in fact, giving it—as the "heart" of nursing. Thus, although the differences in opinion tend to run with differences in work experience, the tendency is not strongly marked. (Statistical tests of the association between conceptions of nursing and type of position fail to show significance.)

We note, parenthetically, that of 26 nurses in Kansas City who were not actively working at the time that they were interviewed, 20 regarded bedside nursing as "real nursing" while only 6 took this view of technical and administrative duties. This rather striking proportion suggests that discontent with the current emphasis on technical and administrative work in nursing may contribute in some cases to the withdrawal of registered nurses from employment at their profession.

This evidence permits us to say that, at least for this sample, which is as representative of nurses in general as careful sampling procedures permit, two fifths of registered nurses actively working at the time they were interviewed held positions which required work of the "wrong" kind. That is, 10 who held technical jobs thought that bedside nursing was the core of nursing service, 10 administrative jobs agreed with them, while nine bedside nurses thought that the essence of contemporary nursing is technical and administrative. That is to say, for this sample, about two nurses in five probably find their work to some extent uncongenial because it requires them to have more to do with patients than they like, or because it allows them less than they wish. The nurse's location in the fields of nursing, then, appears determined in large part by conditions other than her personal preference. This impression is confirmed by other studies of nurses in specialized fields. Personal rather than professional considerations loom as of prime importance among Arkansas operating room nurses:

> . . . The nurse seeking employment in the one-hospital community in Arkansas (the most common community with any hospital service) usually will accept whatever position is available. The probability that this position will be as an operating-room nurse is small, for operating-room nurses comprise less than 10 per cent of those employed. However, the interview data indicate that some nurses became operating-room nurses in just this fortuitous manner. Among the younger and more mobile nurses, a wider selection of place of employment is available, and there is greater opportunity for employment as an operating-room nurse; but for the inexperienced, such positions are usually to be found in the smaller hospitals. For the larger hospitals, the operating-room nurses usually are selected from the available nursing personnel, including the floor nurses who have had experience as operating-room nurses in smaller hospitals, or on occasion, from among the recent graduates of the hospital's school of nursing who have evidenced special interest or aptitude. To summarize, a young, mobile, highly motivated nurse probably can find employment as an operating-room nurse, but such individuals comprised a minority of the operating-room nurses in the hospitals of the sample studied (16, p. 9).

Again, in the case of industrial nurses, whose work might well be most congenial to nurses who dislike dealing with bed-patients, it appears that chance, rather than preference, is a frequent determinant of their field. The sample in the Ohio Valley (21) reports this to be true, and it is easy to extend the conclusion to other comparable categories, such as school and office nurses.

In private duty nursing, there is mixed evidence; private duty is a deliberate and consistent choice of nurses who want and enjoy close contact with patients, but also it is embraced as the most convenient way to nurse while maintaining other duties and responsibilities. At least as seen in Georgia, preference is a strong determinant:

> . . . The private duty nurse is primarily patient-oriented. The nature of her job lends validity to this finding. The general-duty nurse, because of role responsibilities to the total hospital organization, cannot be expected to exhibit such consistant orientation toward the patient. The same limitation would apply to the public health nurse and to the industrial nurse. However, the job orientation of the private duty nurses is scarcely sufficient reason for this sharp focus on the problems of nurse patient care relationship. It is obvious that the field of private duty attracts nurses who are characterized by a real sense of concern for the patient (7, p. 269).

However, some are in private duty for reasons unrelated to the work:

> Frankly I prefer general duty, however, private duty has been more satisfactory for me because it enabled me to be with our children supervising their training and rearing. I did not work until World War II. The past few years working hours on private duty coincided with hours children were at school. I am sure I have selfishly chosen private duty because it left me time to be with my family. Youngest child now in college but am physically unable to work regularly—thus private duty—nevertheless, I love nursing and cannot give it up entirely (7, p. 147).

Similar conclusions are drawn from North Carolina about psychiatric nurses—they are in the field for reasons of personal convenience, good pay, an easy journey to work, and the like (29).

The common trend in these various studies is that, while there are indeed specialized jobs in nursing, there are relatively few specialized nurses who have chosen and followed a specialized field because it was personally congenial. The most conspicuous, and perhaps single, exception may be administrative nursing. Nurses in administrative jobs do not shift easily or often to other nursing fields. This may be explained partly by the fact that they are oftener single than others and are more highly paid. In other words, their careers may be less exposed to outside interruption and may be the most remunerative of all in nursing. On the other hand, it may well be that more dedicated and able nurses come to hold administrative jobs, and so administrative positions are filled by people whose intrinsic motivation in nursing is high. The supposition remains to be tested.

The peculiar impact on their careers is the fact that nurses are, by and large, women, has been discussed in Chapters 7, and 11 and will be touched on again in our conclusions (Chap. 12). Some important interrelationships between the doctor's and the nurse's career were brought out in the final section of Chapter 9.

an over-all pattern

What emerges from the examination of the career patterns of many nurses in many fields and in many localities may be summed up in a few sentences. The range of career opportunities open to nurses has widened and deepened in recent years. Young women who enter nursing are more and more likely to devote more years to work as a nurse. Although most nurses look beyond work as a nurse to a life as wife and mother, many, in fact, return to nursing and carry on double careers, thus contributing to medical service in our society, perhaps more than they had intended when they entered a school of nursing. Lastly, contemporary nursing service has created many specialized fields, but to a less extent, specialized nurses. Rather, nurses tend to take jobs in any branch which satisfies their requirements as to income, location, convenient hours of work, and other considerations apart from nursing itself.

implications and conclusions

The research reports draw attention to situations calling for reform as well as to gaps in our knowledge. Some problems concern the nursing profession itself and its relations to society or to vested interests in it. Others have dimensions considerably less cosmic. In concluding, we will touch upon some of each.

Research is obviously not an end in itself. Its value lies in the light that it throws upon the present state of affairs as an eventual guide to intelligent direction and control. We are most fortunate in that, already, we have the report of a practical application of principles learned in some of the earlier studies in the American Nurses' Association's program.

In the course of work in the Boston Psychopathic Hospital, it was discovered that an especially trained team of otherwise inexperienced attendants, under the direction of one experienced head nurse, may be uncommonly effective in the therapy of acutely ill mental patients (6, 6A, 6B, 6D, 6E). With patients whose basic difficulty is human relations, the problem is essentially to make them aware of each other, in the first place, and then to lead them into friendly, rather than hostile, social relationships. The role of a withdrawn individual's prior interests, his profession and his avocations, in bringing him socially to life, so to speak, was inquired into. Then, once a little society of patients had been brought into being, repercussions caused in it by the transfer or discharge of its "natural" leaders were investigated. An important discovery was that the ratio of attendants to patients makes a difference; beyond a certain balance, the attendants are apt to interact among themselves, sometimes forgetting the patient.

These findings and others about re-socialization of the acutely ill in Boston Psychopathic Hospital were applied by a small team of attendants to an unpromising ward of chronically ill in the Metropolitan State Hospital with very encouraging results (24).

The report of the experiment is valuable for its presentation of not only the undertaking and its outcome as a contribution to psychotherapy, but also the manner in which the experimental personnel was introduced into the hospital and the points at which the co-operation of administration and staff was easy to enlist and where it was difficult. Moreover, the part played in the reactivation of patients by the nurses was compared with that of the attendants.

This study also stands out in the research program because it is one of the few in which the effects of nursing techniques are judged in the light of therapy—for here we have "before" and "after" tests of the patients. In a number of the time studies of nursing functions, for example, the California, the Washington, one of the Arkansas and the Missouri studies 4, 2, 17, 9, a sincere effort was made to assess the state of the patients because obviously the care of the critically ill is the most demanding and time-consuming of all the nurse's work. However, as yet, no assays of the patient's condition have been reported in this research program—with the exception, as noted, of the experiment in the Metropolitan State Hospital in Massachusetts.

We still await a definitive statement of the effect upon the patients and the progress of the relations between the upper and lower echelons of nurse. Does it make any difference to the therapy the hospital effects, if they are castelike and formal, or if they are equalitarian and informal? We do not know yet; but their eventual bearing upon the healing process is the most important consideration of all. We have been brought closer to conclusions by the impressive knowledge of the hospital's social structure which the research monographs have presented us.

The time studies make it perfectly clear how the boundaries between the work of doctor and nurse, and between each rank of nurse and all the other ranks, are shifting (Chap. 6). All down the line, this constant and often unrecognized movement toward re-alignment and reallocation of functions is having unforeseen effects. For one thing, it enters into the nurse's legal position. As nurses are doing more and more of the procedures formerly done only by doctors, they may find themselves from time to time actually breaking the law. Between one state and another of the 48, the procedures which the nurse is forbidden to do vary, but it seems generally true that her work is outgrowing the legal definition of it. For its own protection, the profession might consider an inquiry into the disparity between actual and permitted practice.

The upper echelons of nurses are occupied today largely with supervisory and administrative duties. Indeed, there are smaller hospitals in which every professional nurse has supervisory responsibilities and the tendency is increasing and spreading. Many nurses acquit themselves magnificently in these and in administrative functions; but if they are to be called upon to do parts of the work of another profession—the doctor's, the administrator's—their lives would be more rewarding and less care-ridden were they provided not only corresponding title and salary but also, above all, the equivalent authority.

As a matter of fact, one of the studies points out that many nurses, despite allegations to the contrary, are not ambitious to abandon the patient for desk and front office work and there is no need for a campaign to "win them back to the bedside" (19). Rather, the problem may turn out to be to awaken some to the possibility of their "competing for the important, policy-making positions" (17, p. 98; 22, 19).

The grounds for some head nurses' and supervisors' dread of the responsibilities they have to shoulder and for some general duty nurses' avoidance of promotion may, in many cases, turn out to be the combination of responsibility without comparable authority. The profession itself might consider critically the balance of power between nurses and the hospital's medical and administrative staffs. It may mean bearding the doctors in their den! Of course it means more research!

As to the division of nursing and the relations between graduate and practical nurses, the research monographs contain innumerable hints. The Alabama study established the fact that the practical nurses there like the work they do best and show no disposition to "usurp" professional tasks. This is often, but not always, confirmed by the other surveys. However, it gives assurance that a harmonious division of tasks is possible and indeed, here and there, a reality.

A considerable array of tasks (at present being undertaken by nurses of all ranks) might be redefined as the work of hospital divisions, such as the dietary or the housekeeping department, and thus may be removed at one fell swoop from the controversy over the division of labor. These appear as "nonnursing" functions in the survey of New York hospitals, where they are shown to occupy one fourth of the time of professional nurses and one third of the time of practical nurses. Obviously, their transfer to nonnursing personnel would bring about great economies in the use of the more highly trained staff. However, it is not to be assumed that all tasks which *can* be delegated *should* be delegated; the judgment on where to draw the line rests, of course, with the profession.

A pertinent finding appears in the report on three hospitals in the state of Washington (2). In Hospital "A," a 200-bed institution, 199 hours in two weeks of the time of nursing personnel were reported to be devoted to the distributing of food and water—a little more than the full time of two employees in a 40-hour week. Errand-running would make a full-time job for one person in Hospital "A" and a half-time job in the other two hospitals surveyed. In one hospital, 49 per cent of the time spent on errands came from the professional staff; in the second, it was 21 per cent and in the third 30 per cent. The research team noted that in the 28-bed hospital with no central supply department, seven per cent of total nursing time was spent on tasks related to hospital equipment and supplies; but it fell to one per cent in the larger institution which, though there was more errand-running, was able to make it the specific duty of the central supply service.

If record-keeping and other paper work make nurses unhappy by interposing itself between them and the care of their patients, there might be a serious inquiry into its indispensability. Certainly, in business and governmental bureaucracies, habits of duplicating and triplicating and form-filling of all sorts have now and then been shown to serve no real purpose and occasionally an original and radically minded prisoner of the desk revolts and throws a lot of it into the "circular file"! It seems not to be as fateful a gesture as was supposed! However, to repeat, any reallocation must in the end be inspired not merely by the hope of economizing in the expenditure of the professional nurses' time but also by the consideration of the whole situation as it bears on healing.

Evidence piles up in the research reports of the best educated and most sophisticated nurses as being chained to desks and filing cabinets while—this is to overstate the case grossly for the moment!—it is left to practical nurses and aides to supply the human warmth and comfort that so many laymen think of when they think of ladies in white caps and uniforms. One suspects that this may be the time for something more than the reallocation of tasks. Psychiatry is to be thanked for reminding the medical profession, split as it is into specialties usually named for parts of the body, of the supreme importance of "the whole person." This the medical men signalize by publicly exalting that mythical character, the dear old "family doctor," who successfully tackles any organ or area of the human frame. To some extent, the "traditionalizer," the private duty nurse and the industrial nurse characteristically deal in human relations and often speak so of their work. If, then, the bedside tasks are in large measure to become the kingdom of the auxiliaries, the professional nurses might turn to the cultivation of skills in human understanding and appreciation. Already "total care" is being presented to young student nurses as calling for knowledge of sociology and social psychology. This is a latter-day meaning of the phrase, "total care," which formerly used to describe, for example, the work of the private nurse who tidied up the sickroom and did a bit of light laundering for her patient in between her more directly personal attentions to him.

There are several grounds on which this new direction might recommend itself. In the first place, much of physical illness is already conquered. As this book is being written, the newspapers report that Boston proper, a city of about 800,000, had no deaths from poliomyelitis, diphtheria, scarlet fever, typhoid fever, whooping cough, mumps, measles or chickenpox in 1957 and not even a single case of poliomyelitis. There will be plenty of sick people still, but the balance of illness is daily being weighted more heavily by chronic illness, afflictions of old age, and the still incurable diseases. However, these are, for the most part, the very ailments that call for recognizing and easing fear and stress; and in the second place, our most pervasive enemy nowadays is mental disease. It is unnecessary to say that the nursing of the neurotic and the psychotic means, above all, imparting comfort, courage and confidence.

The point is made also in the study of the New York maternity center. Noting that the medical sciences have made childbirth safe, the authors suggest that the nurse's responsibility from early pregnancy to shortly after delivery has now become the unmet need of young parents: advice and encouragement together with information (20, p. 224). Consistently, they pass on an idea of clinic patients—that nothing could comfort a young woman more than to have the ministrations of one and the same nurse for as much of the maternal cycle as possible. This may not be feasible, but a good second best is the assignment of one nurse to attend a woman at each antepartal visit and one, even if not the same nurse, to her from the beginning of labor to the time when she leaves the hospital. As it is, in many cases in large hospitals, the patient passes through the hands of a procession of nurses, none of whom are ever with her long enough to develop warm relationships (20, pp. 138, 205).

The crux of these suggestions is not more care of the patient but a different kind of care, a prerequisite of which is a new emphasis on social psychology in the nursing schools.

Many nurses who read this book—or better still, the monographs which it discusses—will find all sorts of hints at answers to practical questions. For they are only hints; not answers. Answers involve judgments which none but nurses should make for themselves.

For instance, those who recruit will learn from what economic and social classes today's nurses are drawn, what they expected of the profession when they embraced it and what they actually found it to be. They might deduce, then, that there should be energetic recruiting among such young women; but this is not the only possibility; they might equally conclude to till other fields, hitherto, perhaps, overlooked (6F, pp. 9-10). This is for them to decide.

Psychiatric nursing appears to attract nurses for reasons little related to the work itself (29, pp. 48, 56-66). This may be evidence that the field is not being presented as a challenging possibility in nursing schools and in-service programs. However, there may be other explanations.

According to her tastes and temperament, today's nurse can pick and choose her place among the specialties both in and out of the hospital. For she is, at present at any rate, offering her services in a seller's market; but the profession may not be taking account of a point made in a Missouri study (9, p. 148), that the small-town hospital is, perhaps without planning it, limiting itself to routine cases and passing on to urban hospitals, with their superior facilities and more diversified professional services, the critically ill and the cases calling for new or massive surgery. These are the clinically "interesting" patients that challenge the "professionalizers" among the nurses, and it is possible that the latter are already drifting there of their own free will. This is not the place, perhaps, for intervention; but it might be well if the facts of "nurse drift"—to give a more imaginative name to geographical mobility—were brought to light. In any case, some disillusionment and heartbreak surely could be avoided if young nurses, in particular, were employed in the kind of nursing that they prefer.

The plight of the married nurse who must leave her profession long enough to raise her family brings in the dilemma on whose horns all professional women are likely to be impaled. It already has been observed (Chap. 10), that to apply a single standard of professional involvement equally to wives and mothers, husbands and fathers, is unrealistic. The research monographs have shown that much of nursing is contributed by married nurses; indeed only about one in four nurses is single (Chap. 2, Table 6). As the Pennsylvania study shows, it is only after the nurse has the second child, that she barely contrives to get back to her patients (19). For it is firmly established that the married do not abandon their profession; they merely take time out. Since this is the case, withdrawal for domestic reasons might as well be faced as one of the facts of life and in-service refresher courses might be offered to restore to quick usefulness the nurse who, duty done, returns to the profession. Nursing and the other women's professions, like teaching and social work, might lead in seeking ways to lighten the burden of the working mother.

There are other continuing problems. To mention one of the less apparent, Habenstein and Christ note, en passant, that the layout of a nursing unit enters into the human relations of the personnel (9, pp. 31, 150). A hospital with classified quarters—lounges and dining-rooms for graduate nurses and duplicate accommodation for the auxiliaries—may turn out to be a mistake; that is, if easy and friendly relations between the ranks are thought to be a good thing. Built-in space-dividers may make casual association between superiors and subordinates impossible. What is the effect of hospital architecture? It is hardly necessary to speak of its bearing on the saving of labor. We are told (2) of procedures that are repeated 500 times or more in two weeks, of routines that require dozens of trips, not always short, between three or four fixed points—all of which could be made quicker and easier by better designing in the first place, or by the re-disposition of existing facilities.

Of course, the unanswered questions call for further inquiries. The work already done provides some lessons to guide those who make them. We know now, for one thing, that good descriptive reporting of the scene in which studies are made illuminates the conclusions and makes them intelligible. How instructive, for example, are some of the accounts we have of life and work in hospitals in small towns! To pick an illustration at random (but not from a small town), who, on learning that Charity Hospital, in New Orleans, is a 19-storied building housing 3,200 patients, would imagine, without being told, the fantastically informal atmosphere in which its myriad sick are nursed? What an opportunity this paradox presents for inquiry into what difference it makes to the patient if the hospital is impersonal and if he is made to feel anonymous. The New Orleans study (18) inhibits one from saying, now, that bigness or smallness determines the atmosphere of a hospital. Only by full description of settings and relationships will we begin to sense the less formal and less tangible flavor and mood of hospitals.

In the same way, sympathetic and convincing reporting of interviews—best of all in the speaker's own words—tells us as nothing else can, the circumstances under which the nurse's work is changing. Matters that many nurses will find startling—for instance, the entrusting of grave responsibilities and complicated techniques to auxiliaries—are shown to be sometimes the wise and logical, as well as the only recourse, when the situation is told as a human experience. Then we can visualize the hard-pressed head nurse who has insufficient professional help and we see the middle-aged trustworthy practical nurse to whom she turns; and, by the same token, her desperate plight when she has no other auxiliaries who can rise to the occasion. The research monographs which we have discussed in this book contain some stories of such matters which rise to literary heights and which, like literature, broaden our understanding.

Our remarks are in no sense meant to disparage tables of facts and figures. Quantitative work is likewise important and valuable, its purpose being to permit easy and objective comparison; but for insight and understanding there is no substitute for case description (17, pp. 320-1). Nurses know this because they habitually tell *about* a patient as well as state his pulse and temperature, when reporting to the physician. The best of the research accounts are fine vignettes, undoubtedly requiring artistic talent, and that is a good deal to ask. However, a well-designed questionnaire can guide a quite unexceptional field worker to securing pedestrian, perhaps, but still useful and informative interviews.

In the first years of the American Nurses' Association's five-year program, most of the research was done by social scientists of various disciplines: sociology, anthropology, psychology, and in few cases by nurses themselves. As time went on, nurses very quickly fitted themselves to do social research and came to play a larger part in the program themselves. We can expect that there will be increasing numbers from within the profession who can be counted upon for sound and enlightening studies. Of course, this calls for explicit instruction in method (cf., 10), but, over and above that, for association with workers outside of nursing who are already sophisticated in these things (cf. 6G). Meanwhile, the research program already has acquainted 20,000 nurses, in huge government or voluntary installations and in tiny institutions in the country, from New Hampshire to California and from Minnesota to Louisiana, who have kept diaries and filled time sheets, been interviewed and observed, with the ways of research. Their part is, of course, as indispensable to the increase of knowledge as is the field worker's. For every nurse is already in the field. To be a field worker, there must be added the ability to stand off and look at herself and others and to report what she sees without fear or favor.

By its own research undertaking, nursing has taken a long stride towards professional autonomy. But autonomy is not isolation or exclusiveness. The stereotype of the members of any profession carrying on alone the research which will improve its practice is as obsolete as that of the nurse keeping a lone vigil in an isolated sickroom; it might happen but it isn't the best way to do research or to heal the sick. The research upon which modern medicine draws is done not by physicians alone (although there are more research-minded physicians than ever before), but by biochemists, physicists, physiologists and many others who pretend to no skill in the healing arts. Indeed, in any professional practice there is always a fusion of the contributions from within and from without.

All professional arts draw upon various kinds of scientific and practical knowledge. So is it, and so will it be with nursing. Nurses in the future will do more and more of their own research; but they, too, are turning for fundamentals to other disciplines, not in themselves related to nursing; and the better the education and training of the nurse who does research, the better must be the work of the others who join in her enterprise.

references

studies sponsored by the american nurses' association

1. New York University: A Study of Nursing Functions in twelve Hospitals in the State of New York, New York, N.Y., New York University, 1952.
2. Washington State Nurses Association: A Study of Nursing Functions, Seattle, Wash., Washington State Nurses' Association, 1953.
3. Gordon, H. Phoebe: Who Does What—The Report of a Nursing Activities Study, American Journal of Nursing, 53:564-566, 1953.
4. California State Nurses' Association: Nursing Practice in California Hospitals, San Francisco, Calif., California State Nurses' Association, 1953.
5. The Governmental Research Center, University of Kansas: The Study of Activities of Registered Professional Nurses in Small Kansas Hospitals, Lawrence, Kan., University of Kansas, 1953.
6. Boston Psychopathic Studies: Metropolitan State Hospital Project— Report to A.N.A.
    6A. Kandler, Harriet; Behymer, Alice F.; Kegeles, S. Stephen; and Boyd, Richard W.: A Study of Nurse-Patient Interaction in a Mental Hospital, American Journal of Nursing, 52:1100-1103, 1952.
    6B. Morimoto, Francoise R., and Greenblatt, Milton: Personnel Awareness of Patients Socializing Capacity, The American Journal of Psychiatry, 110:443-447, 1953.
    6C. Kegeles, S. Stephen: A Conception of Social Processes in Hospitalized Psychiatric Patients (Mimeographed).
    6D. Robinson, Alice M.; Mellow, June; Hurteau, Phyllis; and Fried, Marc A.: Research in Psychiatric Nursing—The Psychiatric Head Nurse, American Journal of Nursing, 55:704-707, 1955. (Not A.N.A.)
    6E. The Nurse as a Socializing Catalyst, Boston Psychopathic Studies (Part of unpublished manuscript).
    6F. Kandler, Harriet M.: Why Students Chose Nursing as a Career: Analysis of Opinions of Sixty Students (Unpublished).
    6G. Greenblatt, Milton: The Nurse in Research—With Remarks on Interdisciplinary Projects (Unpublished).

278

7. Couey, Elizabeth, and Stephenson, Diane D.: The Field of Private Duty Nursing, Atlanta, Ga., Georgia State Nurses' Association, 1955.

8. Hanson, Helen C., and Stecklein, John E.: A Study of Nursing Functions in General Hospitals in the State of Minnesota, Minneapolis, Minn., The University of Minnesota, 1955.

9. Habenstein, Robert W., and Christ, Edwin A.: Professionalizer, Traditionalizer and Utilizer, Columbia, Mo., University of Missouri, 1955.

10. Ford, Thomas R., and Stephenson, Diane D.: Institutional Nurses: Role Relationships and Attitudes in three Alabama Hospitals, University, Ala., University of Alabama, 1953.

11. Deutscher, Irwin: Evaluation of Nurses by Male Physicians, Kansas City, Mo., Community Studies, Inc., 1955.

12. ————: Public Images of the Nurse, Kansas City, Mo., Community Studies, Inc., 1955.

13. Vanderbilt University School of Nursing: A Study of the Professional Activities of the Faculty of the School of Nursing of Vanderbilt University, Nashville, Tenn., Vanderbilt University, 1955.

14. Stewart, Donald, and Needham, Christine E.: Source Book for the Function of the General Duty Nurse in ten Arkansas Hospitals, Fayetteville, Ark., University of Arkansas, 1955.

15. ————: The Auxiliary Nursing Personnel, Fayetteville, Ark., University of Arkansas, 1955.

16. ————: The Operating Room Nurse—The Function of the Operating Room Nurse in ten Arkansas Hospitals, Fayetteville, Ark., University of Arkansas, 1955.

17. ————: The General Duty Nurse, Fayetteville, Ark., University of Arkansas, 1955.

18. Reissman, Leonard, and Rohrer, John H.: Change and Dilemma in the Nursing Profession, New York, G. P. Putnam's Sons, 1957.

19. Bressler, Marvin, and Kephart, William M.: Career Dynamics, Philadelphia, Pa., University of Pennsylvania, 1955. Published by the Pennsylvania Nurses' Association. [1955.] This final volume was not available to the authors in preparation of the present book. Since manuscript was used, page references are omitted.

20. Lesser, Marion S., and Keane, Vera R.: Nurse-Patient Relationships in a Hospital Maternity Service, St. Louis, The C. V. Mosby Company, 1956.

21. Barschak, Erna: Today's Industrial Nurse and Her Job, New York, G. P. Putnam's Sons, 1957.

22. Theriault, George F.: A Study of Functions of Nurses in eleven New Hampshire Communities (Manuscript), Hanover, New Hamp., Dartmouth College, 1957. Since manuscript was used, page references are omitted.

23. Couey, Fred, and Couey, Elizabeth D.: Human Relations in Private Duty Nursing, Atlanta, Ga., Georgia State Nurses Association, 1956.
24. Metropolitan State Hospital Project (Manuscript), Boston, Mass., 1957. (Manuscript.)

studies sponsored by the american nurses' foundation

25. Deutscher, Irwin: A Survey of the Social and Occupational Characteristics of a Metropolitan Nurse Complement, Kansas City, Mo., Community Studies, Inc., 1956.
26. McPartland, Thomas S.: Formal Education and the Process of Professionalization: A Study of Student Nurses, Kansas City, Mo., Community Studies, Inc., 1957.
27. ———: Patterns of Career Dynamics in Nursing, Kansas City, Mo., Community Studies, Inc. (Forthcoming).
28. Christ, Edwin A.: Nurses at Work, Columbia, Mo., University of Missouri, 1956.
29. Martin, Harry W., and Simpson, Ida Harper: Patterns of Psychiatric Nursing: A Survey of Psychiatric Nursing in North Carolina, Chapel Hill, N.C., University of North Carolina, 1956.
30. Pumroy, Shirley S., and Suttell, Barbara J.: The Private Duty Nurse —Her Role in the Hospital Environment, Washington, D.C., American Institute for Research, 1956.
31. Smith, Wendell: The Industrial Nurse: An Analysis of Her Functions, Lewisburg, Pa., Bucknell University, 1957.
32. Johnson, Walter L.: Public Health Nursing Turnover, American Journal of Nursing, **57**:464-466, 1957.

other studies

33. Bullock, Robert P.: What Do Nurses Think of Their Profession, Columbus, Ohio, The Ohio State University Research Foundation, 1954.
34. Spohn, Roberta R.: A Study of Private Duty Nurses, New York, N.Y., American Nurses' Association, 1954.